SRA Open Court Reading

Book 5

Cooperation and Competition

•

Back Through the Stars

•

Heritage

•

The Civil War

•

New Frontiers

•

Journeys and Quests

SRA Open Court Reading

Book 5

Program Authors

Carl Bereiter
Marilyn Jager Adams
Marlene Scardamalia
Robbie Case
Anne McKeough
Michael Pressley
Marsha Roit
Jan Hirshberg
Ann Brown
Joe Campione
Iva Carruthers
Gerald H. Treadway, Jr.

SRA

A Division of The McGraw-Hill Companies

Columbus, Ohio

Acknowledgments

Leonard Baskin: Illustrations from ALBERIC THE WISE AND OTHER JOURNEYS by Norton Juster, illustrated by Leonard Baskin. Reprinted with permission of Leonard Baskin.

Curtis Brown, Ltd.: "The West Side" by Peggy Mann. Copyright © 1972 by Peggy Mann. First appeared in *How Juan Got Home*. Published by Coward-McCann. Reprinted by permission of Curtis Brown, Ltd.

Clarion Books/Houghton Mifflin Company.: "Half Slave and Half Free" from LINCOLN: A Photobiography. Copyright © 1987 by Russell Freedman. Reprinted by permission of Clarion Books/Houghton Mifflin Company. All rights reserved. "So I Became a Soldier," from THE BOYS' WAR by Jim Murphy. Text copyright © 1990 by Jim Murphy. Reprinted by permission of Clarion Books/Houghton Mifflin Company. All rights reserved. VOYAGER TO THE PLANETS by Necia H. Apfel. Copyright © 1991 by Necia H. Apfel. Reprinted by permission of Clarion Books/Houghton Mifflin Company. All rights reserved.

Frances Collin, Literary Agent: "A Meeting in Space" from BARBARY by Vonda N. McIntyre. Reprinted by permission of Frances Collin, Literary Agent. Copyright © 1986 by Vonda N. McIntyre.

Dial Books for Young Readers, a division of Penguin Putnam Inc.: "Emancipation" from TO BE A SLAVE by Julius Lester. Copyright © 1968 by Julius Lester. Used by permission of Dial Books for Young Readers, a division of Penguin Putnam Inc. TANYA'S REUNION by Valerie Flournoy, illustrated by Jerry Pinkney. Copyright © 1995 by Valerie Flournoy, text. Copyright © 1995 by Jerry Pinkney, illustrations. Used by permission of Dial Books for Young Readers, a division of Penguin Putnam Inc.

Dutton Children's Books, a division of Penguin Putnam Inc.: "The Flower-Fed Buffaloes," from GOING TO THE STARS by Vachel Lindsay. Copyright © 1926 by D. Appleton & Co., renewed 1954 by Elizabeth C. Lindsay. A Hawthorn Book. Used by permission of Dutton Children's Books, a division of Penguin Putnam Inc.

Farrar, Straus & Giroux, Inc.: "The Great Dog" and "The Scorpion" from THE HEAVENLY ZOO: LEGENDS AND TALES OF THE STARS by Alison Lurie, pictures by Monika Beisner. Text copyright © 1979 by Alison Lurie. Illustrations copyright © 1979 by Monika Beisner. Reprinted by permission of Farrar, Straus & Giroux, Inc. "When Shlemiel Went to Warsaw" from WHEN SHLEMIEL WENT TO WARSAW AND OTHER STORIES by Isaac Bashevis Singer. Copyright © 1968 by Isaac Bashevis Singer. Reprinted by permission of Farrar, Straus & Giroux, Inc.

Fulcrum Publishing, Inc.: From THE ABACUS CONTEST by Priscilla Wu. Text copyright © 1996 by Priscilla Wu. Reprinted with permission of Fulcrum Publishing, Inc.

Donna Gamache: "Juggling" by Donna Gamache, from Cricket, The Magazine for Children, Vol. 21, No. 10. Copyright © 1994 by Donna Gamache. Reprinted with permission of Donna Gamache.

Greenwillow Books, a division of William Morrow & Company, Inc.: MCBROOM AND THE RAINMAKER from HERE COMES MCBROOM! by Sid Fleischman. Text copyright © 1973 by Sid Fleischman. By permission of Greenwillow Books, a division of William Morrow & Company, Inc..

Harcourt Brace & Company: Text from BILL PICKETT: RODEO RIDIN' COWBOY, copyright © 1996 by Andrea Davis Pinkney, reprinted by permission of Harcourt Brace & Company. "The Marble Champ" from BASEBALL IN APRIL AND OTHER STORIES, copyright © 1990 by Gary Soto, reprinted by permission of Harcourt Brace & Company. "Women" from REVOLUTIONARY PETUNIAS AND OTHER POEMS, copyright © 1970 by Alice Walker, reprinted by permission of Harcourt Brace & Company.

HarperCollins Publishers: "CHINATOWN" from CHILD OF THE OWL by LAURENCE YEP. COPYRIGHT © 1977 BY LAURENCE YEP. Used by permission of HarperCollins Publishers. "HARRIET TUBMAN" from HONEY, I LOVE by ELOISE GREENFIELD. TEXT COPYRIGHT © 1978 BY ELOISE GREENFIELD. Used by permission of HarperCollins Publishers. "OPERA AND KARATE" from THE LAND I LOST by HUYNH QUANG NHUONG. TEXT COPYRIGHT © 1982 BY HUYNH QUANG NHUONG. Used by permission of HarperCollins Publishers. "PARMELE" from CHILDTIMES: A THREE-GENERATION MEMOIR by ELOISE GREENFIELD. COPYRIGHT © 1979 BY ELOISE GREENFIELD AND LESSIE JONES LITTLE. Used by permission of HarperCollins Publishers. "THE SEARCH" from …AND NOW MIGUEL by JOSEPH KRUMGOLD. COPYRIGHT © 1953 BY JOSEPH KRUMGOLD. Used by permission of HarperCollins Publishers. "STORKS" from THE WHEEL ON THE SCHOOL by MEINDERT DEJONG. TEXT COPYRIGHT © 1954 BY MEINDERT DEJONG. Used by permission of HarperCollins Publishers.

"UNDER SIEGE" from VOICES FROM THE CIVIL WAR by MILTON MELTZER. COPYRIGHT © 1989 BY MILTON MELTZER. Used by permission of HarperCollins Publishers.

HarperCollins Publishers, Inc., a division of HarperCollins Publishers: "OLD YELLER AND THE BEAR" from OLD YELLER by FRED GIPSON. Copyright © 1956 by Fred Gipson. Copyright renewed. Reprinted by permission of HarperCollins Publishers, Inc.

SRA/McGraw-Hill

A Division of The McGraw-Hill Companies

Send all inquiries to:
SRA/McGraw-Hill
8787 Orion Place
Columbus, Ohio 43240

Printed in the United States of America.

ISBN 0-02-830957-X

3 4 5 6 7 8 9 VHP 04 03 02 01 00

Program Authors

Carl Bereiter, Ph.D.
University of Toronto

Marilyn Jager Adams, Ph.D.
BBN Technologies

Michael Pressley, Ph.D.
University of Notre Dame

Marsha Roit, Ph.D.
National Reading Consultant

Robbie Case, Ph.D.
University of Toronto

Anne McKeough, Ph.D.
University of Toronto

Jan Hirshberg, Ed.D.
Reading Consultant

Marlene Scardamalia, Ph.D.
University of Toronto

Ann Brown, Ph.D.
University of California at Berkeley

Joe Campione, Ph.D.
University of California at Berkeley

Iva Carruthers, Ph.D.
Northeastern Illinois University

Gerald H. Treadway, Jr., Ed.D.
San Diego State University

Table of Contents

Fine Art 56

Table of Contents

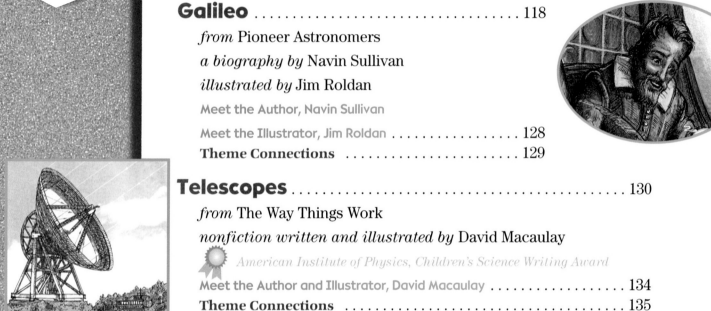

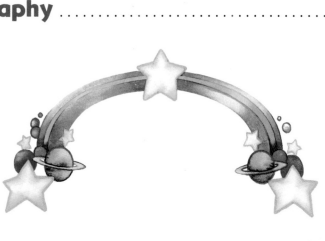

Table *of* **C**ontents

Table *of* Contents

Table *of* Contents

Table of Contents

Cooperation and Competition

Sometimes we need to cooperate with each other to get things done. Sometimes, though, we find ourselves competing with each other. Sometimes we need to do both at the same time—cooperate with teammates while competing against an opposing team. Cooperation and competition play important roles in our lives and they take on many different faces. How do you see competition and cooperation at work in your life?

Class President

by Johanna Hurwitz
illustrated by Richard Hull

To Delia and Bill Gottlieb
They get my vote every time!

Julio Sanchez is sure that fifth grade is going to be his best year yet. On the first day of school, his homeroom teacher Mr. Flores announces that this year the fifth grade will be electing a class president. To get ready for the election, the students are to be thinking about who might make a good leader.

In the meantime, while playing in a soccer game at recess, Julio's classmate Arthur breaks his glasses. The fifth grade pitches in to pay for the glasses by holding a bake sale. But on the day of the bake sale, Arthur's mom finds out his glasses can be replaced for free.

Now the class has two things to decide: who to elect as class president and what to do with the bake sale money no longer needed to pay for Arthur's glasses. . . .

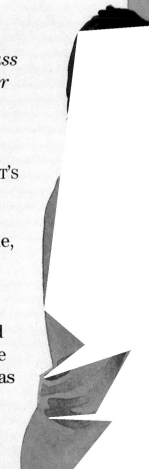

On Monday, Arthur came to school with new glasses. Cricket came to class with a big poster that said, VOTE FOR CRICKET, THAT'S THE TICKET.

The election was going to be held on Friday. That meant there were only four days more to get ready. In the meantime, they learned about how to make a nomination and how to second it. It was going to be a really serious election.

At lunch, Cricket took out a bag of miniature chocolate bars and gave them out to her classmates. Julio took his and ate it. But it didn't mean he was going to vote for Cricket. He wondered if there was anything Lucas could give out that was better than chocolate. Nothing was better than chocolate!

"If you're going to run against Cricket, we've got to get to work," Julio told Lucas on their way home. Julio wasn't very good at making posters, as Cricket and Zoe were, but he was determined to help his friend.

The next morning, a new poster appeared in Mr. Flores's classroom. It said, DON'T BUG ME. VOTE FOR LUCAS COTT. Julio had made it.

Before lunch, Mr. Flores read an announcement from the principal. "From now on, there is to be no more soccer playing in the school yard at lunchtime."

"No more soccer playing?" Julio called out. "Why not?"

Mr. Flores looked at Julio. "If you give me a moment, I'll explain. Mr. Herbertson is concerned about accidents. Last week, Arthur broke his glasses. Another time, someone might be injured more seriously."

Julio was about to call out again, but he remembered just in time and raised his hand.

"Yes, Julio," said Mr. Flores.

"It's not fair to make us stop playing soccer just because someone *might* get hurt. Someone might fall down walking to school, but we still have to come to school every day."

Julio didn't mean to be funny, but everyone started to laugh. Even Mr. Flores smiled.

"There must be other activities to keep you fellows busy at lunchtime," he said. "Is soccer the only thing you can do?"

Lucas raised his hand. "I don't like jumping rope," he said when the teacher called on him.

All the girls giggled at that.

"You could play jacks," suggested Cricket. Everyone knew it wasn't a serious possibility, though.

"Couldn't we tell Mr. Herbertson that we want to play soccer?" asked Julio.

"You could make an appointment to speak to him, if you'd like," said Mr. Flores. "He might change his decision if you convince him that you are right."

"Lucas and I will talk to him," said Julio. "Right, Lucas?"

"Uh, sure," said Lucas, but he didn't look too sure.

The principal, Mr. Herbertson, spoke in a loud voice and had eyes that seemed to bore right into your head when he looked at you. Julio had been a little bit afraid of Mr. Herbertson since the very first day of kindergarten. Why had he offered to go to his office and talk to him?

Mr. Flores sent Julio and Lucas down to the principal's office with a note, but the principal was out of the office at a meeting.

"You can talk to him at one o'clock," the secretary said.

PRINCIP

At lunch, Cricket had more chocolate bars. This time, she had pasted labels on them and printed in tiny letters, *Cricket is the ticket.* She must be spending her whole allowance on the campaign, Julio thought.

After a few more days of free chocolate bars, everyone in the class would be voting for Cricket.

At recess, the girls were jumping rope. You could fall jumping rope, too, Julio thought.

Back in the classroom, Julio wished he could think up some good arguments to tell the principal. He looked over at Lucas. Lucas didn't look very good. Maybe he was coming down with the flu.

Just before one o'clock, Julio had a great idea. Cricket was always saying she wanted to be a lawyer. She always knew what to say in class. Julio figured she'd know just what to do in the principal's office, too. He raised his hand.

"Mr. Flores, can Cricket go down to Mr. Herbertson's office with Lucas and me? She's running for president, so she should stick up for our class."

"Me?" Cricket said. "I don't care if we can't play soccer."

"Of course," teased Lucas. "You couldn't kick a ball if it was glued to your foot."

"Cricket," said Mr. Flores, "even if you don't want to play soccer, others in the class do. If you are elected, you will be president of the whole class, not just the girls. I think going to the meeting with Mr. Herbertson will be a good opportunity for you to represent the class."

So that was why at one o'clock Julio, Lucas, and Cricket Kaufman went downstairs to the principal's office.

Mr. Herbertson gestured for them to sit in the chairs facing his desk. Cricket looked as pale as Lucas. Maybe she, too, was coming down with the flu.

Julio waited for the future first woman President of the United States to say something, but Cricket didn't say a word. Neither did Lucas. Julio didn't know what to do. They couldn't just sit here and say nothing.

Julio took a deep breath. If Cricket or Lucas wasn't going to talk, he would have to do it. Julio started right in.

"We came to tell you that it isn't fair that no one can play soccer at recess just because Arthur Lewis broke his eyeglasses. Anybody can have an accident. He could have tripped and broken them getting on the school bus." Julio was amazed that so many words had managed to get out of his mouth. No one else said anything, so he went on. "Besides, a girl could fall jumping rope," said Julio. "But you didn't say that they had to stop jumping rope."

"I hadn't thought of that," said Mr. Herbertson.

Cricket looked alarmed. "Can't we jump rope anymore?" she asked.

"I didn't mean that you should make the girls stop jumping rope," Julio went on quickly. He stopped to think of a better example. "Your chair could break while you're sitting on it, Mr. Herbertson," he said.

Mr. Herbertson adjusted himself in his chair. "I certainly hope not," he said, smiling. "What is your name, young man?"

"Julio. Julio Sanchez." He pronounced it in the Spanish way with the *J* having an *H* sound.

"You have a couple of brothers who also attended this school, Julio, don't you?" asked the principal. "Nice fellows. I remember them both."

Julio smiled. He didn't know why he had always been afraid of the principal. He was just like any other person.

"Julio," Mr. Herbertson went on, "you've got a good head on your shoulders, just like your brothers. You made some very good points this afternoon. I think I can arrange things so that there will be more teachers supervising the yard during recess. Then you fellows can play soccer again tomorrow." He turned to Cricket. "You can jump rope if you'd rather do that," he said.

Cricket smiled. She didn't look so pale anymore.

Julio and Lucas and Cricket returned to Mr. Flores's classroom. "It's all arranged," said Cricket as soon as they walked in the door.

The class burst into cheers.

"Good work," said Mr. Flores.

Julio was proud that he had stood up to Mr. Herbertson. However, it wasn't fair that Cricket made it seem as if she had done all the work. She had hardly done a thing. For that matter, Lucas hadn't said anything, either. For a moment, Julio wished he hadn't offered to be Lucas's campaign manager. He wished he was the one running for class president. He knew he could be a good leader.

There was bad news on election day. Chris Willard was absent. Since there were twelve girls and twelve boys in Mr. Flores's class, it meant there were more girls than boys to vote in the election. If all the girls voted for Cricket and all the boys voted for Lucas, there would be a tie. Since one boy was absent, Lucas could be in big trouble. Julio hoped it didn't mean that Lucas had lost the election before they even voted.

Then Mr. Flores told the class that the Parent-Teacher Association was going to be holding a book fair in a few weeks. With more than seventeen dollars from the bake sale, the class could buy a good supply of paperbacks for a special classroom library. Cricket seemed to think it was a great idea, but Julio didn't think it was so hot. After all, there was a school library up one flight of stairs. Why did they need extra books, especially books the students had to pay for out of their *own* money?

Julio thought that the class should vote on the way the money was spent. Before he had a chance to say anything, it was time for lunch.

Lunch was chicken nuggets, whipped potatoes, string beans, and Jell-O squares. Cricket and Zoe didn't even touch their lunches. Julio knew they were talking about the election. Julio clapped Lucas on the back. "You're going to win, pal," he said. "I just know it." He really wasn't so sure, but he felt it was his job to give his candidate confidence. After all, he had convinced Lucas to run for class president in the first place.

Lucas shrugged, trying to act cool. "Maybe yes, maybe no," he said. But Julio could see that he was too excited to eat much lunch, either. Julio polished off his friend's tuna-fish sandwich and his orange. "I need to keep up my strength to vote for you," he told Lucas.

Cricket had more chocolate bars. "Are you going to vote for me?" she asked everyone.

"Maybe yes, maybe no," said Julio, taking his bar.

When they returned from lunch, Mr. Flores called the class to order. It was time for the election to begin. Mr. Flores reminded them about *Robert's Rules of Order*, which was the way school board and other important meetings were conducted.

"You may nominate anyone you choose," he said, "even if your candidate doesn't have a poster up on the wall. Then you can make a speech in favor of your candidate and try to convince your classmates."

Uh-oh, thought Julio. He was ready to nominate Lucas but he didn't know if he would be able to make a speech. He wasn't good with words, as Cricket and Lucas were.

Zoe Mitchell raised her hand. "I nominate Cricket Kaufman," she said. No surprise there. Julio wondered if Zoe had wanted to run herself.

"Does anyone second the nomination?" Mr. Flores asked.

Julio thought the class election sounded like a TV program, not the way people talked in real life.

Sara Jane seconded the nomination, and Mr. Flores wrote Cricket's name on the chalkboard.

"Are there any other nominations?" he asked.

Sara Jane raised her hand again.

"Do you have a question, Sara Jane?" asked Mr. Flores.

"Now I want to nominate Zoe Mitchell."

"You can't nominate someone when you have already seconded the nomination of someone else," Mr. Flores explained. "That's the way parliamentary procedure works."

Cricket looked relieved. She hadn't been expecting any competition from Zoe.

Julio raised his hand. "I nominate Lucas Cott," he said.

"Does anyone second the nomination?"

"Can I second myself?" asked Lucas.

"I'll second the nomination," said Anne Crosby from the back of the classroom.

"*Ooooh*," giggled one of the girls. "Anne likes Lucas."

"There is no rule that girls can nominate only girls and boys nominate only boys," said Mr. Flores. He wrote Lucas's name on the board. "Are there any other nominations?" he asked.

Arthur Lewis raised his hand. "I want to nominate Julio Sanchez," he said.

"Julio?" Sara Jane giggled. "He's just a big goof-off."

"Just a minute," said Mr. Flores sharply. "You are quite out of order, Sara Jane. Does anyone wish to second the nomination?"

Julio couldn't believe that Arthur had nominated him. Even though Arthur had said that Julio should run for president, Julio hadn't thought he would come right out and say it in front of everyone.

Cricket raised her hand. "Julio can't run for president," she said. "He was born in Puerto Rico. He isn't an American citizen. You have to be an American citizen to be elected President. We learned that last year in social studies."

"Yeah," Lucas called out. "You also have to be thirty-five years old. You must have been left back a lot of times, Cricket."

"Hold on," said Mr. Flores. "Are we electing a President of the United States here, or are we electing a president of this fifth-grade class?"

Cricket looked embarrassed. It wasn't often she was wrong about anything.

Julio stood up without even raising his hand. He didn't care if he was elected president or not, but there was one thing he had to make clear. "I am so an American citizen," he said. "All Puerto Ricans are Americans!"

Julio sat down, and Arthur raised his hand again. Julio figured he was going to say he had changed his mind and didn't want to nominate him after all.

"Arthur?" called Mr. Flores.

Arthur stood up. "It doesn't matter where Julio was born," he said. "He'd make a very good class president. He's fair, and he's always doing nice things for people. When I broke my glasses, he was the one who thought of going to Mr. Herbertson so that we could still play soccer at recess. That shows he would make a good president."

"But Julio is not one of the top students like Zoe or Lucas or me," Cricket said.

"He is tops," said Arthur. "He's tops in my book."

Julio felt his ears getting hot with embarrassment. He had never heard Arthur say so much in all the years that he had known him.

"Thank you, Arthur," said Mr. Flores. "That was a very good speech. We still need someone to second the nomination. Do I hear a second?"

Lucas raised his hand.

"I second the nomination of Julio Sanchez," he said.

Mr. Flores turned to write Julio's name on the board. Lucas was still raising his hand.

Mr. Flores turned from the board and called on Lucas again.

"Do you wish to make a campaign speech?" he asked Lucas.

"Yes, I'm going to vote for Julio, and I think everyone else should, too."

"Aren't you even going to vote for yourself?" asked Cricket.

"No," said Lucas. "I want to take my name off the board. Julio is a good leader, like Arthur said. When we went to see Mr. Herbertson, Cricket and I were scared stiff, but Julio just stepped in and did all the talking."

"Are you asking to withdraw your name from nomination, Lucas?" asked Mr. Flores.

"Yes, I am. Everyone who was going to vote for me should vote for Julio."

Julio sat in his seat without moving. He couldn't say a word. He could hardly breathe.

"Are there any other nominations?" asked Mr. Flores.

Zoe raised her hand. "I move that the nominations be closed."

"I second it," said Lucas.

Then Mr. Flores asked the two candidates if they wanted to say anything to the class.

Cricket stood up. "As you all know," she said, "I'm going to run for President of the United States some day. Being class president will be good practice for me. Besides, I know I will do a much, much better job than Julio." Cricket sat down.

Julio stood. "I might vote for Cricket when she runs for President of the United States," he said. "But right now, I hope you will all vote for me. I think our class should make decisions together, like how we should spend the money that we earned at the bake sale. We should spend the money in a way that everyone likes. Not just the teacher." Julio stopped and looked at Mr. Flores. "That's how I feel," he said.

"If I'm president," said Cricket, "I think the money should go to the Humane Society."

"*You* shouldn't tell us what to do with the money, either," said Julio. "It should be a class decision. We all helped to earn it."

"Julio has made a good point," said Mr. Flores. "I guess we can vote on that in the future."

Mr. Flores passed out the ballots. Julio was sure he knew the results even before the votes were counted. With one boy absent, Cricket would win, twelve to eleven.

Julio was right, and he was wrong. All the boys voted for him, but so did some of the girls. When the votes were counted, there were fourteen for Julio Sanchez and nine for Cricket Kaufman. Julio Sanchez was elected president of his fifth-grade class.

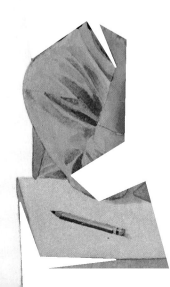

"I think you have made a good choice," said Mr. Flores. "And I know that Cricket will be a very fine vice-president."

Julio beamed. Suddenly he was filled with all sorts of plans for his class.

Mr. Flores took out his guitar. As he had said, they were going to end each week with some singing. Julio thought he had never felt so much like singing in all his life. However, even as he joined the class in the words to the song, he wished it was already time to go home. He could hardly wait to tell his family the news. Wait till he told them who was the fifth-grade class president. Julio, that's who!

At three o'clock, he ran all the way home.

Class President

Meet the Author

Johanna Hurwitz was born in New York, New York. It's not surprising that Ms. Hurwitz knew from the age of ten that she wanted to be a writer. Her parents met in a bookstore. She grew up in a New York City apartment where the walls were lined with books. Her father was a journalist and bookseller, and her mother was a library assistant.

She began her career with books working at the New York City Public Library while still in high school. She then got two degrees in Library Science. She published her first book while in her 30s and has been writing books for children ever since. In one interview she revealed, "It seems as if all my fiction has grown out of real experiences." She has written books about her children's love of baseball, her own childhood and summer vacations, her mother's childhood, and even her cats and their fleas!

Meet the Illustrator

Richard Hull teaches illustration at Brigham Young University. He has also worked as an art director and graphic designer with a magazine for fifteen years. Other books Mr. Hull has illustrated include *The Cat & the Fiddle & More*, *My Sister's Rusty Bike*, and *The Alphabet from Z to A (With Much Confusion on the Way)*. He and his wife currently reside in Orem, Utah.

Theme Connections

Think About It

With a small group of classmates, discuss what you have learned about cooperation and competition as leadership qualities.

- Which characters in the story acted cooperatively?
- Which characters acted competitively?
- Why did the students want Julio to be their class president?
- What qualities did Julio have that made him a good president?
- Why did students select Julio instead of Cricket?

Check the Concept/Question Board to see if there are any questions that you can answer now. If the selection or your discussions about the selection have raised any new questions about cooperation and competition, put these on the Concept/Question Board. Maybe the next selection will help answer the questions.

Record Ideas

What have you learned about cooperation and competition? Record your thoughts in your Writing Journal.

Make a Poster

Decide with your group who you want to support for class president—Julio or Cricket. Make a poster that shows why the students should vote for him or her.

The Marble Champ

from *Baseball in April and Other Stories*
by Gary Soto
illustrated by Maren Scott

Lupe Medrano, a shy girl who spoke in whispers, was the school's spelling bee champion, winner of the reading contest at the public library three summers in a row, blue ribbon awardee in the science fair, the top student at her piano recital, and the playground grand champion in chess. She was a straight-A student and——not counting kindergarten, when she had been stung by a wasp——never missed one day of elementary school. She had received a small trophy for this honor and had been congratulated by the mayor.

But though Lupe had a razor-sharp mind, she could not make her body, no matter how much she tried, run as fast as the other girls'. She begged her body to move faster, but could never beat anyone in the fifty-yard dash.

The truth was that Lupe was no good in sports. She could not catch a pop-up or figure out in which direction to kick the soccer ball. One time she kicked the ball at her own goal and scored a point for the other team. She was no good at baseball or basketball either, and even had a hard time making a hula hoop stay on her hips.

It wasn't until last year, when she was eleven years old, that she learned how to ride a bike. And even then she had to use training wheels. She could walk in the swimming pool but couldn't swim, and chanced roller skating only when her father held her hand.

"I'll never be good at sports," she fumed one rainy day as she lay on her bed gazing at the shelf her father had made to hold her awards. "I wish I could win something, anything, even marbles."

At the word "marbles," she sat up. "That's it. Maybe I could be good at playing marbles." She hopped out of bed and rummaged through the closet until she found a can full of her brother's marbles. She poured the rich glass treasure on her bed and picked five of the most beautiful marbles.

She smoothed her bedspread and practiced shooting, softly at first so that her aim would be accurate. The marble rolled from her thumb and clicked against the targeted marble. But the target wouldn't budge. She tried again and again. Her aim became accurate, but the power from her thumb made the marble move only an inch or two. Then she realized that the bedspread was slowing the marbles. She also had to admit that her thumb was weaker than the neck of a newborn chick.

She looked out the window. The rain was letting up, but the ground was too muddy to play. She sat cross-legged on the bed, rolling her five marbles between her palms. Yes, she thought, I could play marbles, and marbles is a sport. At that moment she realized that she had only two weeks to practice. The playground championship, the same one her brother had entered the previous year, was coming up. She had a lot to do.

To strengthen her wrists, she decided to do twenty push-ups on her fingertips, five at a time. "One, two, three . . ." she groaned. By the end of the first set she was breathing hard, and her muscles burned from exhaustion. She did one more set and decided that was enough push-ups for the first day.

She squeezed a rubber eraser one hundred times, hoping it would strengthen her thumb. This seemed to work because the next day her thumb was sore. She could hardly hold a marble in her hand, let alone send it flying with power. So Lupe rested that day and listened to her brother, who gave her tips on how to shoot: get low, aim with one eye, and place one knuckle on the ground.

"Think 'eye and thumb'—and let it rip!" he said.

After school the next day she left her homework in her backpack and practiced three hours straight, taking time only to eat a candy bar for energy. With a popsicle stick, she drew an odd-shaped circle and tossed in four marbles. She used her shooter, a milky agate with hypnotic swirls, to blast them. Her thumb *had* become stronger.

After practice, she squeezed the eraser for an hour. She ate dinner with her left hand to spare her shooting hand and said nothing to her parents about her dreams of athletic glory.

Practice, practice, practice. Squeeze, squeeze, squeeze. Lupe got better and beat her brother and Alfonso, a neighbor kid who was supposed to be a champ.

"Man, she's bad!" Alfonso said. "She can beat the other girls for sure. I think."

The weeks passed quickly. Lupe worked so hard that one day, while she was drying dishes, her mother asked why her thumb was swollen.

"It's muscle," Lupe explained. "I've been practicing for the marbles championship."

"You, honey?" Her mother knew Lupe was no good at sports.

"Yeah. I beat Alfonso, and he's pretty good."

That night, over dinner, Mrs. Medrano said, "Honey, you should see Lupe's thumb."

"Huh?" Mr. Medrano said, wiping his mouth and looking at his daughter.

"Show your father."

"Do I have to?" an embarrassed Lupe asked.

"Go on, show your father."

Reluctantly, Lupe raised her hand and flexed her thumb. You could see the muscle.

The father put down his fork and asked, "What happened?"

"Dad, I've been working out. I've been squeezing an eraser."

"Why?"

"I'm going to enter the marbles championship."

Her father looked at her mother and then back at his daughter. "When is it, honey?"

"This Saturday. Can you come?"

The father had been planning to play racquetball with a friend Saturday, but he said he would be there. He knew his daughter thought she was no good at sports and he wanted to encourage her. He even rigged some lights in the backyard so she could practice after dark. He squatted with one knee on the ground, entranced by the sight of his daughter easily beating her brother.

The day of the championship began with a cold blustery sky. The sun was a silvery light behind slate clouds.

"I hope it clears up," her father said, rubbing his hands together as he returned from getting the newspaper. They ate breakfast, paced nervously around the house waiting for 10:00 to arrive, and walked the two blocks to the playground (though Mr. Medrano wanted to drive so Lupe wouldn't get tired). She signed up and was assigned her first match on baseball diamond number three.

Lupe, walking between her brother and her father, shook from the cold, not nerves. She took off her mittens, and everyone stared at her thumb. Someone asked, "How can you play with a broken thumb?" Lupe smiled and said nothing.

She beat her first opponent easily, and felt sorry for the girl because she didn't have anyone to cheer for her. Except for her sack of marbles, she was all alone. Lupe invited the girl, whose name was Rachel, to stay with them. She smiled and said, "OK." The four of them walked to a card table in the middle of the outfield, where Lupe was assigned another opponent.

She also beat this girl, a fifth-grader named Yolanda, and asked her to join their group. They proceeded to more matches and more wins, and soon there was a crowd of people following Lupe to the finals to play a girl in a baseball cap. This girl seemed dead serious. She never even looked at Lupe.

"I don't know, Dad, she looks tough."

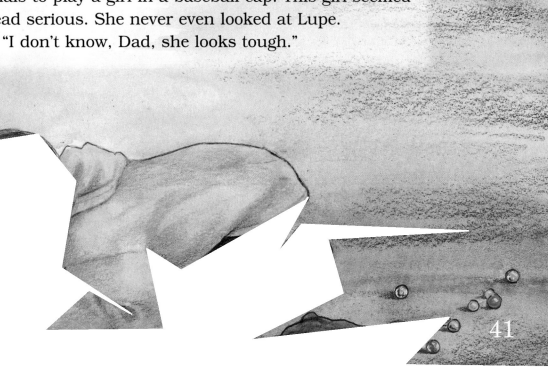

41

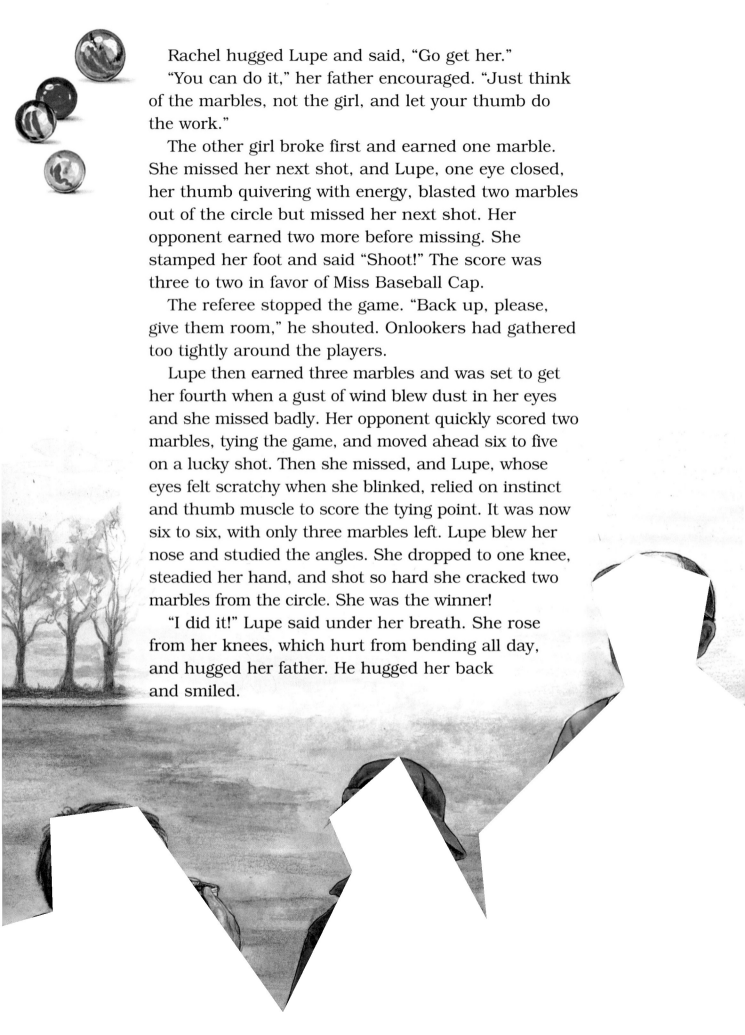

Rachel hugged Lupe and said, "Go get her."

"You can do it," her father encouraged. "Just think of the marbles, not the girl, and let your thumb do the work."

The other girl broke first and earned one marble. She missed her next shot, and Lupe, one eye closed, her thumb quivering with energy, blasted two marbles out of the circle but missed her next shot. Her opponent earned two more before missing. She stamped her foot and said "Shoot!" The score was three to two in favor of Miss Baseball Cap.

The referee stopped the game. "Back up, please, give them room," he shouted. Onlookers had gathered too tightly around the players.

Lupe then earned three marbles and was set to get her fourth when a gust of wind blew dust in her eyes and she missed badly. Her opponent quickly scored two marbles, tying the game, and moved ahead six to five on a lucky shot. Then she missed, and Lupe, whose eyes felt scratchy when she blinked, relied on instinct and thumb muscle to score the tying point. It was now six to six, with only three marbles left. Lupe blew her nose and studied the angles. She dropped to one knee, steadied her hand, and shot so hard she cracked two marbles from the circle. She was the winner!

"I did it!" Lupe said under her breath. She rose from her knees, which hurt from bending all day, and hugged her father. He hugged her back and smiled.

Everyone clapped, except Miss Baseball Cap, who made a face and stared at the ground. Lupe told her she was a great player, and they shook hands. A newspaper photographer took pictures of the two girls standing shoulder-to-shoulder, with Lupe holding the bigger trophy.

Lupe then played the winner of the boys' division, and after a poor start beat him eleven to four. She blasted the marbles, shattering one into sparkling slivers of glass. Her opponent looked on glumly as Lupe did what she did best——win!

The head referee and the President of the Fresno Marble Association stood with Lupe as she displayed her trophies for the newspaper photographer. Lupe shook hands with everyone, including a dog who had come over to see what the commotion was all about.

That night, the family went out for pizza and set the two trophies on the table for everyone in the restaurant to see. People came up to congratulate Lupe, and she felt a little embarrassed, but her father said the trophies belonged there.

Back home, in the privacy of her bedroom, she placed the trophies on her shelf and was happy. She had always earned honors because of her brains, but winning in sports was a new experience. She thanked her tired thumb. "You did it, thumb. You made me champion." As its reward, Lupe went to the bathroom, filled the bathroom sink with warm water, and let her thumb swim and splash as it pleased. Then she climbed into bed and drifted into a hard-won sleep.

The Marble Champ

Meet the Author

Gary Soto was born into a Mexican-American family in Fresno, California. Growing up, he worked alongside his parents, grandparents, brothers and sister, as farm laborers in vineyards, orange groves, and cotton fields around Fresno.

As a young person, Mr. Soto was never very interested in books or schoolwork, but he decided to enroll in college anyway. He discovered he wanted to be a writer at the age of 20. In one of his classes he read a poem called "Unwanted." It had a big effect on him. He started taking poetry classes and writing his own poetry. Mr. Soto continues to write for both adults and children, and he produces short films.

Meet the Illustrator

Maren Scott lives in Utah with her husband and three sons. Besides illustrating, she also enjoys designing quilts. She has won many awards for both her art and her quilts. Ms. Scott advises young people interested in being artists to draw everyday. She says, "Draw what you see and don't be concerned about mistakes. It's okay to make mistakes, just learn from them and you'll get better and better!"

Theme Connections

Think About It

With a small group of classmates, discuss some of the experiences you have had when learning a new game.

- How did you learn the game?
- Did you practice to learn it?
- How successful were you at learning it?
- Was cooperation involved in learning it? If so, who cooperated?
- Was competition involved? If so, who did you compete with?

Also, think about this: If you had a marble team, would you want Lupe on it? Why or why not? Would you want to have Lupe as a friend? Why or why not?

Check the Concept/Question Board to see if there are any questions that you can answer now. If the selection or your discussions about the selection have raised any new questions about cooperation and competition, put the questions on the Concept/Question Board. Maybe the next selection will help answer the questions.

Record Ideas

Record in your Writing Journal any ideas you have thought about or discussed. Highlight or underline anything new you have learned. Try to think of ways you can use what you have learned about cooperation and competition in your dramatic play, and explain them.

Find a Quotation

Look through the story and find a statement made by one of the story characters that shows how he or she feels about competition and cooperation. Write the quote on an index card. Under the quote, write whether or not you agree with the quote. Explain why or why not.

The New Kid

by Mike Makley
illustrated by Laurel Aiello

Our baseball team never did very much,
we had me and PeeWee and Earl and Dutch.
And the Oak Street Tigers always got beat
until the new kid moved in on our street.

The kid moved in with a mitt and a bat
and an official New York Yankee hat.
The new kid plays shortstop or second base
and can outrun us all in any race.

The kid never muffs a grounder or fly
no matter how hard it's hit or how high.
And the new kid always acts quite polite,
never yelling or spitting or starting a fight.

We were playing the league champs just last week;
they were trying to break our winning streak.
In the last inning the score was one-one,
when the new kid swung and hit a home run.

A few of the kids and their parents say
they don't believe that the new kid should play.
But she's good as me, Dutch, PeeWee, or Earl,
so we don't care that the new kid's a girl.

Good Sportsmanship

by Richard Armour
illustrated by Laurel Aiello

Good sportsmanship we hail, we sing,
It's always pleasant when you spot it.
There's only one unhappy thing:
You have to lose to prove you've got it.

Juggling

by Donna Gamache
illustrations by Daniel Powers

In gym class on Monday, we started volleyball, and I hit seven straight serves just over the net, hard and fast. Mr. Braden called me over at the end of the class.

"You've got a good serve, Kyle," he said. "How about coming out for the junior team?"

"Sorry, Mr. Braden," I said, without looking at him. "I'm busy every afternoon." I knew the practices were three times a week, right after school, and that's when I delivered papers. I'd started a paper route two years ago when I was ten, but this year I'd taken over a second route—a long one, too. I never finished delivering before 5:30.

"Well, think about it," Mr. Braden called as I left for my next class. "We could use a serve like yours. Couldn't you juggle your time a little?"

My friend Dave was waiting for me outside the gym door. "Did Mr. Braden ask you to join the team?" he asked.

I nodded. "I told him I was busy."

"You're a lot better than I am," said Dave as we got books from our lockers. "I wish you'd join. We need good servers."

Our next class was math, but it was hard to keep my mind on fractions and percentages. I kept thinking about how good it felt to hit that ball and see it sail over the net. Somehow I managed a spin on the ball that made it hard to hit back.

I'd have loved to say yes to Mr. Braden, but I couldn't afford to. I needed that paper route—or rather, my mom and I *both* needed it. We lived alone in a basement apartment about three blocks from school, and Mom worked at the Cramer Clothing

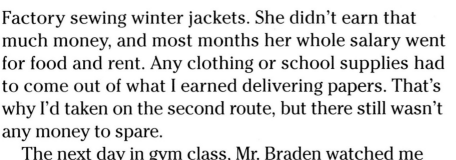

Factory sewing winter jackets. She didn't earn that much money, and most months her whole salary went for food and rent. Any clothing or school supplies had to come out of what I earned delivering papers. That's why I'd taken on the second route, but there still wasn't any money to spare.

The next day in gym class, Mr. Braden watched me again, and when class ended, he called out loudly, "Think about joining the team, Kyle."

Everyone heard him, and soon several other boys started trying to persuade me. "We haven't got any strong servers," said Jason. "Come on and help us out."

"I bet you could learn to spike the ball," said Billy. "You're tall enough."

They didn't seem to hear me when I mentioned my paper routes.

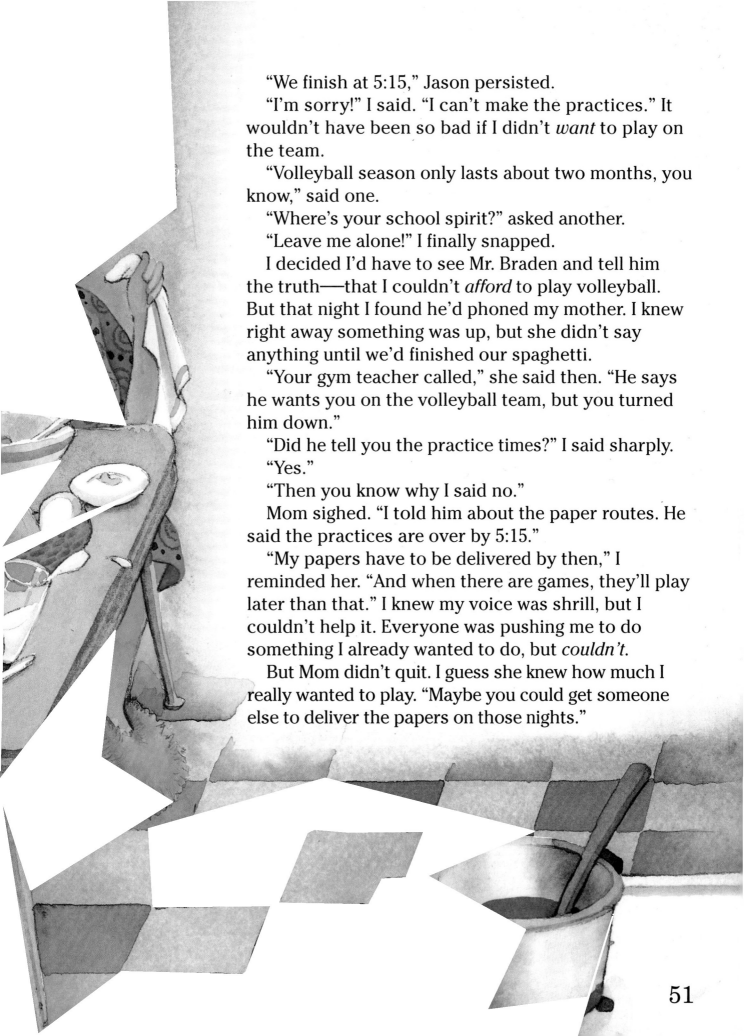

"We finish at 5:15," Jason persisted.

"I'm sorry!" I said. "I can't make the practices." It wouldn't have been so bad if I didn't *want* to play on the team.

"Volleyball season only lasts about two months, you know," said one.

"Where's your school spirit?" asked another.

"Leave me alone!" I finally snapped.

I decided I'd have to see Mr. Braden and tell him the truth—that I couldn't *afford* to play volleyball. But that night I found he'd phoned my mother. I knew right away something was up, but she didn't say anything until we'd finished our spaghetti.

"Your gym teacher called," she said then. "He says he wants you on the volleyball team, but you turned him down."

"Did he tell you the practice times?" I said sharply.

"Yes."

"Then you know why I said no."

Mom sighed. "I told him about the paper routes. He said the practices are over by 5:15."

"My papers have to be delivered by then," I reminded her. "And when there are games, they'll play later than that." I knew my voice was shrill, but I couldn't help it. Everyone was pushing me to do something I already wanted to do, but *couldn't*.

But Mom didn't quit. I guess she knew how much I really wanted to play. "Maybe you could get someone else to deliver the papers on those nights."

"I'd have to pay someone nearly twenty dollars a week to do both routes three times," I said. Abruptly, I shoved my chair back from the table and stamped into my room. I flung myself on the bed and I didn't go out to help Mom with the dishes, either.

The next day in gym class, I deliberately hit all my serves low into the net and I messed up several setups, too. I saw Mr. Braden looking at me in a funny way, but he didn't say anything then. I kept away from Dave all day and ignored the other boys from the team.

At 3:30 I grabbed my homework from my locker and was just heading out the door when my name was called on the intercom. "Kyle Kreerson, please report to Mr. Braden's office."

I thought about ignoring the announcement, but I didn't want to get into trouble. When I reached the office, I saw that Dave was already there. I didn't give Mr. Braden time to speak. I just started right in. "Mr. Braden," I said, "I'm sorry I can't join your team. Will you please stop asking me about it? And ask the other guys to stop pestering me? I'd join if I could. But I *can't!* O.K.?!"

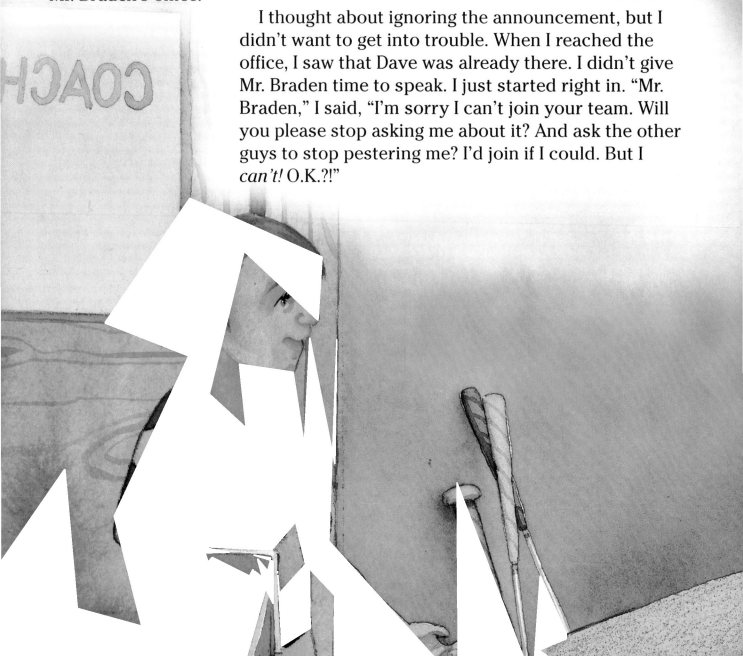

Nobody spoke for a minute, and then Mr. Braden took a deep breath. His face was red, almost like his hair. "Kyle," he said, "I understand. I'm sorry to pressure you, but I called you here to suggest something. Maybe *I* can do the juggling, instead of you."

"What do you mean?"

"As you know, Miss Foxon coaches the girls' team. Right now, they practice after us, but she's offered to trade practice times. That would start our practices at 5:15."

"I'm not finished with my routes by then," I said sharply.

"If you had some help, you could be, right? Dave is offering to help you."

"I can't afford to pay him," I insisted.

"I don't want to be paid," Dave said.

"Then why do it?"

Dave shrugged. "Because I want to. Because I want you on the team. And because you're my friend."

"Enough reasons?" asked Mr. Braden.

I looked at them both for a moment and I felt good for the first time in four days. "When do we start?" I smiled.

Juggling

Meet the Illustrator

Daniel Powers always loved drawing and painting, but he never went to art school until recently. Mr. Powers lives in the high desert country of New Mexico and enjoys hiking there with his wife and two dogs. A couple of times a year he works with children in the schools of the nearby Zuñi Pueblo. He has illustrated many children's books including *Jiro's Pearl, From the Land of the White Birch,* and *Dear Katie, The Volcano is a Girl.*

Theme Connections

Think About It

With a small group of classmates, discuss what you have learned about how obligations affect one's ability to cooperate and compete. During discussion, address the following questions.

- How did Kyle's feelings change from the beginning of the story to the end?
- Would you want to have a teammate like Kyle? Why or why not?
- Would you want to have a friend like Kyle? Why or why not?
- Why wasn't Kyle pleased to be asked to join the volleyball team?
- Why did Kyle's mother encourage him to join the team, even though they needed the money from his job?

Record Ideas

In your Writing Journal, write what you have learned about cooperation and competition from the class discussions. Also, record any new questions or ideas that may have arisen from discussion.

Make a List

Does your group cooperate when working on your unit activity? Make a list of:

- the ways you cooperate
- the ways cooperating helps you learn
- other things your group could do to learn more cooperatively

FINE Art

Small Roman Abacus. Museo Nazionale Romano Delle Terme, Rome, Italy. Photo: SCALA/Art Resource, NY.

Footballers. Ruskin Spear. Private collection. Photo: Christie's Images.

Artist Pyramid. **Josef Hegenbarth.** Oil on canvas. Private collection. Photo: Christie's Images.

Catcher on the Line. **Robert Riggs.** Oil on canvas. Private collection. Photo: Christie's Images.

The Abacus Contest

by Priscilla Wu

illustrated by Yoshi Miyake

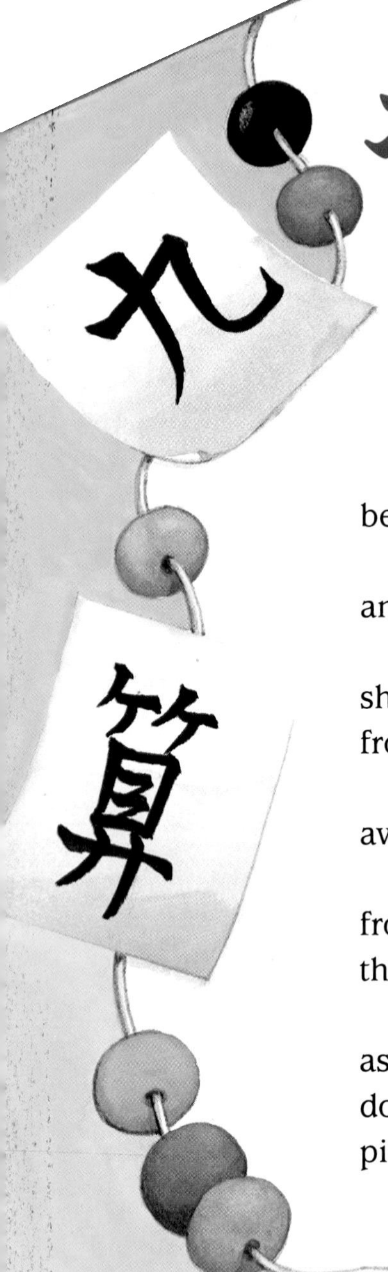

Gao Mai's fingers flew back and forth over the smooth black beads of the abacus.

Suddenly a wire snapped. The beads bounced onto the desk and rolled across the floor.

Gao Mai fell to her knees and crawled around after them. Just as she reached for the last bead, her best friend Li Zhi kicked it away from her hand. The other children giggled. Gao Mai's face burned.

Gao Mai opened her eyes wide and sat up in alarm. What an awful dream!

The comforting aroma of steamy, overcooked rice drifted in from the next room. She pushed aside the heavy quilt, got up from the floor and put on her school uniform.

"Are you ready for the big day?" Gao Mai's mother asked her as she came into the main room of the apartment. Gao Mai sat down at the table and helped herself to dried meat, eel and pickled cucumber.

The dream was fresh in her mind. "I'm not sure," she said.

"Remember what I told you," said Gao Mai's father. "Imagine the abacus is part of you." He smiled at her. "You did so well when we practiced."

It was true. During a few of her many timed drills she was even faster than her father. And he used the abacus every day at the bank.

"Don't worry," said her mother. "You're one of the best abacus students in your class."

"But what about Li Zhi?" asked Gao Mai. "She's beaten me every year."

"Last time it was only by one second. You've improved so much, I'm sure you'll win. Besides," continued her mother, as she lit the incense on the altar where the family ancestors were honored, "you were born under the lucky sign of the horse. I went to the temple yesterday and said a special prayer for you."

Gao Mai looked at her watch. "I have to go."

"Good luck," said her mother.

"Good luck," said her father. "I'll be thinking about you all morning."

Gao Mai ran downstairs to the street and walked quickly through the open market. One farmer had spread a piece of burlap on the pavement and piled it high with cut sugarcane. Her mouth watered as she thought of sucking the sweet juice from the snowy white center. Gao Mai glanced at the fish swimming around in a shallow metal pan. Tonight they would be on someone's plate, maybe even her own.

She reached the school just as the bell rang. Outside her classroom some boys were playing jian zhi. Her classmate, Kun Pei, scored one point after another by kicking the jian zhi into the air over and over again without letting it hit the ground.

Gao Mai walked into the classroom and Kun Pei yelled: "I won!"

During last year's abacus contest Li Zhi had beaten Kun Pei by four seconds, and Gao Mai had beaten him by three seconds. Today she was hoping to beat both of them.

Gao Mai watched Li Zhi's braids bounce as she tapped everyone on the way to her desk. She knew Li Zhi loved practical jokes and could tell by her mischievous look that she might play one at any moment. Gao Mai smiled while thinking of jokes they had played on their classmates together. Last week they had even played one on Li Zhi's mother. Yesterday Li Zhi had invited her to come over after school today so that they could think of a trick to play on her brother, Da Wei.

"Don't forget who won last year," said Li Zhi, sitting down behind her. She tugged on Gao Mai's ponytail and giggled.

"That was last year." Gao Mai leaned away and said, "If you pull my hair again, I'm not going to your house today."

Li Zhi leaned forward to grab Gao Mai's ponytail but only caught the tip. Gao Mai started to say: That's it, I'm not going to your house today. But the teacher arrived and the class stood up to greet him.

"Ni hao?" said Mr. Wang. "While everyone is nice and fresh, we'll begin with the abacus contest." He passed out booklets filled with addition, subtraction, multiplication and division problems.

"Open to the first page and begin with number one. When all the exercises are completed, return your booklet to my desk and I'll write the final time. Ready?" He paused. "Begin!"

Gao Mai's left hand moved down the column of numbers rapidly, wrote the answers and turned the test pages. The fingers on her right hand flew back and forth among the smooth, black beads of the abacus.

In a few minutes she was writing the last answer to the addition problems. Gao Mai began subtracting and a moment later heard pages turning. Everyone was right behind her!

She worked carefully. It was easy to make a subtraction mistake, especially when exchanging a higher bead for lesser ones.

After finishing the last subtraction problem she heard Li Zhi's page turn.

Gao Mai frantically turned to the multiplication but two pages were stuck together. She pulled them apart with shaking hands.

Barely breathing, Gao Mai sped through the multiplication and division. Finally she wrote down the last answer, jumped from her seat and collided with Li Zhi.

Two desks in front of them, Kun Pei rushed up and dropped his booklet on the teacher's desk.

"Oh, no!" yelled Li Zhi. "It's not fair!" She and Gao Mai dropped their booklets on the desk immediately after him.

"Quiet down, everyone," said the teacher.

Gao Mai returned to her desk and slumped in the seat, unaware of the other students handing in their booklets. Her bad dream had come true.

"Time for recess," said Mr. Wang, "while I check the answers."

Gao Mai was the last to go outside.

"Come on," yelled Ping Mei, wanting her to come and jump rope. But she shook her head. Across the playground, Li Zhi motioned for her to come and play tag with some of their friends. But Gao Mai turned away.

As he kicked the jian zhi into the air, Kun Pei bragged to a group of boys about winning the abacus contest. Gao Mai thought of her father's jian zhi at home on top of the TV. Father! Gao Mai knew he'd be disappointed that she hadn't won. The bell rang and everyone piled back into the classroom.

She heard Li Zhi behind her, laughing. "Hurry up, slowpoke!" she said, pushing past her.

Gao Mai secretly wished she could be carefree, like Li Zhi.

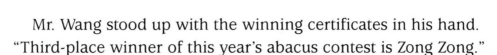

Mr. Wang stood up with the winning certificates in his hand. "Third-place winner of this year's abacus contest is Zong Zong."

The class applauded and a small girl with thick glasses walked quickly to the front of the room and shook hands with the teacher.

"The second-place certificate goes to Kun Pei," Mr. Wang continued.

Kun Pei came forward, looking as if he were about to cry.

"You were first to get your booklet in," Mr. Wang said as he handed him a certificate. "But one answer was wrong."

Gao Mai was confused. She turned around and looked into Li Zhi's bewildered face.

"Now," began the teacher, "we have an unusual situation——one that has never happened to me before. First place in speed and accuracy goes to Li Zhi, last year's first-place winner, and also to Gao Mai, last year's second-place winner."

Gao Mai turned and looked at Li Zhi. They burst out laughing and hurried to the front of the room.

"Here's a first-place certificate for both of you," said Mr. Wang.

As Gao Mai shook hands with the teacher, she decided it was a good day to go to Li Zhi's, after all.

The
Abacus Contest

Meet the Author

Priscilla Wu comes from a family full of writers. Her father and grandfather write books, and her grandmother had some articles published in a newspaper. Says Priscilla, "My dad, I remember him in the basement pounding away on a typewriter. . . . And from my dad's side—he was from the South—there was a tradition of storytelling. I grew up with many stories, or tall tales. . . . And I did the same thing with my own children. We had a lot of storytelling. We used to sit around in the dark at night, and sometimes, rather than read a story, we would tell stories." Priscilla went on to become a writer herself, but not because writing came easily to her. "I wasn't a very good writer in school. I've had to work very hard, and I think it is important to let students know that working hard *does* make a difference."

Meet the Illustrator

Yoshi Miyake was born in Tokyo, Japan. She graduated from the Tokyo Metropolitan University with a degree in chemistry. While in college, she took a correspondence class in art. After graduation, she moved to Chicago to attend the American Academy of Art. She later opened a gallery called American West. Her long-time interest in Native American culture, and her study of the Blackfoot and Sioux languages inspired the theme of this gallery. Yoshi Miyake is the illustrator of more than a dozen children's books.

Theme Connections

Think About It

With a small group of classmates, discuss what you have learned about ways that people cooperate and compete. During discussion, address the following questions.

- Why did Gao Mai believe she had to win the contest?
- What might Gao Mai's parents tell her if she told them how nervous she was?
- How did Gao Mai feel about sharing her victory?
- Have you ever wanted to be first in some activity? Why did it matter so much to you?

Record Ideas

Record what you have learned about the unit theme and the pressures competitors put on themselves. Also, record any new ideas you may have for your unit activity.

Draw a Stick Figure

With a partner from outside your unit activity group, brainstorm the physical feelings people sometimes have before a competition (for example, a queasy stomach or clammy hands). Then, work together to draw a stick person. Identify on it the symptoms you and your partner brainstormed with arrows pointing to parts of the body that are affected.

S.O.R. Losers

from the book by Avi
illustrated by Charles Jordan

Ed Sitrow and his friends have a big problem. All students at South Orange River Middle School are required to play one sport per year—only Ed is no jock and neither are his friends. Playing a sport is sure to mean only one thing for them—total humiliation. Somehow, they manage to slip through their first year at S.O.R. without playing a sport. But when the school catches on, they make up a special soccer team just for Ed's crowd. This soccer team is anything but typical at a school positively famous for its winning teams and all-star athletes. Mr. Lester, the history teacher, has volunteered to be their coach. Little does the team know that they'll be making history of their own.

I should have guessed what was going to happen next when this kid from the school newspaper interviewed me. It went this way.

NEWSPAPER: How does it feel to lose every game?
ME: I never played on a team that won, so I can't compare. But it's . . . interesting.
NEWSPAPER: How many teams have you been on?
ME: Just this one.
NEWSPAPER: Do you want to win?
ME: Wouldn't mind knowing what it feels like. For the novelty.
NEWSPAPER: Have you figured out why you lose all the time?
ME: They score more goals.
NEWSPAPER: Have you seen any improvement?
ME: I've been too busy.

NEWSPAPER: Busy with what?

ME: Trying to stop their goals. Ha-ha.

NEWSPAPER: From the scores, it doesn't seem like you've been too successful with that.

ME: You can imagine what the scores would have been if I wasn't there. Actually, I'm the tallest.

NEWSPAPER: What's that have to do with it?

ME: Ask Mr. Lester.

NEWSPAPER: No S.O.R. team has ever lost all its games in one season. How do you feel about that record?

ME: I read somewhere that records are made to be broken.

NEWSPAPER: But how will you feel?

ME: Same as I do now.

NEWSPAPER: How's that?

ME: Fine.

NEWSPAPER: Give us a prediction. Will you win or lose your last game?

ME: As captain, I can promise only one thing.

NEWSPAPER: What's that?

ME: I don't want to be there to see what happens.

Naturally, they printed all that. Next thing I knew some kids decided to hold a pep rally.

"What for?" asked Radosh.

"To fill us full of pep, I suppose."

"What's pep?"

Hays looked it up. "Dash," he read.

Saltz shook his head.

"What's dash?" asked Porter.

"Sounds like a deodorant soap," said Eliscue.

And then Ms. Appleton called me aside. "Ed," she said, sort of whispering (I guess she was embarrassed to be seen talking to any of us), "people are asking, 'Do they *want* to lose?'"

"Who's asking?"

"It came up at the last teachers' meeting. Mr. Tillman thinks you might be encouraging a defeatist attitude in the school. And Mr. Lester . . ."

"What about him?"

"He doesn't know."

It figured. "Ms. Appleton," I said, "why do people care so much if we win or lose?"

"It's your . . . attitude," she said. "It's so unusual. We're not used to . . . well . . . not winning sometimes. Or . . . not caring if you lose."

"Think there's something the matter with us?" I wanted to know.

"No," she said, but when you say "no" the way she did, slowly, there's lots of time to sneak in a good hint of "yes." "I don't think you *mean* to lose."

"That's not what I asked."

"It's important to win," she said.

"Why? We're good at other things. Why can't we stick with that?"

But all she said was, "Try harder."

I went back to my seat. "I'm getting nervous," I mumbled.

"About time," said Saltz.

"Maybe we should defect."

"Where to?"

"There must be some country that doesn't have sports."

Then, of course, when my family sat down for dinner that night it went on.

"In two days you'll have your last game, won't you," my ma said. It was false cheerful, as if I had a terminal illness and she wanted to pretend it was only a head cold.

"Yeah," I said.

"You're going to win," my father announced.

"How do you know?" I snapped.

"I sense it."

"Didn't know you could tell the future."

"Don't be so smart," he returned. "I'm trying to be supportive."

"I'm sick of support!" I yelled and left the room.

Twenty minutes later I got a call. Saltz.

"Guess what?" he said.

"I give up."

"Two things. My father offered me a bribe."

"To lose the game?"

"No, to win it. A new bike."

"Wow. What did you say?"

"I told him I was too honest to win a game."

"What was the second thing?"

"I found out that at lunch tomorrow they are doing that pep rally, and worse. They're going to call up the whole team."

I sighed. "Why are they doing all this?" I asked.

"Nobody loves a loser," said Saltz.

"Why?" I asked him, just as I had asked everybody else.

"Beats me. Like everybody else does." He hung up.

I went into my room and flung myself on my bed and stared up at the ceiling. A short time later my father came into the room. "Come on, kid," he said, "I was just trying to be a pal."

"Why can't people let us lose in peace?"

"People think you feel bad."

"We feel *fine!*"

"Come on. We won't talk about it any more. Eat your dinner."

I went.

Next day, when I walked into the school eating area for lunch there was the usual madhouse. But there was also a big banner across the front part of the room:

Make the Losers Winners
Keep Up the Good Name of
S.O.R.

I wanted to start a food fight right then and there.

I'm not going through the whole bit. But halfway through the lunch period, the president of the School Council, of all people, went to the microphone and called for attention. Then she made a speech.

"We just want to say to the Special Seventh-Grade Soccer Team that we're all behind you."

"It's in front of us where we need people," whispered Saltz. "Blocking."

The president went on. "Would you come up and take a bow." One by one she called our names. Each time one of us went up, looking like cringing but grinning worms, there was some general craziness, hooting, foot stomping, and an occasional milk carton shooting through the air.

The president said: "I'd like the team captain, Ed Sitrow, to say a few words."

What could I do? Trapped, I cleared my throat. Four times. "Ah, well . . . we . . . ah . . . sure . . . hope to get there . . . and . . . you know . . . I suppose . . . play and . . . you know!"

The whole room stood up to cheer. They even began the school chant.

"Give me an S! Give me an O . . . "

After that we went back to our seats. I was madder than ever. And as I sat there, maybe two hundred and fifty kids filed by, thumping me hard on the back, shoulder, neck and head, yelling, "Good luck! Good luck!" They couldn't fool me. I knew what they were doing: beating me.

"Saltz," I said when they were gone and I was merely numb, "I'm calling an emergency meeting of the team."

Like thieves, we met behind the school, out of sight. I looked around. I could see everybody was feeling rotten.

"I'm sick and tired of people telling me we have to win," said Root.

"I think my folks are getting ready to disown me," said Hays. "My brother and sister too."

"Why can't they just let us lose?" asked Macht.

"Yeah," said Barish, "because we're not going to win."

"We might," Lifsom offered. "Parkville is supposed to be the pits too."

"Yeah, said Radosh, "but we're beneath the pits."

"Right," agreed Porter.

For a moment it looked like everyone was going to start to cry.

"I'd just like to do my math," said Macht. "I like that."

There it was. Something clicked. "Hays," I said, "you're good at music, right."

"Yeah, well, sure—rock 'n' roll."

"Okay. And Macht, what's the lowest score you've pulled in math so far?"

"A-plus."

"Last year?"

"Same."

71

"Lifsom," I went on, getting excited, "how's your painting coming?"

"I just finished something real neat and . . . "

"That's it," I cut in, because that kid can go on forever about his painting. "Every one of us is good at something. Right? Maybe more than one thing. The point is, *other* things."

"Sure," said Barish.

"Except," put in Saltz, "sports."

We were quiet for a moment. Then I saw what had been coming to me: "That's *their* problem. I mean, we are good, good at *lots* of things. Why can't we just plain stink in some places? That's got to be normal."

"Let's hear it for normal," chanted Dorman.

"Doesn't bother me to lose at sports," I said. "At least, it didn't bother me until I let other people make me bothered."

"What about the school record?" asked Porter. "You know, no team ever losing for a whole season. Want to be famous for that?"

"Listen," I said, "did we want to be on this team?"

"No!" they all shouted.

"I can see some of it," I said. "You know, doing something different. But I don't like sports. I'm not good at it. I don't enjoy it. So I say, so what? I mean if Saltz here writes a stinko poem–and he does all the time–do they yell at him? When was the last time Mr. Tillman came around and said, 'Saltz, I *believe* in your being a poet!'"

"Never," said Saltz.

"Yeah," said Radosh. "How come sports is so important?"

"You know," said Dorman, "maybe a loser makes people think of things *they* lost. Like Mr. Tillman not getting into pro football. Us losing makes him remember that."

"Us winning, he forgets," cut in Eliscue.

"Right," I agreed. "He needs us to win for *him*, not for us. Maybe it's the same for others."

"Yeah, but how are you going to convince them of that?" said Barish.

"By not caring if we lose," I said.

"Only one thing," put in Saltz. "They say this Parkville team is pretty bad too. What happens if we, you know, by mistake, win?"

That set us back a moment.

"I think," suggested Hays after a moment, "that if we just go on out there, relax, and do our best, and not worry so much, we'll lose."

There was general agreement on that point.

"Do you know what I heard?" said Eliscue.

"What?"

"I didn't want to say it before, but since the game's a home game, they're talking about letting the whole school out to cheer us on to a win."

"You're kidding."

He shook his head.

There was a long, deep silence.

"Probably think," said Saltz, "that we'd be ashamed to lose in front of everybody."

I took a quick count. "You afraid to lose?" I asked Saltz.

"No way."

"Hays?"

"No."

"Porter?"

"Nope."

And so on. I felt encouraged. It was a complete vote of no confidence.

"Well," I said, "they just might see us lose again. With Parkville so bad I'm not saying it's automatic. But I'm not going to care if we do."

"Right," said Radosh. "It's not like we're committing treason or something. People have a right to be losers."

We considered that for a moment. It was then I had my most brilliant idea. "Who has money?"

"What for?"

"I'm your tall captain, right? Trust me. And bring your soccer T-shirts to me in the morning, early."

I collected about four bucks and we split up. I held Saltz back.

"What's the money all about?" he wanted to know. "And the T-shirts."

"Come on," I told him. "Maybe we can show them we really mean it."

When I woke the next morning, I have to admit, I was excited. It wasn't going to be an ordinary day. I looked outside and saw the sun was shining. I thought, "Good."

For the first time I *wanted* a game to happen.

I got to breakfast a little early, actually feeling happy.

"Today's the day," Dad announced.

"Right."

HOME ECONOMICS

"Today you'll really win," chipped in my ma.

"Could be."

My father leaned across the table and gave me a tap. "Winning the last game is what matters. Go out with your head high, Ed."

"And my backside up if I lose?" I wanted to know.

"Ed," said my ma, "don't be so hard on yourself. Your father and I are coming to watch."

"Suit yourselves," I said, and beat it to the bus.

As soon as I got to class Saltz and I collected the T-shirts. "What are you going to do with them?" the others kept asking.

"You picked me as captain, didn't you?"

"Mr. Lester did."

"Well, this time, trust *me*."

When we got all the shirts, Saltz and I sneaked into the home ec room and did what needed to be done. Putting them into a bag so no one would see, we went back to class.

"Just about over," I said.

"I'm almost sorry," confessed Saltz.

"Me too," I said. "And I can't figure out why."

"Maybe it's—the team that loses together, really stays together."

"Right. Not one fathead on the whole team. Do you think we should have gotten a farewell present for Mr. Lester?"

"Like what?"

"A begging cup."

It was hard getting through the day. And it's impossible to know how many people wished me luck. From all I got it was clear they considered me the unluckiest guy in the whole world. I kept wishing I could have banked it for something important.

But the day got done.

It was down in the locker room, when we got ready, that I passed out the T-shirts.

Barish held his up. It was the regular shirt with "S.O.R." on the back. But under it Saltz and I had ironed on press letters. Now they all read:

S.O.R.
LOSERS

Barish's reaction was just to stare. That was my only nervous moment. Then he cracked up, laughing like crazy. And the rest, once they saw, joined in. When Mr. Lester came down he brought Mr. Tillman. We all stood up and turned our backs to them.

"Oh, my goodness," moaned Mr. Lester.

"That's sick," said Mr. Tillman. "Sick!" His happy beads shook furiously.

"It's honest," I said.

"It's defeatist," he yelled.

"Mr. Tillman, I asked, "is that true, about your trying out for pro football?"

He started to say something, then stopped, his mouth open. "Yeah. I tried to make it with the pros, but couldn't."

"So you lost too, right?"

"Yeah," chimed in Radosh, "everyone loses sometime."

"Listen here, you guys," said Mr. Tillman, "it's no fun being rejected."

"Can't it be okay to lose sometimes? You did. Lots do. You're still alive. And we don't dislike you because of that."

"Right. We got other reasons," I heard a voice say. I think it was Saltz.

Mr. Tillman started to say something, but turned and fled.

Mr. Lester tried to give us a few final pointers, like don't touch the ball with our hands, only use feet, things that we didn't always remember to do.

"Well," he said finally, "I enjoyed this."

"You did?" said Porter, surprised.

"Well, not much," he admitted. "I never coached anything before. To tell the truth, I don't know anything about soccer."

"Now you tell us," said Eliscue. But he was kidding. We sort of guessed that before.

Just as we started out onto the field, Saltz whispered to me, "What if we win?"

"With our luck, we will," I said.

And on we went.

As we ran onto the field we were met with something like a roar. Maybe the whole school wasn't there. But a lot were. And they were chanting, "Win! Win! Win!"

But when they saw the backs of our shirts, they really went wild. Crazy. And you couldn't tell if they were for us or against us. I mean scary . . .

Oh yes, the game . . .

We had been told that Parkville was a team that hadn't won a game either. They looked it. From the way they kicked the ball around—tried to kick the ball around—it was clear this was going to be a true contest between horribles.

The big difference was their faces. Stiff and tight. You could see, they *wanted* to win. Had to win. We were relaxed and fooling around. Having a grand old time.

Not them.

The ref blew his whistle and called captains. I went out, shook hands. The Parkville guy was really tense. He kept squeezing his hands, rubbing his face. The whole bit.

The ref said he wanted the usual, a clean, hard game, and he told us which side we should defend. "May the best team win," he said. A believer!

Anyway, we started.

(I know the way this is supposed to work . . . . There we are, relaxed, having a good time, not caring really what goes on, maybe by this time, not even sweating the outcome. That should make us, in television land—winners. Especially as it becomes very clear that Parkville is frantic about winning. Like crazy. They have a coach who screams himself red-faced all the time. Who knows. Maybe he's going to lose his job if they lose.)

Well . . .

A lot of things happened that game. There was the moment, just like the first game, when their side, dressed in stunning scarlet, came plunging down our way. Mighty Saltz went out to meet them like a battleship. True to form (red face and wild) he gave a mighty kick, and missed. But he added something new. Leave it to my buddy Saltz. He swung so hard he sat down, sat down on the ball. Like he was hatching an egg.

We broke up at that. So did everyone else. Except the Parkville coach. He was screaming, "Penalty! Penalty!"

So they got the ball. And, it's true, I was laughing so much they scored an easy goal. It was worth it.

"Least you could have done is hatched it," I yelled at Saltz.

"I think they allow only eleven on a team," he yelled back.

Then there was the moment when Porter, Radosh and Dorman got into a really terrific struggle to get the ball–from each other. Only when they looked up did they realize with whom they were struggling. By that time, of course, it was too late. Stolen ball.

There was the moment when Parkville knocked the ball out of bounds. Macht had to throw it in. He snatched up the ball, held it over his head, got ready to heave it, then–dropped it.

It was a close game though. The closest. By the time it was almost over they were leading by only one. We were actually in the game.

And how did the crowd react? They didn't know what to do. Sometimes they laughed. Sometimes they chanted that "Win! Win!" thing. It was like a party for them.

Then it happened . . .

Macht took the ball on a pass from Lifsom. Lifsom dribbled down the right side and flipped it toward the middle. Hays got it fairly well, and, still driving, shot a pass back to Radosh, who somehow managed to snap it easy over to Porter, who was right near the side of the goal.

Porter, not able to shoot, knocked the ball back to Hays, who charged toward the goal–only some Parkville guy managed to get in the way. Hays, screaming, ran right over him, still controlling the ball.

I stood there, astonished. "They've gotten to him," I said to myself. "He's flipped."

I mean, Hays was like a wild man. Not only had he the cleanest shot in the universe, he was desperate.

And so . . . he tripped. Fell flat on his face. Thunk!

Their goalie scooped up the ball, flung it downfield and that was the end of that.

As for Hays, he picked himself up, slowly, too slowly.

The crowd grew still.

You could see it all over Hays. Shame. The crowd waited. They were feeling sorry for him. You could feel it. And standing there in the middle of the field—everything had just stopped—everybody was watching Hays—the poor guy began to cry.

That's all you could hear. His sobs. He had failed.

Then I remembered. "SOR LOSER!" I bellowed.

At my yell, our team snapped up their heads and looked around.

"SOR LOSER!" I bellowed again.

The team picked up the words and began to run toward Hays, yelling, cheering, screaming, "SOR LOSER! SOR LOSER! SOR LOSER!"

Hays, stunned, began to get his eyes up.

Meanwhile, the whole team, and I'm not kidding, joined hands and began to run in circles around Hays, still giving the chant.

The watching crowd, trying to figure out what was happening, finally began to understand. And they began to cheer!

"SOR LOSER   SOR LOSER   SOR LOSER!"

As for Hays, well, you should have seen his face. It was like a Disney nature-film flower blooming. Slow, but steady. Fantastic! There grew this great grin on his face. Then he lifted his arms in victory and he too began to cheer. He had won—himself.

Right about then the horn blared. The game was over. The season was done. Losers again. Champions of the bloody bottom.

We hugged each other, screamed and hooted like teams do when they win championships. And we were a lot happier than those Parkville guys who had won.

In the locker room we started to take off our uniforms. Mr. Lester broke in.

"Wait a minute," he announced. "Team picture."

We trooped out again, lining up, arm in arm, our *backs* to the camera. We were having fun!

"English test tomorrow," said Saltz as he and I headed for home. "I haven't studied yet. I'll be up half the night."

"Don't worry, I said. "For *that*, I believe in you."

"You know what?" he said. "So do I."

And he did. Aced it. *Our* way.

S.O.R. Losers

Meet the Author

Avi was born in New York City and raised in Brooklyn. His twin sister Emily nicknamed him Avi when they were children. To this day, it is the only name he uses. He was shy, uninterested in sports, and not a very good student. He failed at one school and nearly "flunked out" of another one before anybody realized he suffered from dysgraphia. This learning disability made writing very difficult for Avi. It caused him to reverse letters in words or spell them incorrectly. Reading, however, was not a problem. Though he hated Fridays in school because they were spelling test days, he loved Fridays because they were library days. He read everything he could find and even started his own library of favorite books.

Meet the Illustrator

Charles Jordan is mostly a self-taught artist, though he did take art classes in the public schools he attended while growing up. His love of drawing, along with the support of his parents and teachers, led him to seek a career as an illustrator. Mr. Jordan won an award for his work from the magazine, *Highlights for Children*. He has also won an award for Artist of the Year from the National Science Teachers Association. He currently resides in Pennsylvania with his wife and two children.

Theme Connections

Think About It

With a small group of classmates, discuss what you have learned about different people's views on cooperation and competition. During discussion, address the following questions:

- Why did the soccer players choose to cooperate with each other?
- How would the story have been altered if the soccer players had chosen to try to win?
- Would you cooperate with the players if you were on this soccer team? Why or why not?
- If someone decided not to cooperate, would he or she be a bad team member?

Record Ideas

Working with a partner, identify two or three examples of humorous situations in the story. In your Writing Journal, write a short description of the situations and tell why you find each humorous.

Create a Comic Strip

Work with a partner—someone not on your unit project—and create a short comic strip about your favorite segment of the story. Use only dialogue to convey the messages of cooperation or competition. Post your comic strips on the Concept/Question Board.

Storks

from *The Wheel on the School*
by Meindert DeJong

To start with there was Shora. Shora was a fishing village in Holland. It lay on the shore of the North Sea in Friesland, tight against the dike. Maybe that was why it was called Shora. It had some houses and a church and tower. In five of those houses lived the six school children of Shora, so that is important. There were a few more houses, but in those houses lived no children—just old people. They were, well, just old people, so they weren't too important. There were more children, too, but young children, toddlers, not school children—so that is not so important either.

The six children of Shora all went to the same little school. There was Jella; he was the biggest of the six. He was big and husky for his age. There was Eelka. He was slow and clumsy, except his mind; his mind was swift. There was Auka, and right here at the beginning there is nothing much to say about Auka—he was just a nice, everyday boy. You could have fun with him. There were Pier and Dirk; they were brothers. Pier and Dirk looked about as much alike as second cousins. But Pier liked what Dirk liked, and Dirk did what Pier did. They liked to be together. They were twins.

Then there was Lina. She was the only girl in the little Shora school. One girl with five boys. Of course, there was also a teacher, a man teacher.

Maybe to begin with, we really should have started with Lina. Not because she was the only schoolgirl in

Shora, but because she wrote a story about storks. There were no storks in Shora. Lina had written this story about storks of her own accord——the teacher hadn't asked her to write it. In fact, until Lina read it out loud to the five boys and the teacher, nobody in school had even thought about storks.

But there one day, right in the middle of the arithmetic lesson, Lina raised her hand and asked, "Teacher, may I read a little story about storks? I wrote it all myself, and it's about storks."

Lina called it a story, but it was really an essay, a composition. The teacher was so pleased that Lina had written a little piece of her own accord, he stopped the arithmetic lesson right there and let Lina read her story. She began with the title and read on:

Do You Know About Storks?

Do you know about storks? Storks on your roof bring all kinds of good luck. I know this about storks; they are big and white and have long yellow bills and tall yellow legs. They build great big messy nests, sometimes right on your roof. But when they build a nest on the roof of a house, they bring good luck to that house and to the whole village that that house stands in. Storks do not sing. They make a noise like you do when you clap your hands when you feel happy and good. I think storks clap their bills to make the happy sounds when they feel happy and good. They clap their bills almost all the time except when they are in the marshes and ditches hunting

for frogs and little fishes and things. Then they are quiet. But on your roof they are noisy. But it is a happy noise, and I like happy noises.

That is all I know about storks; but my aunt in the village of Nes knows a lot about storks, because every year two big storks come to build their nest right on her roof. But I do not know much about storks, because storks never come to Shora. They go to all the villages all around, but they never come to Shora. That is the most that I know about storks, but if they came to Shora, I would know more about storks.

After Lina had finished reading her story, the room was quiet. The teacher stood there looking proud and pleased. Then he said, "That was a fine story, Lina. A very fine composition, and you know quite a lot about storks!" His eyes were pleased and bright. He turned to big Jella. "Jella," he said, "what do you know about storks?"

"About storks, Teacher?" Jella said slowly. "About storks—nothing." He looked surly and stubborn, because he felt stupid. He thought he ought to explain. "You see," he told the teacher, "I can't bring them down with my slingshot. I've tried and tried, but I just can't seem to do it."

The teacher looked startled. "But why would you want to shoot them down?"

"Oh, I don't know," Jella said. He wriggled a little in his seat. He looked unhappy. "Because they move, I guess."

"Oh," the teacher said. "Pier," he said then, "Dirk, what do you twins know about storks?"

"About storks?" Pier asked. "Nothing."

"Dirk," the teacher said.

"Just the same as Pier," Dirk said. "Nothing."

"Pier," the teacher said, "if I had asked Dirk first, what would have been your answer?"

"The same as Dirk's," Pier answered promptly. "Teacher, that's the trouble with being twins—if you don't know something, you don't know it double."

The teacher and the room liked that. It made everybody laugh. "Well, Auka," the teacher said, "how about you?"

Auka was still chuckling and feeling good about what Pier had said, but now he looked serious. "All I know is that if storks make happy noises with their bills like Lina said in her story, then I would like storks, too."

The teacher looked around and said: "Well, Eelka, there in the corner, that leaves only you."

Eelka thought awhile. "I'm like Lina, Teacher; I know little about storks. But if storks would come to Shora, then I think I would learn to know a lot about storks."

"Yes, that is true," the teacher said. "But now what do you think would happen if we all began to think a lot about storks? School's almost out for today, but if, from now until tomorrow morning when you come back to school, you thought and thought about storks, do you think things would begin to happen?"

They all sat still and thought that over. Eelka raised his hand. "But I'm afraid I can't think much about storks when I don't know much about storks. I'd be through in a minute."

Everybody laughed, but the teacher's eyes weren't pleased. "True, true," he said. "That's right, Eelka. We can't think much when we don't know much. But we can wonder! From now until tomorrow morning when you come to school again, will you do that? Will you wonder why and wonder why? Will you wonder why storks don't come to Shora to build their nests on the roofs, the way they do in all the villages around? For sometimes when we wonder, we can make things begin to happen.

"If you'll do that—then school is out right now!"

There they were out in the schoolyard—free! Jella peered again over the roofs on the houses at the distant tower rising beside the dike. He couldn't believe it. But the big white face of the tower clock spelled out three—a little past three. "Boy," Jella said in wonderment, "he let us out almost a whole hour early, just because of storks." Jella was beginning to appreciate storks. "What'll we do?" he said eagerly to the other boys.

But Lina took charge. Since she had started it with her essay about storks, she felt responsible. It was a wonderful day, the sky was bright and blue, the dike was sunny. "Let's all go and sit on the dike and wonder why, just like the teacher said."

Nobody objected. They all dutifully set out for the dike, still feeling happy because of the hour of freedom that had so suddenly and unexpectedly come to them. Still grateful enough to the storks and Lina to be obedient to her and sit on the dike and think about storks. But Jella lagged behind, and that was unusual. Big Jella was generally in

the lead. Going down the village street he stared at every house he passed as if they were something new in the new freedom. But he dutifully climbed the dike and dutifully sat down at the end of the row of boys. Lina sat at the other end.

They sat. Nobody seemed to know just how to begin to wonder without the teacher there to start them off. Jella stared up at the sky. There wasn't a cloud in the sky. There were no storks. There wasn't even a gull. Jella looked at the sea stretching empty before him—there wasn't a ship in the sea.

Jella looked along the quiet row. Everybody was just sitting, hugging his knees. Everybody looked quiet and awkward and uncomfortable. Suddenly Jella had had enough. He looked along the row of boys at Lina. "The teacher didn't say we had to sit in a row on the dike to wonder, did he?"

"No," Lina said, "but I thought, well, he's never given us a whole hour off from school before, and I thought . . ."

"Well, then," Jella said . . . It just didn't feel right to sit when you were free. But the quiet sea and the quiet sky suggested nothing to him. Then fortunately a slow canalboat came pushing around a faraway bend in the canal. The two men on deck lowered the sail and the mast, so the boat could slide under the low bridge. The men picked up poles to push the boat along under the bridge. Jella jumped up. Now he had an idea. "Hey, let's all go get our poles and go ditch jumping!"

All the boys, with the exception of Eelka, jumped up eagerly. Here was something to do—fun in the freedom.

"You, too, Eelka. Run and get your pole," Jella said. "And tell Auka to get mine, too. I'll wait here."

Lina stared at Jella in dismay. Even Eelka had to go. When it came to ditch jumping, Eelka generally was left out—he was too fat and slow and clumsy. "But I thought we were going to wonder why storks don't come to Shora?" Lina said. If even Eelka had to go along, she was going to be left behind all alone.

Lina glared down the dike after the running boys. "All right for you, Eelka," she yelled unhappily. She looked darkly at Jella. "Boy, if the teacher finds out that you . . ." She swallowed her words. It was a bitter, lost feeling to be left behind all alone in the surprise free hour.

Lina had a sudden hopeful thought. It must be that Jella wanted them all in on the ditch jumping, so that if the teacher found out, they'd all catch it together. Maybe he'd let her in on it, too! Maybe that was why he had stayed here with her on the dike. "Jella," Lina asked, "can I go, too? Why, if it wasn't for me, you'd be sitting in school right now. And I could get my mother's clothes pole. It's long and smooth and . . ."

"Naw," Jella said immediately. "Girls are no good at jumping. It's a boy's game."

"I'd be just as good as Eelka. Better even," Lina said indignantly.

"Yeah, I guess so. But Eelka doesn't mind getting wet, but girls worry about wet feet and their dresses flying.

And they squeal and scream, and then they get scared and go giggly."

Jella seemed to have thought a lot about it. Lina could see it was totally no use wheedling or arguing. She drew her wooden shoes primly up under her, hugged her knees, and stared wretchedly out at the sea. "Teacher said we were to wonder why the storks don't come. He even said if we wondered really hard things might begin to happen."

"We'll wonder while we jump ditches," Jella said shortly. He was a bit uneasy. But now the boys were coming back, Auka with two vaulting poles. Jella started to leave. "And we don't care if you do tell the teacher! He didn't say we were supposed to sit like dopes on the dike."

So Jella did care——he was even worried she would tell. She was no tattletale! Lina did not deign to turn around to answer. But she couldn't help looking down the dike when Eelka came dragging his long vaulting pole. "All right, for you, Eelka," she said stormily.

That was the trouble with being the only girl: you got left out of things. And if Eelka didn't also get left out, there was nothing for her to do but sit by herself or play with her little sister Linda and the other little children. What was the fun of that? Well, she'd show them. She'd sit right here and think and wonder really hard. Tomorrow morning when the teacher asked, up would go her hand, but there they'd all sit stupid and with their mouths full of teeth. It did not seem much of a threat. The excited voices of the boys came drifting back to her.

Lina fixed her eyes hard upon a distant hazy swirling far out above the sea, wanting it to be a stork but knowing all the time it was just a sea gull. She wouldn't play with Eelka again for a week! Maybe ten days even, maybe three weeks! Even if in all that time Jella and the rest left Eelka out of every one of their games. She wouldn't bother with Eelka either. She just wouldn't bother!

She stared hard at the gull. It was still a gull; it wasn't a stork. Suppose a whole big flock of storks came flying up out of the sea. The boys, jumping ditches, wouldn't even see them. But Lina had to admit to herself it wouldn't make much difference if they saw the storks or not. The storks wouldn't stay in Shora, and the boys couldn't make them stay, so what was the difference. Lina sighed. It was hard being the only girl in Shora.

She took off one of her wooden shoes and sat staring moodily into it. She caught herself doing it. It was a lonely habit. She often sat staring into her shoe. It somehow made her feel better and seemed to help her to think better, but she didn't know why. She often wished she could wear her wooden shoes in the schoolroom instead of just socks. The wooden shoes had to be left out in the portal. Lina was sure it would help no end if she could pull off one of her shoes and stare and dream into it awhile—especially before doing an arithmetic problem. Lina sighed. You couldn't dream with arithmetic. With arithmetic you could only think. It made arithmetic sort of scary. Hard and scary and not very exciting.

Storks were exciting! "Wonder why? Wonder why?" Lina said quite hard into her wooden shoe. The words came bouncing back at her out of the hard wooden shell. She whispered it into the shoe; the words came whispering back. She sat dreaming, staring into the shoe. And the sea gull was swirling and sailing far out at sea.

Still thinking and dreaming about storks, she got up in her nice hazy daze and wandered away from the dike, one shoe in her hand. She went slowly down the street, staring intently at the roofs of all the houses as if she'd never seen them before. The village street lay quiet and empty. Lina had it to herself all the way through the village to the little school. The school had the sharpest roof of all, Lina decided. All the roofs were sharp, but the school's was the sharpest.

A thin faraway shout and a shrill laugh came through to her. She turned. In the far, flat distance she could see the boys. Now big Jella, it must be Jella, went sailing high over a ditch. Hard behind him, first sprinting, then sailing high on their poles, came the other three boys. And then there came one more; it must be Eelka. But Eelka disappeared——he must have gone into the ditch. Now there was a lot of shouting and running. Lina caught herself waiting anxiously for Eelka to appear out of the ditch. Then she remembered that she wasn't going to play with Eelka for three weeks. She turned her back to the distant boys. "I hope he went in up to his neck," she heard herself saying half-aloud. It surprised her. For now it didn't matter whether or not Eelka went into the water

up to his neck; it didn't matter that the boys were having fun. She knew why the storks didn't come to build their nests in Shora. The roofs were all too sharp! But not only did she know the reason why, she also knew what to do about it! They had to put a wagon wheel on top of one of the roofs——a wagon wheel just like her aunt in Nes had on her roof. Tomorrow morning she would spring it on them in the schoolroom. They'd be surprised!

Lina started to hurry back to the village, almost as if she had to hurry to tell someone. She put her wooden shoe back on to hurry better. There wasn't anyone there, she knew. The boys were playing in the fields; the teacher had gone. She could go home and tell her mother, but she would tell her mother anyway. It just seemed to her there had to be somebody *new* to tell it to——she had that feeling. There wasn't anyone like that. The whole street lay empty. It made her hurrying suddenly seem senseless. Lina slowed herself by staring at a house.

Once more Lina dawdled down the street, once more she stood a dreamy while before each house. Her shoe came off again. She was staring up at the roof of Grandmother Sibble III's house when the old lady came out. It startled Lina.

"I know I'm a nosy old creature," Grandmother Sibble III said, "but there you stand again, staring. I've been watching you wandering from the dike to the school and back again like a little lost sheep."

Lina laughed a polite little laugh. "Oh, I'm not exactly wandering. I'm wondering."

"Oh," said the old lady, mystified. "Well, I guess wondering is always better than wandering. It makes more sense." She chuckled a nice little old lady's chuckle.

They looked at each other. And Lina thought how she had never talked much to Grandmother Sibble III except to say a polite "hello" as she walked by. Now she did not know just what to say to her.

The old lady was still looking at her curiously. "Is that why you have your shoe in your hand?" she said gently. "Because you were wondering so hard?"

In surprise Lina glanced down at her hand holding the wooden shoe. She reddened a little and hastily slipped it on her foot. What must Grandmother Sibble think—not that she was her grandmother, she was just the grandmother of the whole village, the oldest old lady. It certainly must have looked silly, her hobbling down the street on one shoe, carrying the other. No wonder Grandmother Sibble III had come out of the house!

"I . . ." Lina said, trying to explain. She giggled a little. "Oh, isn't it silly?" She fished in her mind for some sensible explanation. None would come. But Grandmother Sibble III wasn't standing there grinning in a superior, adult way. She just looked—well, mystified and inquisitive. Lina decided to tell her. "I guess it does look silly and odd, but it somehow helps me think better to look into my shoe. Then when I get to thinking really hard, I forget to put it back on again," she said defensively.

"Why, yes," the old lady said immediately. "Isn't it funny how odd little things like that help? Now I can think

much better by sort of rocking myself and sucking on a piece of candy, and I've done it ever since I was a little girl like you." She carefully settled herself on the top step of her brick stoop. She looked as if she was settling herself for a good, long chat. "Now of course, I've just got to know what it was you were thinking about so hard it made you forget your shoe." She chuckled her little old chuckle again. "And if you don't tell me, I won't sleep all night from trying to guess."

They laughed together. Grandmother Sibble patted the stoop next to her. "Why don't you come and sit down with me and tell me about it."

Lina eagerly sat down——close, exactly where the old lady had patted. Old Grandmother Sibble was nice, she thought to herself. It was a nice surprise. She didn't talk to you as if you were a tiny tot, almost a baby, and miles of years away, the way grownups usually did. She even understood silly girl things like looking into a wooden shoe. She understood it the way a girl friend——if you had a girl friend——would understand. A girl friend who also had silly tricks and secretly told you about them. Aloud Lina said, "I was thinking about storks, Grandmother Sibble. Why storks don't come and build their nests in Shora."

Grandmother Sibble looked thoughtful. "Well, that is a thing to ponder all right. No wonder you had your shoe off. We here in Shora always without storks."

"But I figured out why," Lina told the old lady proudly. "Our roofs are too sharp!"

"Well, yes . . . Yes, I guess so," the old lady said carefully, sensing Lina's sharp excitement. "But that could be remedied by putting a wagon wheel on the roof, couldn't it? The way they do in the other villages?"

"Yes, I'd thought of that," Lina said promptly. "My aunt in Nes has a wagon wheel on her roof, and storks nest on it every year."

"Ah, yes," the old lady said, "but doesn't your aunt's house have trees around it, too?"

"Yes, it has," Lina said, looking in surprise at the little old lady. Why, Grandmother Sibble must have been thinking about storks, too. It seemed amazing, the old, old lady thinking about storks. "I guess I never thought about trees. Well, just because there are no trees in Shora—so I didn't think about trees." Lina's voice faded away. Here was a whole new thing to think about.

"Would a stork think about trees?" the old lady wanted to know. "It seems to me a stork would think about trees. And it seems to me that in order to figure out what a stork would want, we should try to think the way a stork would think."

Lina sat bolt upright. What a wonderful thing to say! Lina fumbled for her shoe while she eagerly looked at the old lady.

"You see, if I were a stork, even if I had my nest on a roof, I think I would still like to hide myself in a tree now and then and settle down in the shade and rest my long legs. Not be on the bare peak of a roof for everybody to see me all the time."

Lina pulled her feet up under her and looked down confusedly at her wooden shoes. She really needed her wooden shoe right now. Her thoughts were racing.

"You see, years ago," Grandmother Sibble was explaining, "oh, years and years ago when I was the only girl in Shora, the way you are the only girl now, there were trees in Shora and there were storks! The only trees in Shora grew on my grandmother's place. My grandmother was then the only grandmother of Shora. She was Grandmother Sibble I, just like I am now Grandmother Sibble III and you would someday be Grandmother Sibble IV if your mother had named you Sibble instead of Lina. I asked her to! Oh, I had no business asking—we're not even related—but it just seems there should always be a Grandmother Sibble in Shora. But that's beside the point.

"The point is, my grandmother's little house stood exactly where your school stands now but, oh, so different from your little naked school. Really different! My grandmother's house was roofed with reeds and storks like reeds. And my grandmother's house was hidden in trees. And storks like trees. Weeping willow trees grew around the edge of a deep moat that went all around my grandmother's house. And in the shadowy water under the hanging willows, pickerel swam in the moat. And over the moat there was a little footbridge leading right to my grandmother's door. And in one of the willows there was always a stork nest, and there was another nest on the low reed roof of my grandmother's house. As a little girl I used to stand on the footbridge

and think that I could almost reach up to the low roof of the little house and touch the storks, so close they seemed."

"Oh, I didn't know. I never knew," Lina said breathlessly.

Grandmother Sibble did not seem to hear. Her eyes were looking far, far back. She shook her head. "A storm came," she said. "As storms so often come to Shora. But this was a real storm. The wind and waves roared up the dike for longer than a week. For a whole week the water pounded and the salt spray flew. The air was full of salt; you even tasted the salt on your bread in your houses. And when it was all done, there were only three willows left at Sibble's Corner—that is what they called my grandmother's house, because everybody gathered there of a warm summer day to sit and chat and rest from work in the only shade in Shora, to talk and to lean their tired backs against the only trees. Then even those three left-over trees sickened and died. I guess their leaves had just taken in too much salt that long week of the storm.

"Later, after Grandmother Sibble I died, they came and tore down her house and chopped out the old rotted stumps of the willows and filled the moat with dirt. Then there was nothing for years and years, until they built your naked little school on the same spot. But the storks never came back."

Lina sat wide-eyed, hugging her knees, staring straight ahead, drinking it in, dreaming it over—the things the old lady had said—dreaming the picture. It sounded like a faraway tale, and yet it had been! Grandmother Sibble III had seen it! She had thought as a little girl that she

could reach up and touch the storks, it had been so real and so close. Right in Shora!

"I never knew. I never knew," Lina whispered to herself. "And even a little footbridge," she told herself and hugged her knees.

Grandmother Sibble III roused herself. "So you see you mustn't think our sharp roofs is the whole story, must you?" she said softly. "We must think about other things, too. Like our lack of trees, our storms, our salt spray. We must think about everything. And to think it right, we must try to think the way a stork would think!"

Grandmother Sibble said "we"!

"Then have you been thinking about storks, too?" Lina asked in astonishment.

"Ever since I was a little girl. And ever since then I've wanted them back. They're lucky and cozy and friendly and, well, just right. It's never seemed right again—the village without storks. But nobody ever did anything about it."

"Teacher says," Lina told the old lady softly, "that maybe if we wonder and wonder, then things will begin to happen."

"Is that what he said? Ah, but that is so right," the old lady said. "But now you run in the house. There's a little tin on my kitchen shelf and in it there are wineballs. You get us each a wineball out of the tin. Then I'll sit on my stoop and you sit on yours, and we'll think about storks. But we'll think better each on his own stoop, because often thinking gets lost in talking. And maybe your teacher is right—that

if we begin to think and wonder, somebody will begin to make things happen. But you go find the candy tin; I can think much better sucking on a wineball. And you take one, too. You watch if it doesn't work much better than looking inside an old wooden shoe."

Lina had never been in Grandmother Sibble III's house before, never in the neat kitchen. There was the shelf, and there was the candy tin. There were storks on the candy tin! Pictures of storks in high sweeping trees were all around the four sides of the candy tin. On the lid was a village, and on every house there was a huge, ramshackle stork nest. In every nest tall storks stood as though making happy noises with their bills up into a happy blue sky.

Lina kept turning the candy tin to see the pictures again and again. Suddenly she woke up to the fact that she was staying in Grandmother Sibble's house a long, long time. Her first time in Grandmother Sibble's house, too! What would she think? She hastily shoved the candy tin back on its shelf and hurried to the stoop.

"Grandmother Sibble, storks on your candy tin! And on every roof a nest! Oh . . ." Suddenly Lina realized she'd forgotten the wineballs. She raced back. It was hard not to look at the storks, but she kept her face partly turned away and picked out two round, red wineballs. Then she ran back. "I forgot all about the wineballs," she apologized.

"Yes, I know," Grandmother Sibble said gently, for she saw that Lina—though looking straight at her while handing her her wineball—was not seeing her at all. Lina had dreams in her eyes. Lina was seeing storks on every

roof in Shora. The old lady quietly let Lina wander off the stoop and to her own house. Lina had dreams in her eyes and would not hear words anyway.

On her own stoop Lina looked back for the first time. There sat Grandmother Sibble III rocking herself a little and sucking on her wineball. But the dream Lina was dreaming was not just about storks—not directly. Later she would think about storks, try to think the way a stork would think, as Grandmother Sibble had said. But now she thought about Grandmother Sibble, who had a candy tin in her house with storks on it and who had known storks and who, when she was a little girl, had imagined she could reach up and almost touch the storks.

But that was not the wonder either, not quite. The real wonder was that, just as the teacher had said, things *had* begun to happen. Begin to wonder why, the teacher had said, and maybe things will begin to happen. And they had! For there sat Grandmother Sibble III on the stoop of her little house, and suddenly she had become important. She wasn't just an old person any more, miles of years away, she was a friend. A friend, like another girl, who also wondered about storks.

Lina looked again at the little old lady, sitting there on the stoop. She marveled; she sat feeling nice and warm about a little old lady who had become a friend. It was a lovely feeling, as sweet as a wineball, as sweet as a dream. Lina took one shoe off and peered into it. Why, storks did bring good luck! The storks had made a friend for her. Why, now when the boys left her out of their games, she could go to Grandmother Sibble, and they

would sit and talk and chat. Lina looked up out of the shoe triumphantly. Why, yes!

In the morning it was school again. There they were in the schoolroom again, the five boys and Lina and the teacher. But this Saturday morning they did not start out by singing the old, old song about the country—"my lovely spot of ground, my fatherland, where once my cradle stood." No, they sat quietly as the teacher stood looking at each one of them in turn. And then he said, "Who wondered why? And where did it lead you?"

Lina's hand shot up. To her amazement every hand shot up with hers, even Jella's and Eelka's. The teacher looked so happy and pleased about it, it made Lina furious. "Why, Teacher, they never did! They went ditch jumping."

She clapped her hand to her mouth, but it was too late. She wasn't a tattletale. It was just that it had come boiling up out of her, because it had made her so furious. They were fooling the teacher, and it was making him happy.

The teacher looked at her a short moment. He seemed surprised. He turned away from her to Jella. Jella sat there in the front seat, big and stubborn and angry. He was really angry with her. But the teacher was saying, "Well, Jella, and what did you think was the reason why storks do not come to Shora?"

"Oh, I didn't think," Jella told the teacher honestly. "I asked my mother."

The teacher smiled. "Well, next to thinking, asking is the way to become wise. What did your mother say?"

"She said storks don't come to Shora because they never did. She said storks go back every year to the same

nesting spots. So if they never came to Shora, they never will. So there's just nothing to be done about it, she said."

Lina sat in her seat, trembling with eagerness to tell them that storks had once come to Shora, to tell them what Grandmother Sibble had said. She wanted to wave her hand frantically. But all the boys were angry with her, and even the teacher had been surprised and disappointed. It was a woebegone feeling, but still she had to do something. She quivered with eagerness. Then she *was* waving her hand, almost getting up out of her seat, but the teacher didn't take notice. She had to tell them! Lina heard herself saying out loud, "Oh, but storks did once upon a time come to Shora!"

They all turned to her, even the teacher. The next moment Lina was excitedly telling the room the story that Grandmother Sibble had told her about Sibble's Corner and the storks and the willow trees all around and the moat with the footbridge. About storks right here in the exact spot where the school now stood! She even told about the pickerel in the moat.

Jella in the front seat turned right around when he heard about the pickerel. He forgot he was angry with her; he forgot he was in school. He just said right out loud, without permission, "Oh, boy, pickerel! Were they big, Lina?"

All the boys had big excited eyes. They seemed to be much more interested in the pickerel than in the storks. All but Eelka. Eelka raised his hand, and now he was saying in his slow way, "What Lina said about trees. You know, Teacher, that is exactly what I thought when I

wondered why. Storks don't come to Shora because we have no trees!"

Eelka's desk was next to Lina's. She twisted in her seat to stare at him. How did he dare? He'd wondered why! He'd gone jumping ditches!

It was as if Eelka knew what she was thinking, for he calmly told the teacher, "I don't suppose I would have thought of trees. It was really when I jumped right smack into the middle of a ditch and went under that I thought of it. I really got soaked, and I wished there was a tree to hang my clothes on. But there aren't any trees, so I had to go home dripping wet. Boy, did I catch it from my mother!"

The teacher laughed as long and hard as the class. Even Lina had to laugh.

"Well, Eelka," the teacher said, "even though you had to do your thinking under water, it was still good thinking." His eyes were bright with laughter as he turned to the class. "All right, now. Does everyone agree with Eelka that the number one reason why storks do not come to Shora is because we have no trees?" He turned to the blackboard and wrote in big letters:

The Reasons Why Storks Do Not Come to Shora

Under the words he put a big number one and waited.

"I still think the number one reason is what my mother said," Jella spoke up.

"Ah, but Lina has just told us that storks used to come to Shora. In fact, Jella, Grandmother Sibble III has seen storks nesting above the spot where you are sitting now. Where our school now stands. Imagine it!" said the teacher.

"I guess maybe my mother was wrong," Jella said slowly. He seemed to hate to have to admit it. He looked up at the ceiling in a troubled way.

Then Auka raised his hand and quietly said, "Then the number one reason is still NO TREES."

"That's what Grandmother Sibble thinks, too," Lina told the class honestly. "She says storks like shelter and trees and hiding and a shady place to rest their long legs. She said she would if she were a stork! And Grandmother Sibble told me the way to find out what a stork would want is to try to think like a stork."

The teacher stood looking at Lina. "Is that what Grandmother Sibble III told you? I think that is wonderful," he said. He turned back to the class. "Well, are we agreed then that the number one reason for no storks in Shora is no trees?" He turned toward the board with his chalk as if to write it down.

Lina frantically waved her hand to stop him. "Not trees—roofs!" she almost shouted when the teacher did not turn. "Teacher," she said desperately to the teacher's back, "even though Grandmother Sibble and everybody thinks it is trees, it has to be roofs. Storks don't just build nests in trees, they build their nests on roofs, too. But our roofs in Shora are too sharp! Oh, it just has to be roofs," she pleaded. "Because we can put wheels on the roofs for storks to build their nests on, but we can't do anything soon about trees." Breathlessly she told the class about Grandmother Sibble's candy tin with the

picture of a whole village on its lid and stork nests on every roof—because there was a wheel on every roof for the storks to build their nests on!

Pier and Dirk said almost together, "Oh, man, imagine a nest on every roof in Shora!"

"Even on the roof of our school!" Auka shouted.

"But that's just it. That's just it!" Lina all but shouted at them. "There's not a single wheel on any roof in Shora, because, just like Grandmother Sibble, everybody else must have figured it was no trees. So nobody ever put up a wheel. Nobody even tried! But how can we know if we don't try?"

Lina sat back waiting breathlessly, hopefully looking at the teacher. Oh, she had to be right! Teacher had to think it was right.

The teacher liked their excitement. He stood before the blackboard turning the piece of chalk in his hand in no hurry to write anything down. He looked at the boys who were still looking in surprise at Lina. He looked at Lina. "Aha," he said proudly. "Little Lina." And then he wrote on the blackboard Lina's reason in big white letters:

No Wheels on Our Sharp Roofs

He turned back to the class. "Could it be?" he asked. "If we put wheels on our sharp roofs, could there be storks on every roof in Shora, the way Lina saw it in the picture on the candy tin?"

"Aw, that was just a picture," Jella said, scornfully. "You can put anything in a picture. All that is is a dream."

"Ah, yes, that's all it is," the teacher said. "As yet! But there's where things have to start—with a dream. Of course, if you just go on dreaming, then it stays a dream and becomes stale and dead. But first to dream and then to do—isn't that the way to make a dream come true? Now sit for a moment, picture it for a moment: our Shora with trees and storks. Now Shora is bare, but try to see Shora with trees and storks and life. The blue sky above and the blue sea stretching behind the dike and storks flying over Shora. Do you see it?"

"Trees won't grow in Shora," Jella argued stubbornly. "It's the salt spray and the wind storms. There's only one tree in Shora, and that's a small cherry tree in the back yard of legless Janus. But the yard's got a high wall around it, so high you can hardly climb it. The cherry tree grows against the sunny wall of the house, and Janus pets it and guards it. He won't let a bird or a kid get even one cherry. Not one!"

"Well, but doesn't that show us something?" the teacher said. "That to raise trees in Shora we must perhaps protect them. And couldn't we raise trees that could withstand the storms and salt spray—stouter and stronger than willows? There must be trees that grow along the sea. Or maybe we would have to protect the willows with a windbreak of poplar trees. The point is, if trees once grew here, couldn't we make them do it again?"

"Oh, but that would take too long," Dirk said. "That would take years."

"Making dreams become real often takes long," the teacher said. "I don't mean that it should be done at once.

Our first problem is how to make just one pair of storks come to nest in Shora. That is what we are trying to do right now by first thinking out the reasons why the storks don't nest in Shora. But after that . . . If trees once grew where our school now stands, wouldn't they grow there again? Think of it. Trees all around our school!"

"And a moat with pickerel in it," Jella promptly added. "We boys could even dig it ourselves, and Lina could make hot chocolate milk for the diggers."

"Yes, Jella, now you are getting into the spirit of it. For that matter, we could even plant our own little trees. But first, before we can even start to think of all that, what must we do?"

"Find a wheel to put on a roof," Lina promptly cried.

"Ah, hah," the teacher said. "Now we are getting to something that we can do. Now do you see? We wondered why and we reasoned it out. Now we must do. Now we must find a wagon wheel, and then we must put it up on a roof. But behind doing that lies the long dream—storks on every roof in Shora. Trees! Maybe even a moat around the school. Can you picture our Shora like that?"

Excitement was in his voice; excitement was in the whole room. Lina couldn't sit still. She squirmed and squirmed, and then her hand shot up. "And a footbridge leading right to the door! We'd go over the footbridge to school. Teacher," she pleaded. "Teacher, I could get Grandmother Sibble's candy tin. Then we could all see what Shora would be like with storks and trees."

The teacher nodded. "Run then, Lina."

Grandmother Sibble III had no objections whatever to Lina's taking the candy tin to school. "Oh, no, child, keep

it there as long as you like. Keep it until you get real storks in Shora." She opened the tin and took out a wineball. "Why, enough left for a wineball for each of you."

In the schoolroom they passed the candy tin around from hand to hand, and each one looked at all the pictures on the sides and on the lid. Each took out one wineball before reluctantly passing the tin on. The teacher took out the last wineball and then put the candy tin on the top ledge of the blackboard, on its side, so that the village with the trees and the storks on every roof could be seen from every point in the room. And underneath the tin, he wrote on the blackboard in big letters: "COULD IT BE?"

He turned back to the class. "Imagine a zebra in Shora," he said. "Imagine the long necks of two giraffes poking over the top of the dike. Imagine a giraffe running along our dike."

"Imagine a lion in Shora!" Auka said.

"Yes, Auka, even imagine a lion in Shora," the teacher surprisingly agreed. "A good lion, a gentle lion in our street. But isn't it almost like that with storks? Do you know where our storks come from—where they are when they aren't in Holland? Imagine the heart of Africa. The head of a big river deep in Africa, where it isn't a river any more but little rivulets and reedy swampland and marshes that go to make the beginnings of a big river. That's where our storks are now. Right there among the zebras and the herds of gazelles, among the lions and the buffaloes. Do you see our stork? There's an old rhinoceros right behind him, skulking in the brush. Do you see the stork

standing on the banks of the river where the river begins? Just beyond him in the swampy river is a herd of hippopotamuses, snorting and blowing in the deeper water. And the stork lives among them! Until a time comes and the big noble bird spreads his great wings, flaps his big wings, and comes out of the wilds of Africa to live among us. A great wild bird, yet tame and gentle, living among us in a village. Isn't it wonderful? And maybe, just maybe—— It's still a dream. We haven't even a wheel as yet; we don't even know what roof we'll put it on."

"Oh, yes, we do! Oh, yes, we do!" the whole class shouted. "It's got to go right on the roof of our school."

"Why, yes," the teacher said. "Why, yes, class! Then who's going to look for a wagon wheel? Look for a wagon wheel where one is and where one isn't; where one could be and where one couldn't possibly be?"

They were all too breathless to say a word. But Jella hastily swallowed his wineball whole, then blurted it out for all of them. "We all are. From the moment school is out until we find one."

The teacher nodded and nodded. "That's how we'll begin to make a dream come true. We'll begin at noon. It's Saturday, and we have our free afternoon before us. We'll have a whole afternoon to try to find a wagon wheel. We'll really work at it, because that is how to start to make a dream come true . . ."

Storks

Meet the Author

Meindert DeJong was born in the village of Wierum, Friesland in Holland. When he was eight, his family immigrated to America and settled in Grand Rapids, Michigan. His family was very poor, so he and his brothers had to work to help support them.

He had a strict Calvinist upbringing and attended Calvinist schools all the way through college. He graduated during the Great Depression, so there were no jobs to be found when he finished school. Instead he tried to support himself by tinning, grave digging, and farming. When World War II broke out, he was sent to China as an official historian for the Chinese-American Air Force. After the war, he returned to the U.S. and his wife Hattie in Grand Rapids. He traveled to the Netherlands and Mexico and eventually moved to Chapel Hill, North Carolina.

His books reflect his own personal experiences. He loves and respects animals and humanity and writes with the theme of peace and goodwill towards others always in mind.

Theme Connections

Think About It

With a small group of classmates, discuss how people learn through cooperation and competition. During discussion, address the following questions.

- Did Lina change throughout the story? How?
- How did feeling excluded affect Lina's competitiveness?
- Did feeling competitive help Lina learn about storks?
- How did cooperation help the children and the town?

Record Ideas

Answer the following questions in your Writing Journal.

- Why could the old woman help the children find out about the storks?
- Do you think that young people can learn from their elders?
- What have you learned from an older friend or your grandparents?

Descriptive Writing

Working with your unit activity group, review the story and identify passages where its setting is described.

Now work independently. Write a description of the setting for your dramatic play. Use all five senses to describe your setting, modeling it after the setting description in "Storks." Then share your setting with members of your group.

Revise your setting to include any of your partners' suggestions that you liked. Ask yourself: Is it better to work cooperatively or competitively when you are learning?

Bibliography

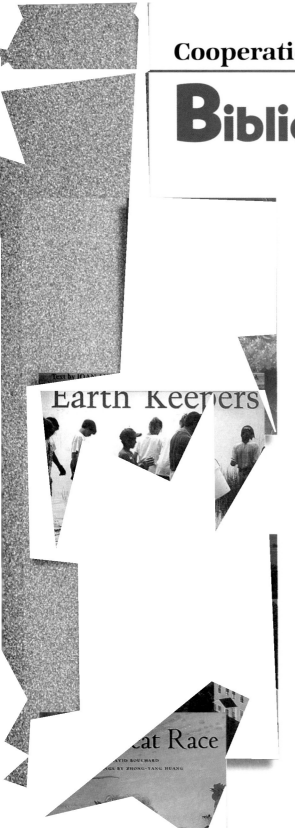

Devil's Bridge

by Cynthia DeFelice. Ben Dagget hopes to win the Striped Bass Derby for a number of reasons, but little does he know how the contest will affect his life.

Earth Keepers

by Joan Anderson and George Ancona. Read about the people who work together to rescue the earth in the places where it is most needed. Their cooperation is crucial to the earth's life.

Flood: Wrestling with the Mississippi

by Patricia Lauber. In 1927 and 1993 the mighty Mississippi unleashed all its power in damaging floods. This is the story of those floods and the people who worked together to repair the damage.

The Great Race

by David Bouchard. Who will win the race and be the first to reach Jade City? Will it be the ox, the rat, the horse, or one of the other creatures in the Chinese zodiac?

Iditarod Dream: Dusty and His Sled Dogs Compete in Alaska's Jr. Iditarod

by Ted Wood. Travel the 158-mile course of the Junior Iditarod with Dusty and his team of dogs and find out who wins the grueling competition.

Philip Hall Likes Me. I Reckon Maybe.

by Bette Greene. A little competition can't hurt a friendship, can it?

Ten Mile Day: And the Building of the Transcontinental Railroad

by Mary Ann Fraser. How do you measure your days? In minutes, hours? Working together, these men measured theirs in miles.

A World In Our Hands: In Honor of the 50th Anniversary of the United Nations: Young People of the World

by the Young People of the World Staff. Young people from 115 different countries celebrate in prose, poetry and art, the mission of the United Nations. They believe that people can make the world a better place to live.

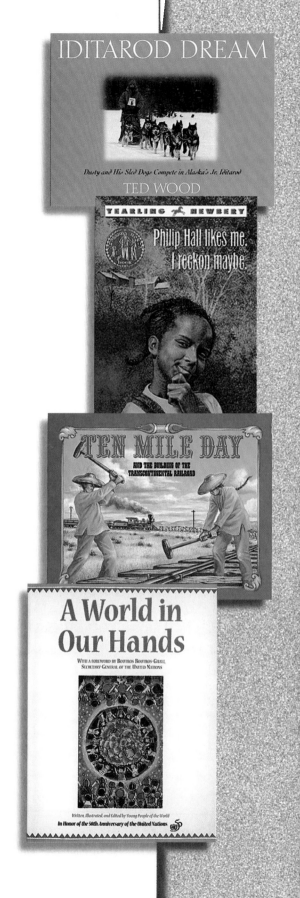

Back Through the Stars

People have been gazing at the stars since the beginning of time. Some people just look and appreciate their beauty. Others ask, "What are those things in the night sky?" "How do they affect our lives?" "How can I find out?" In the search for answers, the science of astronomy was born. Find out how and why.

117

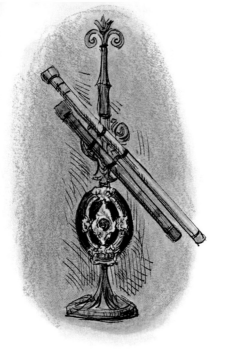

Galileo

from **Pioneer Astronomers**
by Navin Sullivan
illustrated by Jim Roldan

One May evening in 1609, a carriage rattled briskly through the streets of Padua, in Italy. In it was Galileo Galilei, professor of mathematics, returning from a trip to Venice. While he was there, he had received news from a former pupil named Jacques Badovere——news that had sent him hurrying home.

"A marvelous tube is on sale here," wrote Badovere, who was now living in Paris. "This tube makes distant objects appear close. A man two miles away can be seen distinctly. People call these tubes 'Dutch perspectives' or 'Dutch cylinders.' Some say that they were invented by Hans Lippershey, an obscure maker of eyeglasses in Middleburg, Holland. What is sure is that they employ two lenses, one convex and the other concave."

The carriage turned into the Borgo dei Vignali and stopped outside Galileo's house. Pausing only to glance at his garden, Galileo hurried indoors and went to his study.

"One convex and one concave," he repeated as though in a trance. He drew writing paper toward him, dipped a sharpened quill in the ink, and began to draw.

"Suppose the convex lens is placed in front, to gather the light," he muttered. "Then if the concave lens is placed the right distance behind, it should magnify the gathered light."

118

He only had to figure the distance and he would be able to make one of these marvelous "Dutch perspectives" for himself! He had already taken the precaution of bringing a good assortment of eyeglass lenses from Venice.

By the time that Galileo went to bed he felt fairly sure that he had solved the problem. Early the next morning he hurried to his workshop. The place was filled with gadgets he had already invented, including an apparatus for indicating temperature and another for timing the pulse of a patient. Now he would make a tube to demolish distance.

Seizing a handy piece of lead tubing, he cut it down to the length he wanted. Then he took a convex lens and placed it in one end, and placed a concave lens in the other. Excitedly, he held the tube to his eye and peered through. Immediately he gave a cry of delight. It worked! The church tower several streets away might have been just outside.

How much did his tube magnify? Galileo cut different-sized circles of paper and pinned them up on a wall. When he found that his tube made a small circle look the size of a larger one seen with the naked eye, he could figure the magnification by comparing the actual sizes of the circles. In this way he found that his telescope magnified three times.

Proudly he sat down and wrote to his friends in Venice telling them of his success. Then, after getting the lenses mounted in a more imposing tube made of wood, he hurried back to Venice himself. The Venetians were famous as sailors and navigators. This tube would show them ships out at sea long before they could be seen with the naked eye. Surely, thought Galileo, the nobles of Venice would pay well for such a device.

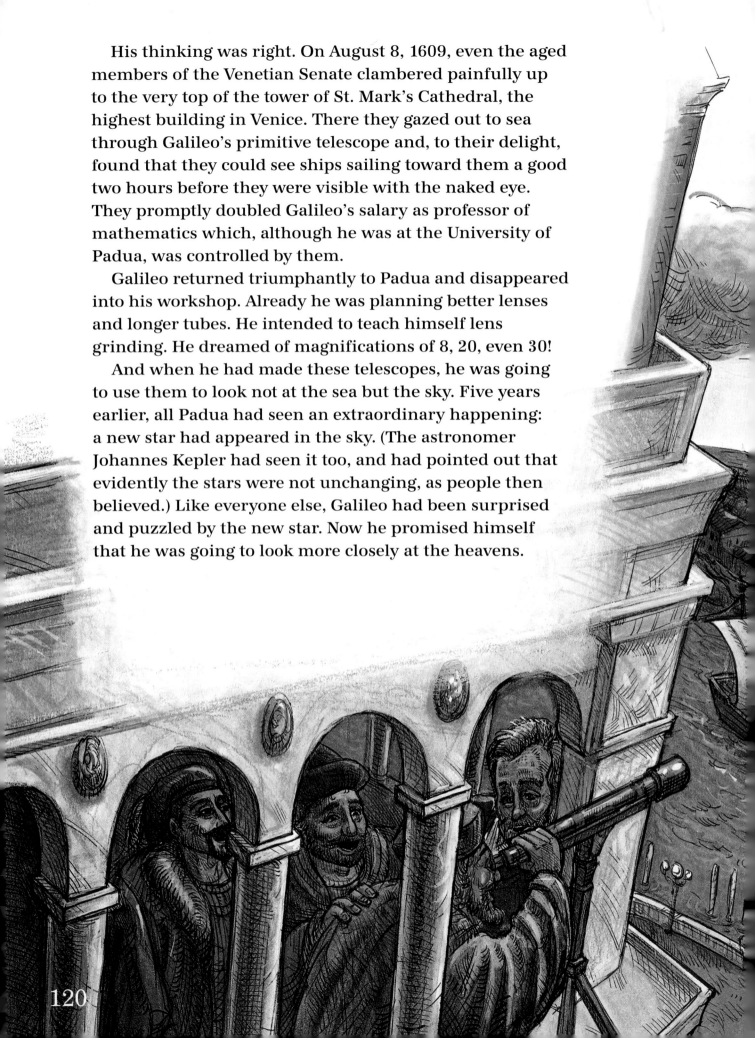

His thinking was right. On August 8, 1609, even the aged members of the Venetian Senate clambered painfully up to the very top of the tower of St. Mark's Cathedral, the highest building in Venice. There they gazed out to sea through Galileo's primitive telescope and, to their delight, found that they could see ships sailing toward them a good two hours before they were visible with the naked eye. They promptly doubled Galileo's salary as professor of mathematics which, although he was at the University of Padua, was controlled by them.

Galileo returned triumphantly to Padua and disappeared into his workshop. Already he was planning better lenses and longer tubes. He intended to teach himself lens grinding. He dreamed of magnifications of 8, 20, even 30!

And when he had made these telescopes, he was going to use them to look not at the sea but the sky. Five years earlier, all Padua had seen an extraordinary happening: a new star had appeared in the sky. (The astronomer Johannes Kepler had seen it too, and had pointed out that evidently the stars were not unchanging, as people then believed.) Like everyone else, Galileo had been surprised and puzzled by the new star. Now he promised himself that he was going to look more closely at the heavens.

It was four days after new moon. Galileo's newest telescope, magnifying 30 times, was resting in its cradle on a tripod stand. He squinted through it at the bright crescent, then drew what he saw by the light of a flickering candle.

The moon was, he knew, lit from one side by the sun. He noticed that the boundary between light and dark on the moon's surface was wavy and uneven. Also, he saw bright spots of light dotted over the dark area. What could they be?

He puzzled over them for a while, and then he made a bold deduction.

"These spots of light are mountain peaks just catching the sunlight," he decided. "And the wavy line at the boundary between light and dark exists because there are mountains there, too. It is sunrise up there and, just as on earth at dawn, the mountain peaks are bathed in sunlight while the valleys are still dark." It seemed incredible. Yet it must be true. There were mountains on the moon, as there were on earth!

Until then no one had seriously supposed that the moon might be something like the earth. People had thought of the moon and planets as heavenly bodies, things quite different in kind from the earth.

How high were the mountains? Galileo could not measure them directly, but he devised a way of comparing them with the diameter of the moon, which was fairly accurately known. When he had worked out the figures, he could hardly believe them. The moon mountains proved to be enormous, much higher than earthly mountains: up to four miles high.

It was a whole new world that Galileo was looking at. But was it full of living creatures or was it dead? He wondered if there was air on it, and shuddered at the idea that it might be cold and silent, a dead world forever circling the earth.

Then he began to explore the sky. Night after night he gazed upward, and what he found was a revelation. With the naked eye only about 2,000 stars are visible at any one time. Even with his relatively low-power telescope, Galileo found myriads more than that.

He examined the belt and sword of Orion: instead of the usual nine stars he found 89! The constellation of the Pleiades, in which sharp-eyed observers could only see seven stars, became a swarm of 43. As for the Milky Way——it was impossible to think of counting the stars in it. Wherever Galileo looked, his telescope showed crowded clusters of stars.

"Many of them are tolerably large and extremely bright," he noted, "but the number of small ones is quite beyond determination."

On January 7, 1610, while he was gazing at the sky an hour after sunset, he noticed that the planet Jupiter was visible. Immediately he turned his telescope onto it, eager to examine one of the planets for the first time.

He saw that it was a small, round disk that did not sparkle like a star. Peering more closely, he saw something else: three bright little points of light were grouped near it, two to the east of Jupiter, one to the west.

(East)   X   XO   X   (West)

At first he told himself that these bright points must be three fixed stars. But the next night, to his astonishment, they were differently grouped: all three were to the west of Jupiter.

(East)   OXXX   (West)

"Can Jupiter have moved past them?" Galileo asked himself in bewilderment. "If so, it is not traveling the way astronomers have always said it does."

He waited impatiently to look again the next night, but to his disappointment the sky was cloudy. However, the following night was clear. He rushed to his telescope and turned it with trembling hands toward Jupiter. This is what he saw:

(East)   X   XO   (West)

For a moment he wondered if he were going crazy. Now there were only two points of light, and both were to the east of Jupiter.

"Is Jupiter moving back and forth like a pendulum?" he muttered.

He searched the sky nearby, checking to see if Jupiter had moved in this way against the background of the fixed stars. It had not; it was on the course that astronomers had always charted for it.

"If Jupiter is not swinging to and fro, then the little points of light are," reasoned Galileo. "And since one of them has disappeared tonight, it is probably hidden by Jupiter——it has probably gone behind the planet. It looks as if these points of light are swinging *around* Jupiter!"

This meant that the points of light could not be stars. To make sure that they were swinging around Jupiter, Galileo began a methodical series of observations.

On the next night, January 11th, he still saw only two of them, but now they had moved farther away from the planet. On the 12th they were closer again, and a third had appeared on the west of the planet. On the 13th, he had another surprise: there were four points of light.

(East)   xoxxx   (West)

He doubted no longer. "These are not fixed stars, but bodies belonging to Jupiter and going around it in various orbits," he decided. "Jupiter has four satellite moons of its own, just as the Earth has one!"

Full of excitement, he settled down to write a short account of all that he had discovered with his telescope. Two months later this was published in Venice, under the title *Messenger from the Stars*. His discoveries amazed the whole of Europe. Soon they were even being discussed in faraway Peking (now Beijing).

Galileo had opened up a new vision of the heavens. He had shown that the moon is a rocky, mountainous globe, that the earth is not unique in having a satellite moon, and that millions upon millions of stars exist. Soon he went further and discovered that Venus appears first as a crescent, then full, then dark, as it circles the sun and reflects light at different angles. He even traced the movement of mysterious spots across the face of the sun. The fact that the sun has spots shocked some people, who felt that a celestial object ought to be without blemish. Galileo, however, was very interested, for the movement of the spots, in one direction, indicated that the sun, like the earth, was spinning round on its axis.

To many people this probing of the skies was exciting. They realized that for the first time people had a means of exploring space. But to others it was unsettling, even dangerous. This was because, although they were living 70 years after Copernicus, they still believed that the earth did not move and was the center of the universe. The Church of Rome officially agreed with this belief, although some of its members did not.

Until now Galileo had not dared to defy the Church openly and declare that the earth moved round the sun.

"I would certainly dare to publish my ideas at once if more people like you existed," he had once written to Kepler. "Since they don't, I shall refrain from doing so."

However, his discoveries made Galileo a much more important man. He decided, finally, that the Church would not dare to curb him, and he began to state publicly that the earth circled the sun.

"Let them try to prove me wrong!" he exclaimed.

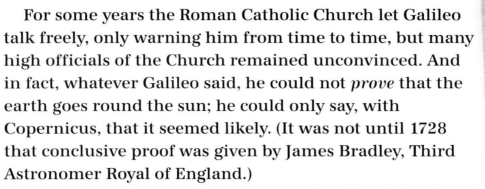

For some years the Roman Catholic Church let Galileo talk freely, only warning him from time to time, but many high officials of the Church remained unconvinced. And in fact, whatever Galileo said, he could not *prove* that the earth goes round the sun; he could only say, with Copernicus, that it seemed likely. (It was not until 1728 that conclusive proof was given by James Bradley, Third Astronomer Royal of England.)

In 1623 a new Pope was elected and the Church hardened against Galileo. He received more severe warnings than before, but would not give way. In 1632 he published a brilliant argument in favor of his beliefs, entitled *Dialogue on the Great World Systems.*

This was open defiance of the Church, and Galileo was summoned to appear before the Inquisition in Rome. Interrogation began on April 12, 1633. Galileo was asked to declare that he was wrong and that the earth stood still. The questioning continued for a month.

The great astronomer was now seventy years old, and he was worn out by fatigue and by fear of the Inquisition. In the end, Galileo did as he was told. Never again did he say in public that the earth moved.

Galileo

Meet the Author

Navin Sullivan has written and edited science books since he was a young man in his twenties. He is fascinated with people who make discoveries about things like outer space, medicine, and the human body. He calls them "pioneers" because they explore new territories in science. He has made it his goal to teach others about these scientists and their discoveries. He does this by writing books, like *Pioneer Astronomers* and *Pioneer Germ Fighters*. He also writes about these discoverers in short stories, magazines, and radio scripts.

Meet the Illustrator

Jim Roldan's first memorable gift as a child was a box of 64 colored crayons. He drew pictures of cartoon characters, animals, comic book heroes, dinosaurs and spaceships. He went on to earn a degree in Fine Art. After a few years working in a graphic design studio, Mr. Roldan started his own business illustrating ads, magazines, posters, books, and the occasional cartoon character. He currently lives and works in New Hampshire where he shares a house with his wife and their two cats.

Theme Connections

Think About It

With a small group of classmates, consider how the telescope made a difference in Galileo's investigations.

- Why did Galileo study the same objects in the sky night after night?
- Would Galileo have made even more discoveries if he could have spoken about his findings publicly?

Check the Concept/Question Board to see if there are any questions there that you can answer now. If the selection or your discussions about the selection have raised any new questions about astronomy, put the questions on the Concept/Question Board. Maybe the next selection will help answer the questions.

Record Ideas

Why was the idea of Earth orbiting the sun controversial in Galileo's time? Record your notes and ideas in your Writing Journal.

Research Ideas

- Study famous astronomers and their discoveries. Find out what tools they used to acquire their information.
- How do you become an astronomer? What different subjects do you have to study?

from *The Way Things Work*
by David Macaulay

TELESCOPES

A telescope gives a close-up view of a distant object, which, in the case of an astronomical telescope viewing a far-off planet or galaxy, is very distant indeed. Most telescopes work in the same basic way, which is to produce a real image of the object inside the telescope tube. The eyepiece lens then views this image in the same way as a magnifying glass. The viewer looks at a very close real image, which therefore appears large. The degree of magnification depends mainly on the power of the eyepiece lens.

REFRACTING TELESCOPE

In a refracting telescope, an objective lens forms the real image that is viewed by the eyepiece lens. The image is upside down, but this is not important in astronomy.

REFLECTING TELESCOPE

In a reflecting telescope, a large concave primary mirror forms the real image that is then viewed by an eyepiece lens. Usually, a secondary mirror reflects the rays from the primary mirror so that the real image forms beneath the mirror or to the side. This is more convenient for viewing.

Reflecting telescopes are important in astronomy because the primary mirror can be very wide. This enables it to collect a lot of light, making faint objects visible. Collecting light from an object is often more important than magnifying it because distant stars do not appear bigger even when magnified.

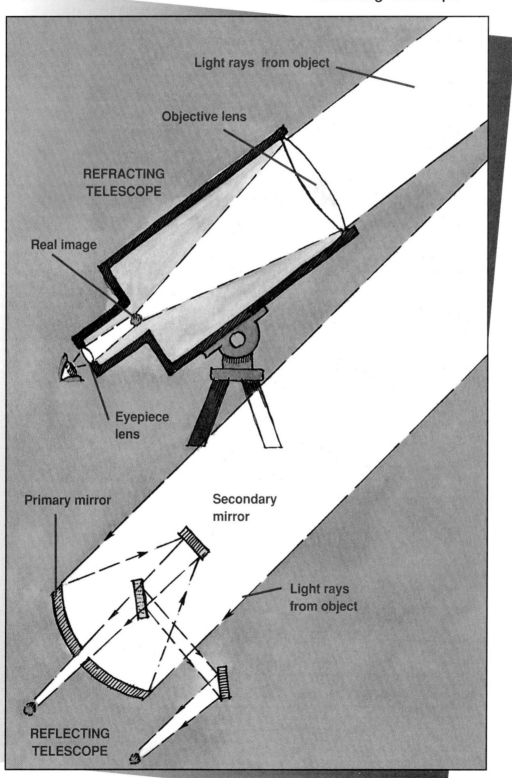

Light rays from object

Objective lens

REFRACTING TELESCOPE

Real image

Eyepiece lens

Primary mirror

Secondary mirror

Light rays from object

REFLECTING TELESCOPE

RADIO TELESCOPE

Many objects in the universe send out radio waves, and a radio telescope can be used to detect them. A large curved metal dish collects the radio waves and reflects them to a focus point above the center of the dish, rather as the curved mirror of a reflecting telescope gathers light waves from space. At this point, an antenna intercepts the radio waves and turns them into a weak electric signal. The signal goes to a computer. Radio telescopes detect very weak waves, and can also communicate with spacecraft.

By detecting radio waves coming from galaxies and other objects in space, radio telescopes have discovered the existence of many previously unknown bodies. It is possible to make visible images of radio sources by scanning the telescope or a group of telescopes across the source. This yields a sequence of signals from different parts of the source, which the computer can process to form an image. Differences in frequency of the signals give information about the composition and motion of the radio source.

Radio Telescope

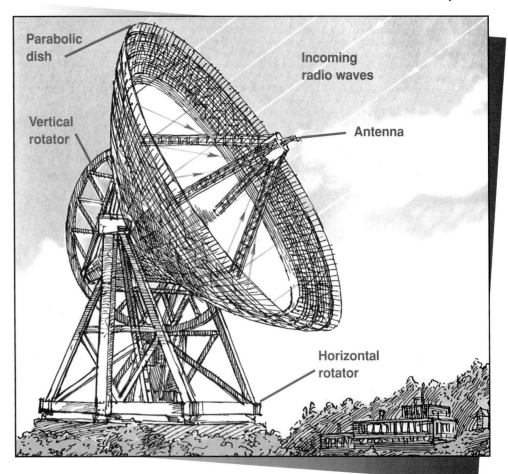

Parabolic dish

Incoming radio waves

Vertical rotator

Antenna

Horizontal rotator

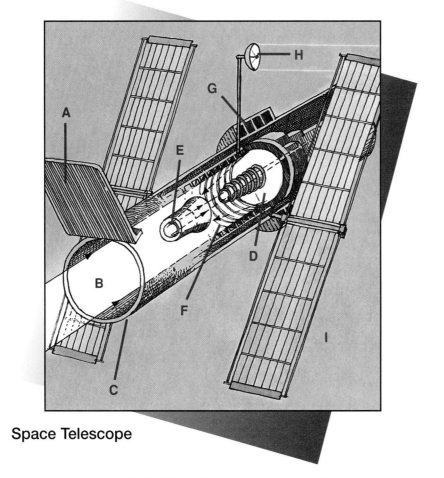

Space Telescope

A. Aperture door. B. Light rays from star or galaxy. C. Telescope tube. The main body of the telescope is 43 feet long and 14 feet across. D. Primary mirror. The space telescope is a reflecting telescope with a main mirror eight feet in diameter. E. Secondary mirror. F. Baffles. These ridges reduce the reflection of stray light from surfaces in the tube. G. Equipment section. Light detectors change the visual images produced by the mirrors into television signals. The space telescope also contains scientific instruments. H. Radio dish. The dish sends telescope images and measurements from instruments back by radio to ground stations below. I. Solar panels. The pair of panels provides electricity to work the instruments aboard the space telescope.

SPACE TELESCOPE

The Hubble space telescope is part optical telescope and part satellite. It promises to revolutionize astronomy because it operates outside the atmosphere, which hampers any observations made from the ground. The space telescope orbits the earth, observing distant stars and galaxies in the total clarity of space. It can peer seven times further into the universe than we can see from the ground, and can also detect very faint objects. The telescope may be able to "see" far back in time by observing ancient light waves from the most distant galaxies. Among these may be light waves produced just after the big bang that blew the universe into existence some 15 billion years ago.

Telescopes

Meet the Author and Illustrator

David Macaulay was born in England, but he moved to America at the age of 11. He went to college in Rhode Island and earned a degree in architecture. Afterward, he worked as a junior high art teacher, and an interior designer. He now writes and illustrates his own books. "Telescopes" was taken from his award-winning book, *The Way Things Work*. In it he explains how telescopes work, along with everything from nail clippers and zippers to a car's automatic transmission. Mr. Macaulay is the author of other fascinating books too, like *Pyramid, Black and White, Underground,* and *Motel of the Mysteries*.

Theme Connections

Think About It

With a small group of classmates, discuss the variety of telescopes and their uses.

- What are some types of information we gather with telescopes?
- What makes the Hubble space telescope different from other powerful telescopes?

Check the Concept/Question Board to see if there are any questions that you can answer now. If the selection or your discussions about the selection have raised any new questions about the unit theme, put the questions on the Concept/Question Board. Maybe the next selection will help answer the questions.

Record Ideas

Why is it important for scientists to learn more about how the universe began? Use your Writing Journal to record your notes and ideas.

Research Ideas

- Find out more about the Hubble space telescope and whether it is considered a successful venture.

The Heavenly Zoo

from *The Heavenly Zoo*
retold by Alison Lurie
illustrated by Monika Beisner

From the earliest times people have looked at the night sky and tried to understand what they saw there. Long before anyone knew that the stars were great burning globes of gas many millions of miles from the earth and from one another, men and women saw the sky as full of magical pictures outlined with points of light.

What shapes ancient people saw in the sky depended on who and where they were. Thus the group of stars that we call the Big Dipper, which is part of the Great Bear, was known to the Egyptians as the Car of Osiris, to the Norse as Odin's Wagon, and in Britain first as King Arthur's Chariot and later as the Plough. Many of the pictures that we see today are very old. The constellation we call the Great Dog was first known as a dog five thousand years ago in Sumeria; Taurus the Bull was already a bull in Babylon and Egypt.

Our ancestors saw all sorts of things in the stars: men and women, gods and demons, rivers and ships. But what they saw most often were beasts, birds, and fish. And for most of these creatures there was a legend of how they came to be there.

THE GREAT DOG

This story is from the Mahabharata, *which was written in India. Parts of this collection of stories were written more than two thousand years ago.*

Once upon a time in India there were five princes who left their kingdom to seek the kingdom of heaven. With them they took only food and drink for the journey; and the prince Yudistira brought his dog Svana.

Now besides Yudistira, who was the eldest, the brothers were Sahadeva the all-wise, who was learned beyond other men; Nakula the all-handsome, famed for his grace and beauty; Arjuna the all-powerful, who had never been defeated in any contest of arms; and Bhima the all-joyful, known far and wide for his good temper and love of pleasure.

So they set forth, and journeyed many days and many nights. Presently they came to a fair, where music was playing and people were drinking and dancing and feasting. Some of them saw Bhima the all-joyful, and called out for him to come and join them. Bhima said to himself, "I will rest here today and be happy, and seek the kingdom of heaven tomorrow." So he entered into the dance. And Yudistira and his brothers Sahadeva and Nakula and Arjuna and his dog Svana went on without him.

They traveled for many days and many nights, till they came to a broad plain where a great army was drawn up in ranks facing the enemy. When the soldiers saw Arjuna the all-powerful they shouted out, summoning him to come and lead them into battle.

Arjuna said to himself, "I will fight today for my country, and seek the kingdom of heaven tomorrow." So he joined the soldiers; and Yudistira and his brothers Sahadeva and Nakula and his dog Svana went on without him.

So they traveled for many days and nights, till they came to a magnificent palace surrounded by a garden full of flowers and fountains; and in this garden a beautiful princess was walking with her attendants. When she saw Nakula the all-handsome she was seized with love and longing, and she cried out for him to come nearer. Nakula too was struck with love, and said to himself, "I will stay with this princess today, and seek the kingdom of heaven tomorrow." So he went into the garden, and Yudistira and his brother Sahadeva and his dog Svana went on without him.

They journeyed on for many weary days and nights, until they came to a great temple. When the holy men who lived there saw Sahadeva the all-wise they ran out, inviting him to come and join them in prayer and study. And Sahadeva said to himself, "I will stay here today, and seek the kingdom of heaven tomorrow." So he went into the temple, and Yudistira and his dog Svana went on without him.

At last Yudistira came to Mount Meru, which is the doorway to heaven. And Indra the Lord of Past and Present appeared before him, and invited him to ascend. Yudistira bowed low and replied, "Very willingly I will do so, if I may bring my dog Svana with me."

"That may not be," said Indra. "There is no place in heaven for dogs. Cast off this beast, and enter into eternal happiness."

"I cannot do that," said Yudistira. "I do not wish for any happiness for which I must cast off so dear a companion."

"You traveled on without your four brothers," said Indra. "Why will you not ascend to heaven without this dog?"

"My lord," replied Yudistira, "my brothers left me to follow the desires of their hearts. But Svana has given his heart to me; rather than renounce him I must renounce heaven."

"You have spoken well," said Indra. "Come in, and bring your dog with you." So Yudistira and Svana ascended into paradise; and Indra, in recognition of their devotion to each other, set in the sky the constellation of the *Great Dog,* whose central star Sirius is the brightest of all in the heavens.

THE SCORPION

This story was told in ancient Greece.

Orion was one of the greatest of the Greek giants. Because he was the son of Poseidon, the god of the sea, he was as much at home in the water as on land. When he wished to get from one island to another he walked across on the bottom of the ocean; he was so tall that his head was always above the waves, and so large and broad that his travels caused high tides.

From childhood on Orion was famous for his beauty and his tremendous strength. He grew up to be a great hunter, able to track and slay all kinds of beasts with the help of his giant hound Sirius. When the island of Chios was oppressed and terrified by lions and wolves, Orion came to its assistance. He tracked down and destroyed every one, so that the people and their flocks could live in safety.

By the time Orion came to the large island of Crete, his fame was so great that Artemis, the goddess of the moon, invited him to go hunting with her. All went well until Orion, who had become vain of his skill, began to boast that he would soon have killed all the wild animals in Crete. Now the scorpion, who was listening, said to himself that this must not be. So he lay in wait for Orion, and stung him to death with his poisoned tail.

But Orion's spirit did not have to go down to dwell in the Underworld with the souls of ordinary mortals. The gods, who loved him, transported him instead to the sky, where he can be seen in his golden armor and sword-belt, holding up his golden shield, with his faithful dog Sirius at his heel. The scorpion who saved the wild animals of Crete was also raised into the heavens, and became a constellation in the southern sky.

Every night, as the *Scorpion* rises, Orion fades and vanishes.

The Heavenly Zoo

Meet the Author

Alison Lurie always felt like an outcast as a child. Born in 1926, she was deaf in one ear due to an injury at birth. This injury also damaged the muscles in her face, causing her mouth to turn sideways and her smile to look like a sneer. Often ignored by other children, she learned from an early age to entertain herself by making up stories and poems. Through writing, she could reinvent her world. This talent led her to study English in college. Today she lives in New York, and is an author and English professor. *The Heavenly Zoo: Legends and Tales of the Stars* was her first children's book. She went on to also write *Clever Gretchen and Other Forgotten Folktales* and *Fabulous Beasts*.

Meet the Illustrator

Monika Beisner is an author and illustrator who lives in England. She is fascinated with mysterious lands and creatures. One of her favorite things to imagine is what it would be like to live in a world where nothing is as you expect it to be. Reading her stories is like walking into just such a world, with a surprise around every corner. Her illustrations are also full of surprises and hidden meanings. The places she paints are odd, but almost life-like. In ways, her pictures are like beautiful puzzles. People who look at their details long enough, find that she tells as many stories through her paintings, as she does with words.

Theme Connections

Think About It

With a small group of classmates, consider what this selection has taught you about the beliefs and values of the ancient Indian and Greek cultures.

- What are some similarities between the two myths presented in this selection?
- Many ancient cultures devised myths about the constellations. Why did people of long ago make up these stories?

Check the Concept/Question Board to see if there are any questions there that you can answer now. If the selection or your discussions about the selection have raised any new questions about astronomy, put the questions on the Concept/Question Board. Maybe the next selection will help answer the questions.

Record Ideas

 Why do cultures preserve myths that are no longer taken seriously as explanations for natural phenomena? Record your notes and ideas in your Writing Journal.

Research Ideas

- Investigate constellation myths from a variety of cultures.
- Find out more about the origins of "The Great Dog," which is thought to be based on actual events that took place between 1400 B.C. and 1000 B.C.

Circles, Squares, and Daggers:

How Native Americans Watched the Skies

by Elsa Marston

You have probably heard about stargazers of the past such as the ancient Egyptians, the builders of Stonehenge, and the Mayas. Did you know that Native Americans, too, made astronomical observatories——long before Europeans arrived?

The study of these ancient observatories is called *archaeoastronomy*. By combining astronomy with archaeology, we are beginning to understand how people of the past observed the skies.

Archaeoastronomy is a very new field. The Native American observatories have been discovered——or their purposes understood——only recently. Most of the sites had been abandoned centuries ago, and their original uses had been forgotten.

Let's look at some of the different ways Native Americans devised to follow the movements of the sun and, in certain cases, the stars.

Medicine Wheels

One of the most dramatic observatories lies on a windswept plateau high in the Bighorn Mountains of Wyoming. It is simply a circle of stones that looks something like a wheel, 80 feet across. In fact, it's called the Bighorn Medicine Wheel ("medicine" means holy or supernatural).

In the center of the wheel is a large pile of stones called a cairn. Twenty-eight lines of stones lead like spokes from the "hub" to the rim. Just outside the circle stand six smaller cairns.

Though the wheel had been known for about a hundred years, it was not until the early 1970s that its secrets began to come clear. An astronomer, John Eddy, discovered how the wheel "works."

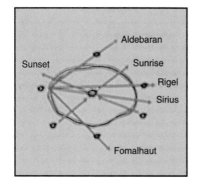

The Bighorn Medicine Wheel. The diagram shows cairns marking sunrise and sunset on the summer solstice and the rising of the bright stars Aldebaran, Rigel, Sirius, and Fomalhaut.

Bighorn Medicine Wheel

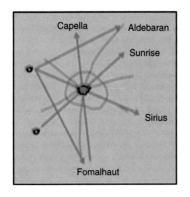

The diagram shows cairns marking sunrise on the summer solstice and the rising of the bright stars Capella, Aldebaran, Sirius, and Fomalhaut.

If you stand at a particular small cairn on the day of the summer solstice (usually June 21st), you will see the sun rise directly over the large cairn in the center of the wheel. At the end of the day, standing at a different pile, you'll see the setting sun line up with the center cairn. The medicine wheel tells almost exactly when the longest day of the year has arrived, the day we say summer begins.

The wheel shows other alignments as well. Pairs of small cairns were found to point to bright stars that shone briefly on the horizon on certain days before and after the summer solstice. These stars appeared roughly 28 days apart. Possibly the 28 "spokes" were supposed to help keep track of these intervals.

The Bighorn Medicine Wheel was probably built around 1700. The Ponca tribe claims that its ancestors constructed the original wheel. Other tribes probably added to it after moving into the area.

There is a similar medicine wheel in Saskatchewan, Canada. The Moose Mountain Medicine Wheel has cairns placed like those of the Bighorn Wheel. This gave a clue to its age. The point on the horizon where a star rises changes slightly over time. The wheel was dated by figuring out when bright stars rose closest to the points shown by the cairns. The calculations agreed with carbon dating for the site. The Moose Mountain Medicine Wheel was probably built around 2000 years ago!

Moose Mountain Medicine Wheel

Circles and Squares

At Cahokia, a major Native American site in western Illinois near St. Louis, archaeologists discovered traces of four large circles of wooden posts. They reconstructed part of one of these circles.

Seen from the center at dawn, the sun lines up with certain posts at the summer solstice and winter solstice (the shortest day of the year, usually December 21st). A third post is aligned with the rising sun at the spring and fall equinoxes (usually March 21st and September 21st, when day and night are of equal length).

Another observatory was discovered near Kansas City, Missouri, in the early 1980s. Again, traces of posts were found, but this time in the shape of a square. About 35 feet long on each side, the square suggested a building such as a fort——except that the corners were open. A triangle of posts had stood in the center, and on the south side of the square was a double row of post marks.

A local astronomy society made a simple reconstruction of the square. They found that on the summer solstice, a person standing a certain distance from the center posts could see the sun rise and set through two of the open corners. The other two corners framed the sunrise and sunset at the winter solstice. On the equinoxes, the sun shone directly between the double lines of posts. Both observatories were made by Native Americans of the Mississippian culture, probably about a thousand years ago.

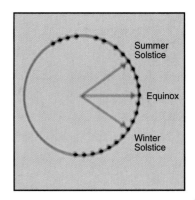

At Cahokia, the sun rises over a post marker at the equinox. The diagram shows posts marking sunrises at the summer and winter solstices.

Cahokia

Sun Daggers

The Anasazi——a name that means simply "ancient ones"——lived in the beautiful but dry country of northern New Mexico, Colorado, Utah, and Arizona around 900 years ago. In Chaco Canyon, New Mexico, they designed an especially clever kind of observatory. It was discovered in 1977 by an artist, Anna Sofaer, who was examining rock carvings.

Near the top of Fajada Butte, a high rock that rises from the canyon floor, three large slabs of stone lean against a vertical rock face. About 9 feet long, they stand on end only a few inches apart, their narrow sides against the rock. On the shadowed rock behind them, two spirals have been cut.

At noon on the summer solstice, a tiny shaft of sunlight falls between two of the slabs. It makes a spot that looks like a dagger——cutting right through the middle of the larger spiral.

The solar marker in Chaco Canyon at noon on the summer solstice.

Fall equinox.

Winter solstice.

Spring equinox.

As the weeks pass, the "dagger" of sunlight moves to the right. Meanwhile, a second vertical streak of light appears. At the fall equinox, it cuts through the smaller spiral. By the winter solstice, the two "daggers" rest on the edges of the larger spiral. It's as though the spiral, now empty of sunlight, is a symbol of winter when the world is cold. Gradually, then, the sun daggers move to the left until, on the longest day of the year, the first one again strikes the center of the larger spiral.

All over the Southwest there are many such figures, called petroglyphs, cut in the rock. Spirals, crosses, rough outlines of humans, lizards, birds——all had meanings.

At many sites, the petroglyphs are touched by spots of sunlight, usually falling between two large rocks. Astronomer Robert Preston and his wife Ann, an artist, discovered many of these sites in Arizona. Light strikes the rock carving at the solstices, the equinoxes, or, in some cases, a point halfway between the fall equinox and the winter solstice.

"Sun Rooms"

The Anasazi thought of other ways to observe the travels of the sun. Between Tucson and Phoenix, Arizona, rises a three-story adobe building known as Casa Grande ("Great House"). At dawn, a person standing inside this ancient structure will see the sun shining through a small hole high in the east wall. The spot of light strikes the opposite wall, moves toward a small hole in that wall, and disappears into it. The spot of sunlight hits this bull's-eye only on the days close to the spring and fall equinoxes.

Casa Grande a little after dawn, at the time of the spring equinox. Sunlight passes through holes in two different walls, one behind the other.

Hovenweep Castle

There is a different type of Anasazi "sun room" at Hovenweep National Monument in Utah. Attached to a large stone structure called Hovenweep Castle is a tower-like room. At sunset on the solstices and equinoxes, the sun's rays enter small holes and a door, shine through the room, and strike doorways in the inside walls. The archaeoastronomer who studied Hovenweep Castle, Ray Williamson, determined that the beams of sunlight could not enter the room in this way merely by chance.

Why?

All over this country, Native Americans came up with ingenious ways to observe the skies. But *why* did they study astronomy?

The skies were the Native Americans' calendar. They had no fixed, written calendar as we do today. They relied on what nature would tell them about the changing times of the year. Important solar events such as the solstices and the equinoxes helped them know when to plant their crops, when to start preparing for the winter, when to move from one place to another.

The sun and stars told Native Americans when important ceremonies were supposed to take place. These ceremonies were usually concerned with the "return" of the sun and start of a new year, and with planting, harvesting, and hunting.

Other special occasions might have been for social purposes such as tribal rituals, gatherings of tribes, trade, or payment of tribute. For example, the most likely function of the Bighorn Medicine Wheel was to keep a calendar so large groups could assemble in summer for trading fairs.

It's probable that only special persons knew how to use the observatories and make the announcements awaited by the people. The observatories must have strengthened the power of the chiefs and religious leaders.

There is a deep religious meaning in Native American astronomy. The sun is a vital symbol in the beliefs of many Native American cultures. And something equally important: Native Americans' understanding of the heavens helped them feel in harmony with the universe——for in many Native American religions, human beings are only one small part of the world, living in peace with the rest of nature.

Today we are coming to recognize Native Americans' achievements in astronomical knowledge——and to appreciate the ways in which they used that understanding.

Circles, Squares, and Daggers:

How Native Americans Watched the Skies

Meet the Author

Elsa Marston was born in Newton, Massachusetts. Although she is a writer and an artist, she has had a wide variety of jobs and interests. She has lived both in Europe and the Middle East. In her lifetime she has taught English, been the head of an art gallery, and organized a jail improvement committee. She is also a nature lover and an active community worker. Her children's books are often based on experiences she has had. She says, "My basic philosophy in writing for young people is that I want to share what is important to me." Her favorite things to write about are the cultures of other people, both in the past and present. With her books, she hopes to "encourage an awareness of the world beyond here and now."

Theme Connections

Think About It

With a small group of classmates, discuss what you have learned about observatories built by early Native Americans.

- Why did Native Americans want to track the movements of the sun and stars?
- What can the astronomical records and observatories that remain tell us about what was important to early Native American civilizations and about how they lived?

Check the Concept/Question Board to see if there are any questions there that you can answer now. If the selection or your discussions about the selection have raised any new questions about the unit theme, put the questions on the Concept/Question Board. Maybe the next selection will help answer the questions.

Record Ideas

How does the effectiveness of ancient Native American observatories compare with modern calendars? Use your Writing Journal to record your notes and ideas about the different ways people track time and their reasons for doing so.

Research Ideas

- Compare the sky-watching methods of ancient Native Americans with those of ancient Greeks.
- Find out more about the importance of heavenly bodies in Native American ceremonies and rituals.

FINE Art

Pictorial Quilt, detail *Falling Stars*. 1895–98. **Harriet Powers.**
Pieced, appliquéd and printed cotton embroidered with cotton and
metallic yarns. 69 × 105 in. Bequest of Maxim Karolik. Courtesy,
Museum of Fine Arts, Boston.

Orion in December. 1959.
Charles Burchfield. Watercolor
and pencil on paper. $39 \frac{7}{8} \times 32 \frac{7}{8}$ in.
National Museum of American Art,
Smithsonian Institution, Washington,
DC. Photo: Art Resource, NY.

The Starry Night.
1889. **Vincent van
Gogh.** Oil on canvas.
$29 \times 36 \frac{1}{4}$ in. The
Museum of Modern Art,
New York. Acquired
through the Lillie P. Bliss
Bequest. Photograph
©1999 The Museum of
Modern Art, New York.

VOYAGER
to the
PLANETS

from the book by Necia H. Apfel

Voyagers 1 and 2 are space probes, spacecraft sent to explore other planets. Space probes carry instruments that collect information and send photographs and other data back to earth. Before the Voyagers, space probes had been sent to gather information from Mars, Venus, Jupiter, Saturn, and Mercury. Voyager 1 flew by Jupiter and Saturn. Voyager 2, however, was the first space probe to go on a "grand tour" of several planets. This selection follows the long journey of Voyager 2 from the time it left Earth.

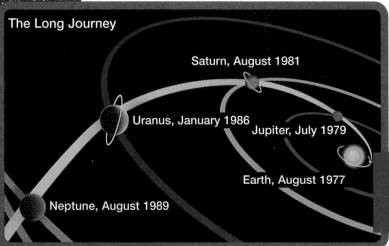

The Long Journey

Saturn, August 1981

Uranus, January 1986

Jupiter, July 1979

Earth, August 1977

Neptune, August 1989

Diagram of Voyager 2's twelve-year journey to Jupiter, Saturn, Uranus, and Neptune.

On August 20, 1977, Voyager 2 was placed atop a Titan 3-E/Centaur rocket at the United States launching site on Cape Canaveral in Florida. The rocket blasted off and rose majestically into the clear blue sky.

All was well. But now the real countdown began. Voyager would take two years to reach its first destination—the giant planet Jupiter.

Voyager is a strange-looking machine with tubes and boxlike structures sticking out all over it. These contain its many instruments, including cameras, radio receivers, and ultraviolet and infrared sensors. The instruments were designed to collect data from places Voyager would visit and to send this information back to Earth, where scientists and engineers were eagerly awaiting the reports.

Sometimes instructions had to be sent from stations on Earth to Voyager, telling it when to change its position, what data to record, or which instruments to use. Voyager was equipped with a big umbrella-shaped antenna to receive these directions.

In designing Voyager, the engineers tried very hard to anticipate any problems or emergencies that might arise on its long journey. But the first difficulty occurred much sooner than they expected. Only eight months after Voyager was launched, its primary radio system stopped working and the backup radio receiver developed a short circuit. These defects drastically reduced Voyager's ability to receive instructions from the scientists. New computer programs had to be sent to Voyager so that it could respond to future commands. The scientists could only hope that the defective radio system would last for the entire journey. Otherwise, there would be no way for them to communicate with Voyager.

With its faulty radio operating weakly, Voyager kept sailing farther into space. After two years it finally arrived at the colorfully banded planet Jupiter, passing closest to it on July 9, 1979.

Jupiter is so big that more than 1,300 Earths could fit inside of it. It has more material in it than all the other planets in the solar system combined. It is truly a giant planet.

Following commands from programmers on Earth, Voyager took pictures of Jupiter's clouds, recorded their temperatures and speeds, and analyzed their composition. The spacecraft found that it is very cold out there, a half-billion miles from the sun. Jupiter receives only one twenty-fifth the sunlight we receive on Earth. Its pretty clouds have temperatures of about –230° F. Deep inside Jupiter it is much warmer, and at the planet's center the temperature rises to 54,000° F. That's around five times as hot as the surface of the sun.

This great heat rising from the interior would make Jupiter's cloud tops look like a multicolored bubbling mixture if the planet were not turning around rapidly on its axis. But Jupiter rotates very fast. A day on Jupiter lasts only ten hours. This rapid rotation causes the clouds to be pulled out into a series of colored bands. Different substances in the clouds give them their varied colors.

The planet Jupiter. The Great Red Spot is just below the planet's equator.

The bands of clouds circling Jupiter are not smooth or featureless. Within them are huge, turbulent storms, whirlpools, and other disturbances. Weather on this giant planet is extremely violent and forceful. The most noticeable storm is called the Great Red Spot. It is so big that it can be observed through telescopes on Earth and has been seen for at least three hundred years.

Long before Voyager was launched, astronomers knew that the Great Red Spot was a giant storm, towering 10 miles above the rest of the clouds that swirl around it. Through their telescopes, they had seen the Red Spot change in size and in brightness, although it never seemed to vanish completely. Voyager's pictures showed the Red Spot to be about the size of Earth, but at other times it was known to be three times the size of Earth. Its color also varied from bright cherry red to very faint reddish hues. Astronomers aren't sure why the Great Red Spot appears red or why it has lasted such a long time.

Although the Great Red Spot drifts around the planet, it is always about the same distance below

A closeup of the Great Red Spot surrounded by turbulent cloud formations.

Jupiter's equator. As it drifts, it also rotates, taking about six days to turn around once. This rotation and drifting cause the gases around the Red Spot to eddy and swirl, somewhat like the way rocks and other barriers cause a rapidly rushing stream of water to froth and foam into small whirlpools and eddies. The photographs taken by Voyager show these eddies and swirls in great detail.

Jupiter is the center of its own miniature solar system. It has at least sixteen moons, three of which were discovered by Voyager. Four of Jupiter's moons are very large, with diameters of several thousands of miles. The other twelve moons are no bigger than a few hundred miles across, and many are much smaller.

We now know that all four of the planets visited by Voyager have ring systems. Saturn's magnificent ring system was discovered about 1610 by Galileo. In 1977, more than 350 years later, faint rings around the planet Uranus were detected through powerful telescopes. Astronomers started theorizing that perhaps Jupiter and Neptune also had ring systems. Voyager proved them right when it discovered rings around both planets.

From afar, all these ring systems appear solid, but they are actually composed of thousands of individual chunks of ice, all following similar orbits around a planet. Saturn's rings are the most spectacular, but all four ring systems are fascinating in different ways.

Voyager found that Jupiter's ring system is just a single ring consisting of several parts with no gaps between them. The brightest part is the outer edge, but even this section is too faint to be detected from Earth. Just outside this edge Voyager found two very small moons. Both moons race rapidly around Jupiter, taking only about seven hours to complete their orbits. By contrast, our moon takes twenty-nine and one-half days to orbit Earth, which is a much smaller planet.

By moving so quickly, these tiny moons prevent any ring particles from straying beyond the ring's outer edge, farther out into space. Astronomers call such moons shepherd satellites because, like sheep dogs with sheep, they keep ring particles confined within certain regions.

Because no shepherd satellites control the inner particles of Jupiter's ring system, they have spread out very thinly, reaching all the way to Jupiter's cloud tops. Only when Voyager was very close to Jupiter could it detect this faint, wispy diffusion of tiny particles.

Leaving Jupiter, Voyager headed farther into the frigid emptiness of space. For two more years it traveled outward another half-billion miles, reaching the ringed planet Saturn in August 1981.

Saturn's rapid rotation, like Jupiter's, causes its clouds to appear as colorful bands. But Saturn has no giant storms like Jupiter's Great Red Spot. It has much smaller storms that look brown and white in Voyager's photographs.

Saturn also has much less material in it than Jupiter. In fact, although it is the second largest planet and has a diameter ten times that of Earth, it is a lightweight planet. Saturn is so light that it would actually float on water if it were put into a swimming pool large enough to hold it.

A thick layer of haze covers Saturn, making its atmospheric markings look much more muted than Jupiter's. Its clouds appear in different shades of butterscotch rather than bright orange, yellow, and white.

Nothing obscures Saturn's magnificent rings. Billions of icy particles orbit the planet in a flat sheet, extending outward more than 45,000 miles. But the

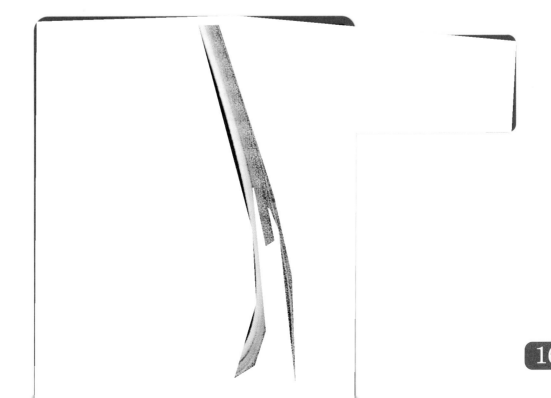

thickness of this sheet is only about one hundred yards, the length of a football field. The rings cast shadows on Saturn's clouds but are thin enough for stars to be seen through them, even from Earth. As Voyager had found at Jupiter, shepherd satellites help herd the tiny particles of Saturn's rings into confined orbits.

Saturn, like Jupiter, has its own solar system, with at least eighteen moons. But Saturn has only one large moon, Titan. The rest are quite small. Eight of these have been called "moonlets" or "the Rocks" because they are very tiny, irregular chunks of rocky material. Some of them are shepherd satellites.

Titan, on the other hand, is bigger than the planet Mercury. It is also the only moon in the solar system that has a thick atmosphere. This atmosphere is so thick, in fact, that Voyager couldn't see Titan's surface at all. Titan's atmosphere is mainly nitrogen, much like Earth's atmosphere, which also contains oxygen. Titan lacks oxygen, the element so vital to life on Earth.

Beneath its thick, smoglike clouds, Titan's surface must be a dark, gloomy place, much like the depths of an ocean on Earth. Because of its nitrogen atmosphere, Titan may be the way Earth was billions of years ago. Of course, Titan is much colder than Earth ever was. Its surface temperature is around –296° F.

Voyager had been carefully aimed so that Saturn could give it a gravity-assist change of direction toward Uranus. Before Voyager 2 reached Uranus, however, the engineers found that the spacecraft had lost much of the lubricant needed to keep its scanning platform operating. Without the ability to turn easily, the cameras mounted on this platform could not be aimed properly. Instead, the entire spacecraft would have to be rotated, a much more difficult maneuver. Also, Voyager's computer software, especially those commands controlling Voyager's stabilization and photographing instructions, had to be redesigned.

The engineers knew that whereas Voyager had been able to spend several days at Jupiter and Saturn, it would have only about six hours at Uranus. And because Uranus is so much farther from the sun than either Jupiter or Saturn, much, much less sunlight reaches it. Taking a picture at Uranus has been compared to photographing a ball park at night by the light of a single candle.

The engineers calculated that Voyager would be moving at about 12 miles per second when it went past Uranus. This meant that in 10 seconds it would move 120 miles. So Voyager's camera had to be moved backward at just the right speed to compensate for this rapid forward motion. All these commands had to be sent to Voyager almost three hours beforehand, because that's how long it takes light or radio waves, traveling at the speed of light, to reach the planet from Earth.

Also, because of the increased distance, Voyager's radio signals back to Earth became much weaker. The engineers had to expand the Deep Space Network that tracked and communicated with Voyager. To do this, they started using powerful radio telescopes, such as the Very Large Array (VLA) in New Mexico and a similar one in Australia. These large series of connected radio telescopes act as one huge telescope, detecting radio waves too faint for a single receiver to pick up. Once again, when Voyager had in effect radioed home for help, the engineers were able to devise new and brilliant solutions. Voyager's engineers were the real heroes of this story.

All these preparations took place while Voyager silently traveled onward. On January 24, 1986, after four and a half long years, the sturdy spacecraft came within about 50,000 miles of Uranus. It was only 10 miles off the desired point after having traveled 2 billion miles from Earth.

Uranus was discovered during the time of the American Revolutionary War. In 1781, the English astronomer Sir William Herschel realized that what previously had been recorded as a star was actually the seventh planet in our solar system. Many years later, five moons were found orbiting Uranus, and then in 1977 Uranus's ring system was detected.

Uranus's main peculiarity, however, was known long before Voyager's journey. It is not the planet's rings or its moons that are unique. It is the planet itself. Unlike other planets, which rotate in an upright position, Uranus rolls along in its orbit like a top spinning on its side. As a result, during half of its eighty-four-year orbit Uranus's north pole faces the sun, and during the other half its south pole is sunlit. Uranus's moons and rings also follow this strange orientation because they all have orbits directly above Uranus's equator.

Astronomers were disappointed at how few features Voyager was able to detect in Uranus's clouds. Layers of thick haze hang over most of the upper clouds, obscuring any details that may exist below. A small amount of methane gas in the haze and clouds gives the planet its soft blue-green color.

Although Voyager found Uranus almost featureless, the visit was not in vain. Besides discovering ten new Uranian moons and obtaining close-up photographs of the five known ones, Voyager was able to distinguish ten very narrow rings of particles in Uranus's ring system. The rings are widely separated by several shepherd satellites that were among the ten new moons found by Voyager.

The planet Uranus. One of Uranus's moons, Miranda, is shown in the foreground.

Particles in the rings are made of ice but are covered with sootlike material, which makes them appear very dark. Most of the particles are about the size of a fist or bigger. One would expect to find smaller particles as well, possibly as small as dust. Astronomers theorize that some process must be sweeping the rings clear, leaving only the larger chunks.

The astronomers would have liked Voyager to linger longer at Uranus. But even as the spacecraft approached Uranus, they were preparing speed and direction commands to be radioed to it. With a gravity-assist from Uranus, Voyager would head toward Neptune.

By the time Voyager arrived at Neptune, the engineers were already jokingly describing the spacecraft as being hard of hearing with a touch of arthritis and a slight loss of memory. Voyager was a very old spacecraft indeed.

However, Voyager came closer to Neptune than it did to any other object in its long journey. It passed 2,700 miles above the cloud tops over Neptune's north pole. That was on August 25, 1989, twelve years after its launch. Voyager was now $2^3/_4$ billion miles from Earth. The spacecraft was so far from the people who sent commands to it that it would have to operate at the very limit of its capability to hear their directions.

Neptune is too far away from us to be seen without a telescope. Sunlight reaching Uranus is very dim, but it is two and a half times as much as the amount of light reaching Neptune. Neptune receives only one-thousandth the amount of light we receive on Earth.

Astronomers thought that Neptune would be featureless like Uranus. They were delightfully surprised. Neptune is about the same size as Uranus and shares the same blue-green color because of a small amount of methane in its clouds. But heat rising from Neptune's hot interior keeps its cloud top temperatures similar to Uranus's temperatures, even though Neptune is more than a billion miles farther away from the sun.

This rising heat drives fierce winds, creating huge storms in Neptune's atmosphere, much like those found on Jupiter. Instead of finding a peaceful-looking planet, Voyager found active cloud structures in a turbulent state.

Neptune's biggest feature is called the Great Dark Spot, which is a huge rotating storm about the size of Earth. Unlike Jupiter's Great Red Spot, the Great Dark Spot is a hole or depression in the clouds. It lets us look deep into Neptune's atmosphere, although all

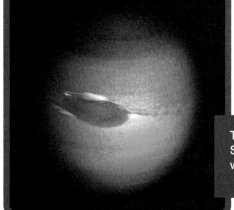

The planet Neptune. The Great Dark Spot is at the equator, just above the white cloud.

we see is darker shades of Neptune's blue-green methane covering.

About 30 miles above the atmosphere, white cirruslike clouds form and dissipate around the Great Dark Spot, similar to the way clouds form on mountainsides on Earth. White wispy clouds are also found near a small triangular-shaped storm, which moves around the planet faster than the Great Dark Spot and has therefore been dubbed Scooter. Another storm, Dark Spot Two, is smaller than the Great Dark Spot and is oval in shape. It has a white cloud hovering above its center.

The thick blue-green clouds covering Uranus and Neptune make up only about 10 to 20 percent of the planets' mass. The rest is rock and ice beneath the clouds. Uranus and Neptune are not true gas planets like Jupiter and Saturn. Scientists believe that they may be the accumulation of thousands of huge boulders that crashed together and formed planets early in the solar system's history.

After Voyager confirmed that both Jupiter and Uranus had ring systems, astronomers were fairly sure that Neptune would have one, too. They were, therefore, not surprised when Voyager detected it. When the spacecraft was still far away from Neptune, the pictures it sent back to Earth showed only sections of rings. Not until Voyager was much closer could the rest of the rings be observed. The brighter sections seen at first were found simply to have more material in them, making them more visible. And once again, Voyager detected shepherd satellites confining two of the first three rings it discovered into very narrow areas. The third ring is much more spread out. Later, after studying Voyager's photographs more closely, astronomers discovered a fourth and fifth ring.

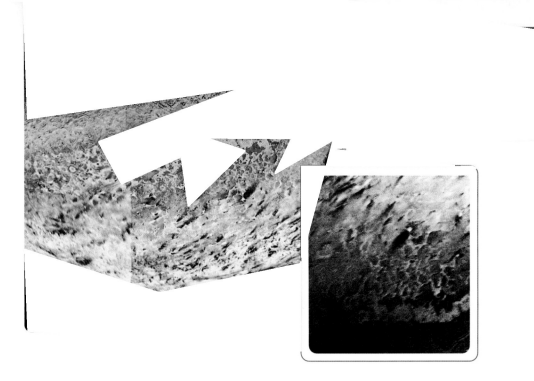

Voyager also found six new moons orbiting Neptune, raising the total number known to eight. But most amazing was what Voyager discovered about Triton, Neptune's largest moon. Although Triton had been observed from Earth many years before, little was known about it other than that it was one of the largest satellites in the solar system. Triton orbits Neptune in a retrograde motion, which means that it goes around Neptune in the direction opposite to Neptune's spin. It is the only major moon in the solar system to have this characteristic, although some of the smaller moons of Jupiter have retrograde motion.

The surface of Triton, as revealed by Voyager, is fascinating. Bright snowfalls only a few decades old contrast with craters billions of years old. In general, however, craters are very scarce on Triton, indicating that its crust is quite young and is constantly changing.

Voyager found several active volcanoes on Triton. The material coming from them is not molten rock like the hot lava that comes out of volcanoes on Earth. Instead, water mixed with other substances is spewed out, making the volcanoes more like geysers.

Voyager also photographed dark plumes of dust-filled nitrogen gas erupting from beneath Triton's surface. The gas rises some 5 miles into the thin atmosphere before being blown more than 150 miles across the moon. The dark plumes are seen as streaks of black on the much lighter landscape.

After Voyager 2 passed Neptune, its program was given a new name—Voyager Interstellar Mission (VIM)—because now it is headed out of the solar system, out to the stars.

Very little will change on Voyager as it sails on through outer space. Eventually its electrical power will be used up and its instruments will cease to function, but there is nothing in space that will stop Voyager from traveling farther and farther from us. Only when it comes close enough to be affected by another star's gravitational attraction will its path be altered. Astronomers have calculated that that won't happen for at least twenty-seven thousand years!

We don't know if there are any intelligent beings elsewhere in the universe, but if there are—and if they find either of the two Voyagers wandering out in space—they will discover, in addition to all the instruments, a very special gold-plated record on the side of each spacecraft. On each record is a recorded greeting from the people on Earth in fifty-five languages as well as many sounds that are common on Earth. These include the roar of a jet plane, the crying of babies, the chirping of crickets, and ninety minutes of a variety of music. Covering this precious record is a diagram showing what Earth people look like and where Earth is in the solar system. The story of Voyager will be an ancient legend before any alien being can possibly find the spacecraft. But maybe, many thousands of years from now . . .

VOYAGER
to the
PLANETS

Meet the Author

Necia H. Apfel thought stars and planets were fascinating, even as a child. However, adults tried to discourage her interest by telling her women did not become astronomers. Despite this, she went on to study astronomy in college. Today, she both teaches and writes about her beloved subject. Children are her favorite students because she says, "they are by far the most exciting and imaginative." She speaks at schools and has given classes to children at the Adler Planetarium, in Chicago. She also writes a monthly column for young readers in *Odyssey* magazine. In it she answers children's questions about astronomy. "Only children can think up the kind of questions I receive," she said. "They are marvelous."

Theme Connections

Think About It

This selection included many facts about the planets that Voyager 2 visited. With a small group of classmates, discuss what you found to be the most interesting discovery.

- Why do scientists on Earth want to gather as much information as possible about the other planets?
- Advances in technology have greatly increased our knowledge of the solar system. What will be the next step in exploring the planets?

Check the Concept/Question Board to see if there are any questions there that you can answer now. If the selection or your discussions about the selection have raised any new questions about astronomy, put the questions on the Concept/Question Board. Maybe the next selection will help answer the questions.

Record Ideas

 Would you spend 12 years of your life traveling to and exploring other planets? Record your notes and ideas in your Writing Journal.

Research Ideas

- Find out more about the experiments conducted with space probes.
- Investigate the challenges of communicating with a space probe from Earth.

A Meeting in Space

from *Barbary*
by Vonda N. McIntyre
illustrated by Thomas La Padula

Orphaned Barbary and her cat Mick have come to the space research station Atlantis to live with her mother's old friend Yoshi and his daughter Heather, who has a serious heart condition. Barbary arrives at an exciting time. An alien spacecraft has entered Earth's solar system. Yoshi's friend Thea, an astronomer, plans to send a probe with a camera to learn more about the alien craft. But when the probe is launched, Barbary finds that Mick is aboard it. In trying to rescue him she herself will play a role in the first meeting between the aliens and Earth people.

Barbary entered the launch chamber. Heather's raft sat on its tracks, waiting to go out again. Barbary floated to it, opened its door, and slid into the seat.

She stared at the controls. She thought she remembered what Heather had done, but she was not certain. She was not even sure she could figure out in which direction to go to find the alien ship, and Mick's raft. Away from the sun, she guessed. But there was an awful lot of nothing out there, and rafts were awfully small.

Heather said the computer could drive the raft—
She turned it on.
"Can you hear me?"
"I can hear you."
"Do you know where the raft with the transmitter is?"

"Yes."

"I want to go there."

"Please wait."

The kaleidoscope patterns appeared. Barbary gritted her teeth. Computers were supposed to know everything instantly.

But if it knew the location of Mick's raft, why was it making her wait? The only reason she could think of was that it was reporting her.

She slapped the switch that turned off the computer. She did not know if that would keep it from reporting her—if that was what it was doing—but it was the only thing she could think of. She would have to find Mick herself. She pulled down the door and sealed it and tried to remember what control Heather had used first.

"Open up!"

Barbary started at the muffled voice and the rap on the transparent roof.

Heather stared in at her. She looked furious.

Barbary opened the hatch.

"Move over!"

"Heather, they're going to shoot Thea's contraption, and Mick's inside it. I have to stop them——"

"Move over!"

Barbary obeyed.

Heather swung in, slammed the hatch shut, and fastened her seat belt.

"Your computer told me part of it, and I figured out the rest." She took over the controls.

"Thea tried to make her camera come back, but it wouldn't."

"Mick probably knocked loose some of the connections." Their raft slid into the airlock. The hatch closed.

175

"I just hope I got here soon enough to get us out," Heather said. "I bet they'll freeze all the hatches in about two seconds, if they haven't already——"

The outer door slid open.

Heather made a sound of triumph and slammed on the power. The acceleration pushed them both back into their seats.

With the raft accelerating and the station growing smaller behind them, Heather glared at Barbary.

"Now," she said. "Why didn't you wake me up?"

"There wasn't time," Barbary said.

"Oh." Heather's scowl softened. "That's a good point."

Barbary squinted into starry space. "How do you know where to go?"

"It's not that hard. From where the station is now, and the direction and speed the ship's approaching, it has to be lined up with Betelgeuse, if Atlantis is directly behind us."

Barbary tried to imagine the geometry of the arrangement Heather described, with all the elements moving independently of one another, and came to the conclusion that it *was* hard, even if Heather was so used to it that she didn't know it.

She peered into the blackness, unable to make out anything but the bright multicolored points of stars.

Heather drew a piece of equipment from the control panel. It looked like a face mask attached to a corrugated rubber pipe. Heather fiddled with a control.

"Here," she said, and pushed the mask toward Barbary. "You can focus with this knob if you need to."

The image of the alien ship floated before her, a sharp, clear three-dimensional miniature, a jumble of spheres and cylinders, panels, struts, and irregularities, some with the hard-edged gleam of metal, some with the softer gloss of plastic, some with a rough and organic appearance, like tree bark. But for all Barbary knew, alien plastic looked like tree bark and their trees looked like steel. If they had trees, or plastic, or steel.

"Can you make it show Mick's raft?"

"That's harder," Heather said, "since I don't know what course Thea used. But I'll try." She bent over the mask, fiddling. "Hey, Barbary," she said.

"Yeah?"

"Were you really going to come out here all by yourself?"

"I guess so. I couldn't think of anything else to do."

"That was brave."

"Dumb, though," Barbary said. She never would have remembered the right controls, and she would have headed off in the wrong direction. "I guess you would have had to come out and get me and Mick both."

"Still, it was brave."

"Did you find Mick yet?" Barbary asked, embarrassed.

"Unh-uh, not yet."

"Can we use his transmitter?"

Heather glanced up, frowning.

"We could," she said, "but we can't, if you see what I mean. We'd have to use the computer, and if we turn it on it would probably lock our controls and take us home. But we'll find him, don't worry."

"Okay," Barbary said. "How long before we catch up to him, do you think?"

"It sort of depends on how fast the raft went out and how rapidly it was accelerating. Which I don't know. But it couldn't have been too fast, or it would use up all its fuel before it got to the ship. Then it wouldn't be able to maneuver, so it would just fly by very fast. Without much time to take pictures. So it has to be going slowly, instead. Anyway, we ought to catch up within a couple of hours. I don't want *us* to run out of fuel—and I don't want to get going so fast that we go right past without seeing Mick."

The raft hummed through silent space. Barbary kept expecting the stars to change, to appear to grow closer as the raft traveled toward them. But the stars were so distant that she would have to travel for years and years before even a few of them looked any closer or appeared to move, and even then they would still be an enormous distance away.

"Heather . . . "

"Yeah?"

"Thanks for coming with me," she said.

"Hey," Heather said, her cheerfulness touched with bravado. "What are sisters for?"

A red light on the control panel blinked on.

"Uh-oh," Heather said.

"What is it?"

"Radio transmission. Somebody from the station calling us. With orders to come back, probably."

They stared at the light. Heather reached for the radio headset.

Barbary grabbed Heather's hand. "If you answer them, they'll just try to persuade us to turn around."

"But we ought to at least tell them that it's us out here," Heather said.

"They probably already know. If they don't, maybe we ought to wait until they figure it out."

"Yoshi will be worried," Heather said sadly, "when he comes home, and he can't find us."

"We're going to have to transmit a message to the aliens anyway," Barbary said. "To tell them we don't mean to bother them, but Mick is in the first raft and we're coming out to rescue him. When we do that, they'll hear us back in Atlantis."

"Uh-huh." Heather gazed into the scanner. "I wonder why they don't want us to come near them? I wonder what they do when somebody does?"

"I guess they could blow us up with death-rays," Barbary said. "But that doesn't seem too civilized."

"And how are we going to explain cats to them? I wonder if they have pets? I wonder what they look like?"

"Maybe they're big cats themselves, like the aliens in *Jenny and the Spaceship,*" Barbary said. "Did you read that?"

"Big *cats?*" Heather said. "That's silly, Barbary. The aliens come from some other star system. They evolved on a whole different planet. They probably don't even have the same chemistry we do. They might breathe cyanide or methane or something. Big *cats?*"

"Okay, okay, forget it," Barbary said. "It was just a book."

The radio light continued to glow. To Barbary, it seemed to be getting brighter and brighter, more and more insistent.

Heather finally put on the headset. When she turned on the radio, she spoke before a transmission from Atlantis could come through.

"Raft to alien ship, raft to alien ship. Um . . . hi. My sister Barbary and I—I'm Heather—are trying to rescue a . . . a sort of friend of ours who got stuck in the first raft by mistake. Now we can't make the raft turn around, so we have to catch up to it to get him." She hesitated. "Please don't be mad or anything. Over and out."

In the instant between the time Heather stopped transmitting and turned off the radio, the receiver burst into noise.

"—do you hear me? You girls get back here right now, or—"

Barbary recognized the voice of the vice president.

Heather clicked off the radio.

"He sounded pretty mad," she said. "I guess now they'll tell Yoshi where we are."

"Heather, what if the aliens try to call us? We won't be able to hear them, if we don't leave the radio turned on."

Heather raised one eyebrow and flicked the switch again.

"—return immediately, and you won't be punished. But if—"

She turned it off.

She shrugged cheerfully. "We wouldn't be able to hear the aliens anyway, with Atlantis broadcasting nonstop at us, unless the aliens just blasted through their signal. I'll try later——maybe the vice president will get tired of yelling at us."

"What do we do now?"

"We just wait," Heather said. "I'll keep looking for Mickey's raft. When we find it we'll know better what we need to do and how long it'll take."

"Let me help look," Barbary said.

"Okay."

Heather showed her how to search the star-field for anomalies. At first glance, they looked like stars. But if one looked at an anomaly at two different times, the bright speck would have moved in relation to the real stars. The scanner could save an image and display it alternately with a later view of the same area. An anomaly would blink from one place on the image to another, and the human eye could see the difference. A computer could, too, but it took processing time or a lot of memory, or both, to do what a person could do in an instant.

181

"Astronomers used to discover new planets and comets and things this way," Heather said. "You can also search by turning up the magnification, but that means you can only see a little bit of space at once. So unless you got really lucky, you'd spend days and days trying to find what you were looking for."

Barbary scanned for the alien ship. When she finally found it she felt pleased with herself, until she remembered how easily Heather had done the same thing.

"Shouldn't Mick's raft be right in between us and the alien ship?" Barbary asked.

"It could be," Heather said. "But it isn't. Nothing moves in straight lines in space, not when there are gravity fields to affect your course. Besides, I'm sure Thea didn't send her camera on a direct line to where the ship is now. She probably planned to arc around it. I mean, she wouldn't want to run into it. There's no way to tell exactly what course she chose. We could call and ask her——"

"As if she'd tell us——"

"She would. But I don't think the VIPs would let her."

"So we just keep looking?"

"Yeah."

Barbary let Heather have the scanner. She knew Heather could find Mick about a hundred times faster than she could.

"What's it like, back on earth?" Heather said abruptly, without looking up. "What's it like to visit a farm, or camp out in the wilderness?" She waited quite a while, as Barbary tried to figure out how to answer her. Finally Heather said in a small voice, "Never mind. I didn't mean to pry."

"It's okay," Barbary said. "It isn't that. It's just a hard question to answer. There are so many different places and different things to see—only I haven't seen most of them. It's hard to get a permit to go out in the wilderness, and you need a lot of equipment, and that costs money. Nobody I knew ever did it."

"What about farms? Did you see cows and horses and stuff?"

"I've never been on a farm, either. There weren't any near where I lived, and they aren't like in movies. They're all automated. Big machines run them. Some of them are covered with plastic to keep the water and the heat in. A couple years ago I snuck off to a zoo. I saw a cow then. It looked kind of bored and dumb. Horses are prettier, but hardly anybody on farms has them anymore. Mostly, rich people keep them to ride."

"How about an ocean?"

"I never saw that, either."

"Oh."

"I wish I could tell you . . ."

"That's all right. I've talked to other people about it, and I've seen pictures and tapes. But I can't figure out what it would be like to see it myself."

"You know, Heather," Barbary said, "an awful lot of people talk about going to the mountains, or going to the ocean, but hardly anybody ever did it. Not anybody I knew, anyway."

COW

"But they could have gone if they wanted."

"Yeah. They could have."

"I usually don't care. But sometimes I wish I could go see the mountains or the ocean, or blue sky."

"Your sky is prettier."

"I bet a blue one would be easier to find a raft in." Heather raised her head from the scanner. She looked exhausted. She had dark circles under her eyes. Barbary felt afraid for her.

"Want me to look?" Barbary asked.

"I'll do it a while longer, then it'll be your turn," Heather said. She stretched, and hunched and relaxed her shoulders a couple of times. "I don't suppose you brought along any sandwiches or anything, did you?"

"No," Barbary said. "I didn't even think of it."

"Oh, well. There are some rations in the survival ball. But they're pretty boring. Probably we should wait till we're really hungry before we use them."

Barbary thought she would get sick if she tried to eat. She felt empty and scared.

Heather bent over the scanner once more. "Hey! Look at this!"

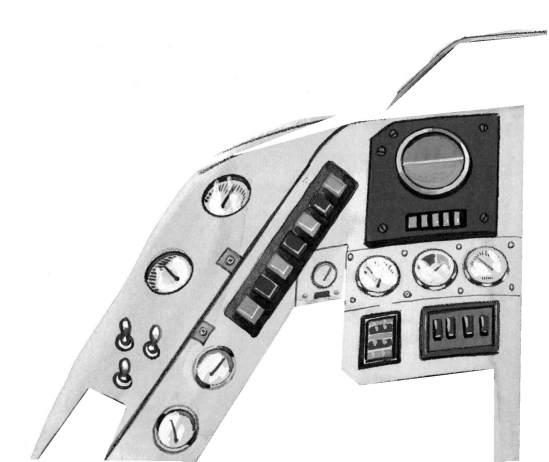

Barbary peered into the scanner.

"I just see stars."

"Keep looking." Heather touched the blink control.

In the center of the picture, one of the bright points jumped.

"Is that Mick?"

"Has to be," Heather said.

Barbary flashed the control again; again the image jumped.

"Now zoom in."

Barbary did so. The raft appeared. The airless distance of space transmitted details sharp and clear, but all she could find was the silver and plastic shape of the raft, and the shadows of Thea's contraption inside. Nothing moved.

"There it is!" she said. She magnified it even more. "I don't see Mick, though."

"Let me look."

Heather teased the scanner controls.

"Can you see him?"

"Umm . . . no," Heather said. "I can't. But there's a lot of stuff in there. He'd practically have to sit on top of it for me to find him."

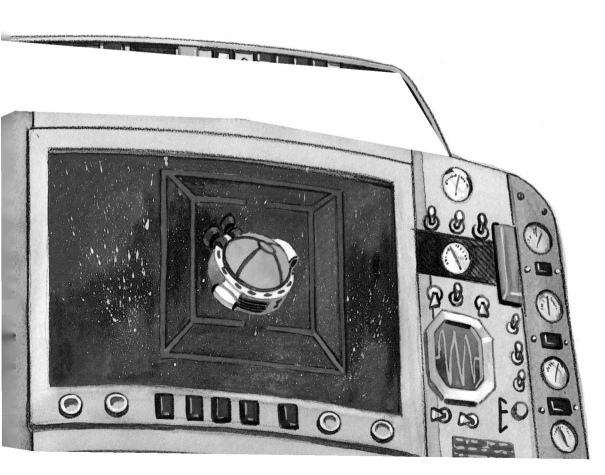

"He's probably sitting under it," Barbary said. "Yowling. Or growling like a wildcat."

Heather laughed. "I bet you're right."

Barbary felt both overjoyed and terrified. Heather had found Mick—but Barbary would not be able to stop worrying till she saw for herself that he was all right.

"Where is he?" she asked. "Right in front of us?"

"No, he's kind of over to the side." Heather pointed. "Thea must have planned to circle all the way around the alien ship, then follow it as far as she could. I'm going to have to turn us pretty hard. Are you strapped in?"

"Uh-huh. How long will it take to get there?"

"A couple of hours, maybe. I'm just guessing, though."

"How do we get him when we get there?"

"We can't. There's no safe way to open a raft in space unless everybody inside is in a space suit or a survival ball, and Mick couldn't get in one by himself. So we'll stick out our claws and grab his raft and turn us both around, and go back."

"Oh," Barbary said. She had been hoping there was some way of getting from one raft to another. But at least she would be able to look inside and see Mick.

"Hang on."

The raft plunged into free fall as Heather cut the acceleration. Barbary flung her hands out before her, for it really did feel as if she were falling. The steering rocket flared on, the stars swung, and the rocket on the other side counteracted their spin. Now, Barbary knew, they were traveling in the same direction as before, but Heather had turned the raft a few degrees to the left.

Heather applied some thrust to the raft. The new acceleration would add to their previous velocity, changing their direction and speed so they would be heading more nearly toward Mickey.

Getting to the right spot in space took a lot of care and calculation. It would have been much easier if they could have flown the raft like an airplane, or like a spaceship in a movie, banking into turns and *swooshing* from place to place. But in a vacuum, without any air, ships could not bank into turns or *swoosh*.

"I don't want to kill any more velocity than I have to," Heather said. "It takes too much fuel. So I'll probably have to correct our course a bunch of times. But for now we're sort of heading for where Mick ought to be when we get there."

Barbary tried to figure out how that worked. It sounded suspiciously like a math word problem, which she had never been very good at. She had never seen the point of figuring out when two trains would pass each other when the only trains left were tourist attractions that she had never ridden anyway. But being able to figure out in her head how to meet another raft in space would be useful. She wished she had paid more attention to word problems in school, and she wondered if it was too late for her to learn how to do what Heather could do.

"Hey, Heather—Heather!"

Heather jerked up from the scanner, blinking and confused.

"Huh? What? I'm awake!" She stopped, abashed.

"No, you're not," Barbary said. "You fell asleep sitting up! Heather . . . look . . . maybe . . ." With a shock, she realized how much danger she and Mick had put Heather in.

"Oh, no!" Heather said. "Don't even say it! We're not turning around and going back like we just came out here to make trouble and then lost our nerve!"

Barbary hunched in her seat. She felt miserable.

"I'm afraid you're going to get sick," she said.

"I'm okay! I'm just a little tired!" Heather snapped. Her expression softened. "Look," she said. "I don't have to do anything for a while. I could take a nap, and you could keep an eye on the scanner. I'll set it so the image of Mick's raft will get closer and closer to the center till we intercept it. If it goes past the center of the focus, wake me up to correct the course." She showed Barbary the faint band of color outlining a square in the center of the scanner. The other raft lay at the left edge of the screen; it moved, almost imperceptibly, centerward.

"That sounds easy enough," Barbary said.

Heather grinned. "It's a lot easier than trying to sleep in a raft, that's for sure." She squirmed around, trying to get comfortable.

"Lie down crosswise and put your head in my lap," Barbary said. "I'll try not to bonk you with the scanner."

"Okay."

Barbary took off her jacket and tucked it around Heather's shoulders. Heather curled up under it, hiding her eyes from the light of the control panel. Her position still did not look very comfortable, but within a few minutes she was fast asleep.

Barbary looked around.

Far behind her, spinning, lit from behind, the station grew smaller. The earth and the moon each showed only a slender crescent of light, for Barbary was on their night sides. The raft's automatic shield hid the sun and prevented it from blinding her.

Even in the observation bubble of the transport ship, she had never felt so alone and so remote. Beauty surrounded her, a beauty too distant and too enormous for her ever to reach or comprehend. She gazed out at the stars for a very long time, till she realized how long she had been staring. She quickly grabbed the scanner. To her relief, the other raft still lay within the field, halfway to the center of the focus.

Barbary increased the magnification, but that sent the raft all the way off the screen. If she moved the focus, she might not get it back to the place where Heather had aimed it. That also meant she could not use the scanner to find the alien ship, to see if it was doing anything threatening or even simply different.

Heather slept on. The radio receiver's light never flickered from its brilliant red. Trying to keep her attention on the scanner, Barbary forced herself to remain calm. But worry raced through her mind. She began to wonder if perhaps the aliens, and not the space station, might be trying to call the raft: to tell her they understood, everything was all right; to tell her they did not understand, please try to explain more clearly; or to tell her they understood, but they did not believe her and did not trust her and did not care anyway, and were going to shoot both rafts with death-rays.

She put on the headset and turned on the radio and the transmitter.

"This is the second raft calling, in case you didn't hear us before." She whispered, trying not to wake Heather. "We're coming out to rescue the first raft so it won't bother you. It's a mistake that it's out here, and we're really sorry. We're trying to fix things."

She turned off the transmitter, leaving the channel open for just a moment.

"Barbary!" Yoshi said. "Is Heather all right?"

"You two turn around and——"

The vice president's voice faded as Barbary cut the power to the radio without replying. She would have liked to reassure Yoshi, but she was afraid to get into a fight with any of the adults, especially Yoshi. . . . Yoshi could say things that would make her want to turn around and go back, so he would not be so disappointed with her.

She glanced behind the raft. The science station was a bright turning toy, part lit, part shadowed, spinning between the more distant crescents of the earth and the moon.

Before her, space lay beautiful but still. Somehow the stars reminded her of snow early in the morning, before dawn, in a quiet, windless winter. She peered into the scanner to reassure herself that the other raft was still there. She squinted, searching for any sign of Mick. But his raft drifted onward, showing no signs of life.

She yawned, then shook her head to wake herself up. She could not go to sleep, though Heather's steady breathing in the silence of the little ship had a hypnotic effect. She yawned again. She pinched herself, hard.

A glimmer of light on metal caught her gaze.

Off to the left, far away but as clear as a close-up model, Mick's raft crept along. Now that she had found it, Barbary did not understand how she could have failed to see it for so long. She could tell it was in motion; she could tell her own raft was approaching it, slowly and at a tangent. In the scanner, the image had touched the outer edge of the focus square.

She started to touch Heather's shoulder, but decided against waking her yet. They still had quite a way to go before their raft intercepted Mick's, and Heather needed the rest.

Still careful not to change the direction of the scanner, Barbary increased the magnification. Now she could see part of the raft in the center of the frame. But the transparent roof had not yet come into view. Barbary stared at the image, willing it to move faster so she could look inside. It crept onto the screen, appearing to move sideways because of its orientation and because she was approaching it from behind and to one side. She wished she could see its front. Often, when Mick had ridden in a car, he crouched up front looking through the windshield. But she supposed he would have trouble crouching on the dashboard of a raft, without any gravity.

Something glided through the picture.

Her heart pounding with excitement, Barbary bent closer over the scanner.

"Mick," she whispered, "hey, come past again, okay?" The portion of the image taken up by transparent raft roof increased. She held her breath.

As if he knew she was coming after him, Mick brought himself up short against the plastic and peered directly at her. He opened his mouth wide. If they had not been

separated by the vacuum of space, she would have heard his plaintive yowl.

"Okay," she said, laughing with relief. "I'm coming to get you, you dumb cat."

The scanner grew foggy. She had come so close to crying that she had misted up the mask. She sat up and reached into it to rub away the condensation with her sleeve. She glanced outside to check the position of Mick's raft.

To her shock, it——and Mick, looking at her——lay no more than twenty meters away. She was gaining on it.

"Heather!" she cried.

She pushed the scanner out of the way and pulled her jacket off Heather's shoulders. She shook her, but Heather remained sound asleep.

"Heather, come on!"

Barbary did not intend to come this far and lose Mick. She did not know if they could turn around and come back for him if they passed his raft. She jammed her hands into the grasps of the claw controls. She reached out; the grapples extended from beneath the raft. She opened her fingers and closed them; the claws followed her motion.

The distance between the rafts diminished to ten meters, then to five.

Barbary reminded herself again and again that the key to doing anything in space was to do it calmly and smoothly. She did not feel calm. She felt terrified and ignorant. Sweat rolled into her eyes. She could not take her hands from the grasps, and she was afraid to take her gaze off the other raft long enough to lean down and rub her forehead on her sleeve.

"Heather——!"

Even if Heather woke now, there was no time for her to take over the controls. As her raft approached Mick's, so much faster than it had seemed to be moving when they were far away, Barbary grabbed for it.

As she clenched her fingers in the grappler controls, the two rafts came together with a tremendous, wrenching *clang*. Barbary gasped, fearing she had rammed hard enough to breach the hull of Mick's raft or her own. The ships began a slow tumble. Around them, the stars spun. Barbary squeezed her eyes tight shut. That was even worse. She opened her eyes again. The claws kept the two vehicles clamped tight together. She could no longer see Mick, for he was underneath her. But as the reverberations of the crash faded, she heard, transmitted through the hulls, Mick's angry, objecting howl.

She laughed with relief. The motion of the rafts was beginning to make her dizzy, though, and the rafts would continue to tumble till someone used the steering rockets to counteract the spiraling twist. Heather would know how to do it.

"Hey, Heather——"

Usually when Heather wanted to sleep some more, she muttered and pulled her blanket over her head. This time, she lay still.

"Heather?"

Heather's hands felt cold as ice and her skin was very pale. Frightened, Barbary leaned down and put her ear to her sister's chest. Her heartbeat sounded weak and irregular. Barbary wished she knew what it was supposed to sound like, or what it usually sounded like.

Afraid to try to wake her again, Barbary covered her with her jacket and pillowed Heather's head in her lap.

"It's okay," she said. "I got Mick, I can get us back." She studied the controls. She would have to figure out how to make the ship stop tumbling, then turn it around. She wished she did not feel so dizzy——

Then she thought, You dummy! If you turn on the radio and the computer, back at Atlantis they'll send out the signal to bring us back. It's what they've wanted all along!

She threw the two switches, and got ready to be bawled out.

The radio remained silent.

As the raft rotated, an enormous shape slid past the roof.

The rotation of the raft slowed, though Barbary felt no vibration from the steering rockets.

The huge shape slid into view again, the rotation stopped, and Barbary found herself gazing through the roof at the looming alien ship.

Barbary put her arms across Heather as if she could protect her.

Slowly, the raft moved toward the irregular, multicolored hull.

The alien ship drew the raft closer, growing larger and larger till its expanse of incomprehensible shapes stretched as far as Barbary could see.

Trembling, she hugged Heather closer. She wrapped her jacket closer around her sister's shoulders, trying to keep her warm. The raft slid between two irregular projections from the alien ship's hull: a spire taller than any building on earth, covered with delicate strands and symbols, and a wavy, faceted shape resembling the crystals that form around a string suspended in a supersaturated solution of sugar and water.

Roof first, Barbary's raft floated toward a wide black slash in the ship's hull. If she did not keep telling herself she was going "up," she felt as if she were falling, upside down and in slow motion.

Intense darkness closed in around her.

The raft's control panel spread a ghostly light on Heather's pale face and Barbary's hands. She heard the echo of Mick's plaintive miaow, and the feathery whisper of Heather's breath.

A faint chime rang, growing louder and closer. Barbary blinked, trying to figure out if she only imagined light outside the raft, or if she were seeing a glow as gentle as dawn. The ringing reached a pleasant level and remained there, while the light brightened till Barbary could see. She had weight as well, but she had not noticed when the gravity appeared. She felt as if she weighed as much as she did on earth, and this increased her concern for Heather.

Her raft hung in a round room whose surface glistened like mother-of-pearl. The columns supporting the ceiling looked like frozen waterfalls or translucent pillars of melted glass. She searched for the opening that had let her in, but it had closed or sealed itself up. From the wind-chime sound transmitted to her through the raft's body, she decided she must be surrounded by an atmosphere, but she did not know if it was oxygen or—as Heather had speculated—methane or cyanide. She had no way to tell whether it was safe to breathe, or poisonous.

Mick miaowed again, louder.

"It's okay, Mick," she said. She swallowed hard, trying to steady her voice. "It's going to be okay."

"Do you hear us?"

The radio spoke with the beautiful voice of the alien's first message to Atlantis.

"Yes," she whispered, her throat dry. "Can you hear me?"

"We sense you. Will you meet us?"

"I want to. I really do," Barbary said. "But I have to get Heather into zero gravity and back to the space

station. She's sick and I can't wake her up. The gravity's too strong for her here. Besides, all the important people are waiting to meet you, and they'll be really angry if I see you first."

"But," the voice said, "you have already seen us."

Barbary stared around the chamber, looking for creatures, great ugly things like the aliens in old movies, or small furry things like the aliens in books. They must be hiding behind the tall glass pillars.

The gravity faded till it was barely enough to give Barbary's surroundings a "down" and an "up."

"Is this gravity more comfortable for you?"

"Yes," Barbary said. "Thanks."

"We believed we calibrated your gravity correctly."

"You did," Barbary said. "At least it felt okay to me. But Heather . . . Heather has to live in lower gravity. Won't you let us go? She's sick! Anyway, I can't see you—" She stopped, amazed.

Though she had not seen them move, the crystal columns had come closer. They clustered around her.

Their rigid forms remained upright, yet they gave the impression of bending down like a group of worried aunts or friendly trees. A long row of crystalline fibers grew along the side of each column. The fibers quivered rapidly, vibrating against and stroking the main body of each being, producing the wind-chime voices.

"Oh," she said. "Oh. I *do* see you. You're beautiful!"

"We will loose your craft if you wish," the voice on the radio said. "But our ship will reach your habitat before your vessel could fly to it, and here the gravity can be controlled."

"Can you hurry? I'm really worried about Heather."

"We will hurry."

Barbary listened to Heather's rapid, irregular heartbeat.

"Can't you help her?" she said to the aliens. She remembered all the movies she had seen where people got hurt and aliens healed them. "Can't you make her well? Aliens are supposed to be able to make people well!"

"But we have only just met you," one of the aliens said, perplexed and regretful. "We know little of your physiology. Perhaps in a few decades, if you wish us to study you . . ."

Barbary thought she should have learned by now not to expect anything to work the way it did in books or movies. She leaned over Heather again, willing her to awaken.

Heather's eyelids fluttered.

"Barbary . . . ?"

Heather opened her eyes. She sounded weak, confused, and tired.

"It's okay, Heather. Anyway, I think it is—what about you?"

"I feel kind of awful. What happened?"

"We're on the alien ship."

A spark of excitement brought some of the color back to her sister's cheeks. She struggled to a sitting position.

"Are there aliens?" Heather whispered. She was shivering. Barbary chafed her cold hands and helped her put on the jacket.

"There are other beings," the gentle voice said. "We hope not to be alien, one to the other, for very long. Will you meet us?"

"Can we breathe your air?" Heather hugged the jacket around her.

"It is not our air. We do not use air. It is your air. You should find it life-sustaining, uninfectious, and sufficiently warm to maintain you."

Barbary gingerly cracked the seal of the roof-hatch. Warm, fresh air filled the raft. Heather took a deep breath. Her shivering eased.

"If you join us," a voice said, no longer from the radio but from one of the crystalline beings, "then we may rotate your vehicles and release the small person in the lower craft. It does not respond to our communications in an intelligible fashion, and it appears to be quite perturbed."

Barbary could not help it: she laughed. Heather managed to smile. Barbary picked her up—her weight was insignificant in this gravity—and carried her from the raft. The aliens made a spot among them for her; they slid across the mother-of-pearl floor as if, like starfish, they had thousands of tiny sucker-feet at their bases. The floor gave off a comforting warmth. Barbary laid Heather on the yielding surface.

"I'm okay, I really am," Heather said. She tried to sit up, but she was still weak. Barbary helped her, letting Heather lean back against her. Heather gazed at the aliens. "Holy cow."

Mick's furry form hurtled across the space between the rafts and Barbary. He landed against her with all four feet extended and stopped himself by hooking his claws into her shirt. Somehow he managed to do it without touching her skin with his claws. He burrowed his head against her, and she wrapped her arms around him and laid her cheek against his soft fur.

"Boy, Mick," she whispered, "did you cause a lot of trouble."

A Meeting in Space

Meet the Author

Vonda N. McIntyre likes to write science fiction because it is about things that haven't happened yet, but could happen in the future. She thinks about what it would be like to live underwater like fish, or be a starship pilot who could travel faster than the speed of light. She believes one day humans will be able to do all of these things. Scientific knowledge already allows them to travel through the oceans' depths, and even to outer space. She hopes her books make others wonder about all the ways science can be used to make the impossible possible.

Meet the Illustrator

Thomas La Padula has been illustrating for magazines, advertising agencies, and publishing houses for the last two decades. He is also a professor at the Pratt Institute where he teaches classes in illustration. Mr. La Padula has participated in numerous group art shows across the country.

Theme Connections

Think About It

With a small group of classmates, imagine what it might be like to set off on a dangerous journey through space.

- Do you think this story presents a realistic idea of life in future centuries?
- How did Barbary's preconceived ideas about the aliens compare with what they were really like?

Check the Concept/Question Board to see if there are any questions there that you can answer now. If the selection or your discussions about the selection have raised any new questions about astronomy, put the questions on the Concept/Question Board. Maybe the next selection will help answer the questions.

Record Ideas

Why might people eventually want to live in space? Use your Writing Journal to record notes and ideas about the possibility of neighborhoods in space.

Research Ideas

- Investigate the physical adjustments that astronauts undergo when traveling in space.
- Find out more about the space station Mir—its successes and its failures.

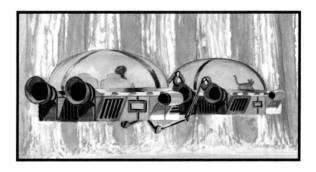

Canis Major   Orion

STARS

by Seymour Simon

Stars are huge balls of hot, glowing gases. Our sun is a star. It is just an ordinary star, not the biggest nor the brightest. But the sun is the star that is nearest to our planet Earth. Earth is part of the sun's family of planets, moons, and comets called the Solar System. All of the other stars that we see in the sky are much farther away from Earth. The stars are so far away from us that even through powerful telescopes they look like small points of light.

People long ago gave names to the brighter stars and learned where and when to look for them. They also gave names to the constellations, groups of stars that seem to form patterns in the sky. Usually these constellations were named after gods, heroes, or animals.

The photograph shows the constellation of Orion, the Hunter. Orion is visible during winter evenings. Look for the three bright stars in a row that form the belt of Orion. The bright red star in the upper left of Orion is named Betelgeuse (most people call it "beetle juice"). The brilliant blue-white star in the lower right is named Rigel. The brightest star in the sky is Sirius, the Dog Star. It is just to the lower left of Orion in the constellation of Canis Major, the Big Dog.

Thousands of years ago Orion looked different than it does today. And thousands of years in the future it will look different than it does now. That's because stars move in space. They move very rapidly, ten or more miles per second. But the stars are so far away from us that we do not notice their motion in our lifetimes.

Imagine traveling in a spaceship going ten miles a second. Even at that speed, it would still take you about three and a half months to reach the sun. But it would take more than seventy thousand *years* to reach the next nearest star, Alpha Centauri.

Alpha Centauri is about twenty-five trillion miles away. There are other stars *millions* of trillions of miles away. These numbers are so big that they are hard to understand. Measuring the distance between the stars in miles is like measuring the distance around the world in inches.

Because of the great distances between stars, scientists measure with the light-year instead of the mile. Light travels at a speed of about 186,000 miles every second. A light-year is the distance that light travels in one year: a bit less than six trillion miles. Alpha Centauri is a little more than four light-years away. The stars shown in this giant cloud of gas in the constellation of Orion are fifteen hundred light-years away.

How many stars do you think you can see on a clear, dark night? Can you see thousands, millions, countless numbers? You may be surprised that in most places only about two thousand stars are visible without a telescope.

When the great scientist Galileo looked through his low-power telescope in the year 1610, he saw thousands and thousands of stars that no one on Earth had ever seen before. As more powerful telescopes were made, millions and millions of other stars were seen.

What look like clouds in the photograph of the Milky Way galaxy are really millions of stars too far away to be seen as separate points of light. With powerful telescopes we can see that the stars are as many as the grains of sand on an ocean beach.

Alpha Centauri

Some of the millions and millions of stars in the Milky Way.

A computer-colored photograph shows a newborn star in the cloud of gas and dust known as Barnard 5.

Stars are born in giant clouds of gas and dust called nebulas. Most of the gas is hydrogen with a small amount of helium. Over millions of years, gravity pulls the gas and dust particles together and squeezes them so that they heat up. When the gas gets hot enough, it sets off a nuclear reaction like that of a super hydrogen bomb and a star is born. This computer-colored photograph shows a newborn star (*arrow*) in the cloud of gas and dust known as Barnard 5.

Stars change as they grow older. For example, young stars (10 to 200 million years old) are very hot—with surface temperatures of more than 12,000 degrees (F)—and are usually blue or blue-white in color. Middle-aged stars like our sun are yellow and not as hot—10,000 degrees (F).

After about ten billion years stars begin to run out of their hydrogen fuel. Most of these old stars collapse upon themselves and they get hotter and hotter. Then, like a piece of popcorn when it "pops," the stars balloon out and become hundreds of times larger. They become what are known as red giant stars.

A red giant star may be 40 or 50 million miles across. Some are even larger. Betelgeuse is a red supergiant star 250 million miles across. If Betelgeuse were put in place of our sun in the center of the Solar System, it would swallow up Mercury, Venus, Earth, and Mars.

Some older stars go through a stage where they keep growing and then shrinking. These stars are called variable stars because at times they appear bright and at other times they are dim.

Other older stars shoot out a large cloud of gas into space. These stars are called planetary nebulas because through low-power telescopes they look like round planets. This photograph taken with a high-power telescope shows the real nature of a planetary nebula. This is the Ring Nebula in the constellation Lyra.

Finally, older stars cool and start collapsing. They shrink down to about the size of a small planet and are called white dwarf stars. As the white dwarfs slowly cool off they become black dwarf stars. And then the stars are dead.

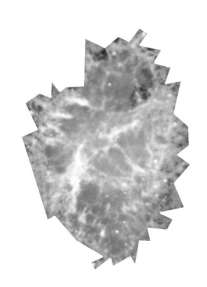

Sometimes a star, usually a white dwarf, suddenly explodes and becomes much brighter. To people long ago it looked like a new bright star had appeared in the sky. They called the star a nova (*nova* means "new"). Even though most novas are too far away for us to see, scientists think that two or three dozen novas appear in the Milky Way every year.

Much rarer are the gigantic explosions known as supernovas. A supernova star flares up and becomes millions of times brighter than normal.

A supernova may appear only once every few hundred years. In the year 1054, Chinese astronomers saw a supernova in the constellation of Taurus. Today we can see the gaseous remains of that exploding star. We call it the Crab Nebula.

Some supernovas shatter completely, leaving behind only the wispy gases of a nebula. But a few supernovas leave a small, tightly packed ball of particles called a neutron star. A tiny drop of a neutron star would weigh a billion tons on earth.

The sudden collapse of a supernova causes a neutron star to spin very rapidly and give off a beam of X-ray radiation. Like the beam from a lighthouse, we can detect the X rays as a pulse. So a rotating neutron star is called a pulsar.

This X-ray photograph shows a pulsar in the middle of the Crab Nebula. The X rays from the pulsar in the Crab blink on and off thirty times every second. The star is visible when the X rays are "on" and invisible when the X rays are "off."

Some stars are much larger than the average star. When such a massive star cools and collapses, it becomes something very special. The star is crushed together by the huge weight of the collapsing gases. Gravity keeps squeezing and squeezing until the star seems to disappear. The star has become a black hole.

Anything passing too close to a black hole will be pulled into it and never get out again. Even light is pulled in and cannot escape, so a black hole is invisible. Yet, scientists think they have located several black holes.

This drawing is of a double star called Cygnus X-1. Only one of the stars is visible: a hot, blue giant star. Near it is a black hole that pulls gases from its neighbor. As the gases are sucked in they become so hot that they give off huge amounts of X rays. Some scientists think that there are many such black holes scattered throughout space.

Crab Nebula

Cygnus X-1

Our sun is an unusual star. It does not have any nearby stars circling it. Most stars have one or more companion stars and they revolve around each other. The star groups are so far from us that most look like single points of light to our eyes.

About half of all the stars we can see are double, or binary, stars. There are also many groups with three, four, a dozen, or even more stars in them. These groups of stars move through space together like flocks of birds in flight. Scientists think that the stars in such a group were all formed at the same time.

Very large groups of stars are called star clusters. This is a photograph of the Pleiades, an open cluster of stars. It contains several hundred stars that form a loose group with no special shape. These are young stars and they are surrounded by clouds of gas and dust.

Here is a different kind of star cluster called a globular cluster. A globular cluster contains many thousands, or even millions, of stars very close together.

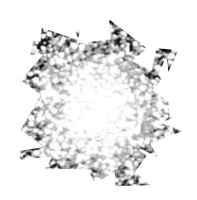

This is the great globular cluster known as M.13 in the constellation of Hercules. It is visible just as a dot of light to the naked eye. But through a telescope we can see that it has at least a million stars. Most of these stars are very old and they have stayed together throughout their lifetime.

The biggest star clusters of all are called galaxies. Galaxies are the largest kind of star systems. Our sun and its planets are a member of a galaxy called the Milky Way. There are more than one hundred billion stars in the Milky Way galaxy.

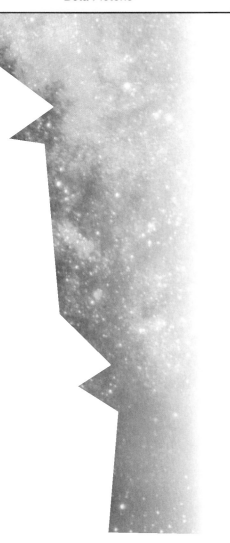

Beta Pictoris

The sun is located almost out on the edges of the Milky Way. All the stars in the Milky Way whirl around the center of the galaxy, each at its own speed. The sun along with the Solar System moves at about 150 miles a second around the center of the galaxy. But the galaxy is so big that the sun takes about 225 million years to go around once.

Are there planets circling other stars in our galaxy? The answer is almost definitely yes. This picture shows a ring of material surrounding the star Beta Pictoris. This material is thought to be a young solar system in the making.

Planets form at the same time and from the same gases as do stars. So scientists think it is likely that some or even many stars have planets circling them. If even a tiny percentage of these planets are similar to Earth, then there may be millions of Earth-like planets in the galaxy.

Do any of these planets have life on them? No one knows. But scientists are using radio telescopes to listen for signals of intelligent life in outer space. They think the signals will come in the form of radio waves much like those of our own radios and televisions. So far scientists have not found anything, but they are not discouraged. Until they have examined every star that may have planets they won't know for sure.

The Milky Way is only one galaxy among millions of others in the universe. Galaxies——large and small, single or in groups and clusters, and in many different shapes——are found in every direction.

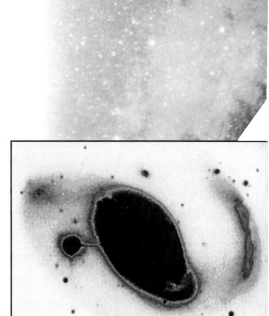

The Andromeda galaxy, shown here, is a spiral galaxy with almost twice as many stars as there are in the Milky Way. The Andromeda galaxy lies in far distant space, almost twelve quintillion miles away. That's 12,000,000,000,000,000,000! Light from this galaxy has been traveling for more than two million years by the time we see it in our telescopes.

How many galaxies are there in the universe? No one knows. But scientists think that there are about one hundred billion other galaxies. And each one of these galaxies contains hundreds of thousands of millions of stars.

Many mysteries confront us in the distant reaches of space. Beyond most of the galaxies that we can see with our largest telescopes are bright starlike objects called quasars. Each quasar gives off more than one hundred times the energy of all the stars in the Milky Way galaxy put together.

This is a computer-colored photo of a quasar-galaxy pair. Scientists think that quasars may be the centers of young galaxies that are just forming. Light from most quasars has been traveling for ten to fifteen billion years by the time it reaches Earth. That means that we are viewing quasars as they were ten to fifteen billion years ago, just after the universe began.

Powerful telescopes orbiting above Earth's atmosphere may soon show us the very edges of the universe and the beginning of time itself. Will all our questions about stars then be answered? It's not likely. Each mystery that we solve about space seems to lead to many more unsolved questions about the nature of the universe.

Quasar-Galaxy Pair

STARS

Meet the Author

Seymour Simon taught science in the New York City schools for 23 years but now devotes all of his time to writing. Simon is the author of nearly 150 science books written especially for students from preschool to junior high. Most of his books are about astronomy and animals. One of the reasons why his books are so wonderful is because they contain many spectacular photos. He likes picture books because, unlike television, they can "freeze" images for as long as the reader wants to look at them. He hopes children will be as amazed as he is by the photos' subjects. He says, "Children need to develop a lifelong enjoyment and appreciation for science. Science is fascinating stuff like dinosaurs, space, earthquakes, and the human body."

Theme Connections

Think About It

With a small group of classmates, discuss what scientists have learned from studying the stars.

- Compare ancient people's impressions of the stars with that of modern scientists.
- Why would it be important for scientists to learn about the life cycles of stars?

Check the Concept/Question Board to see if there are any questions there that you can answer now. If the selection or your discussions about the selection have raised any new questions about astronomy, put the questions on the Concept/Question Board. Maybe the next selection will help answer the questions.

Record Ideas

How does the appearance of stars in the night sky correspond to what you have learned about their composition? Use your Writing Journal to record notes and ideas about any disparities.

Research Ideas

- Find out more about the likelihood that other stars—like our sun—are orbited by planets, forming solar systems that may house intelligent life forms.

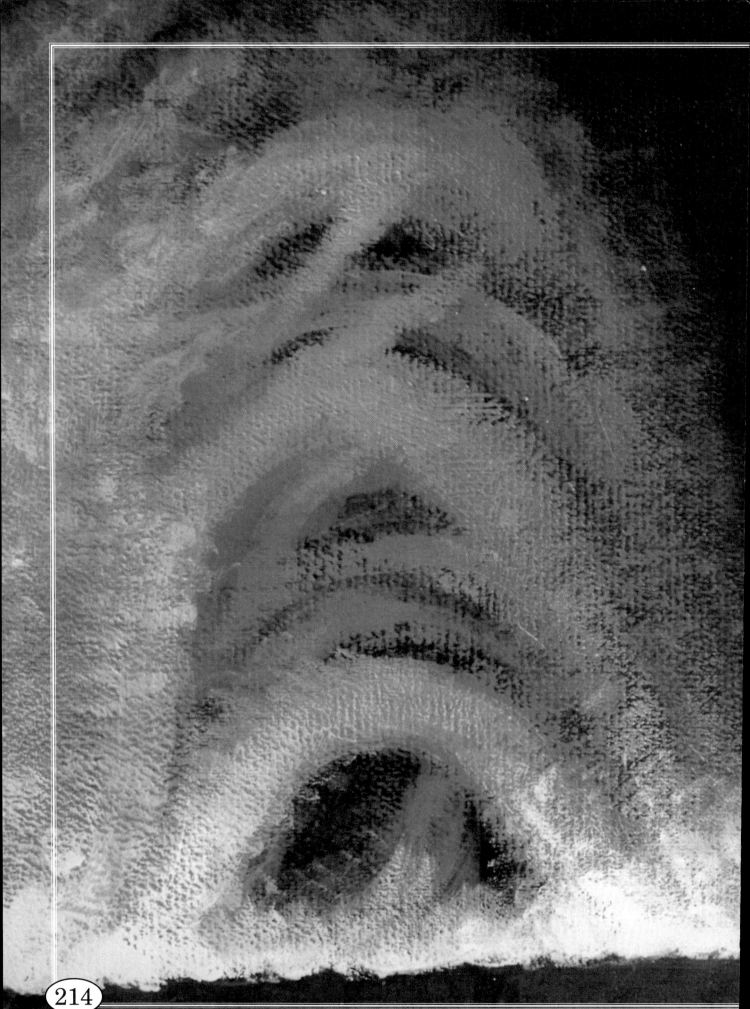

SUN

by Myra Cohn Livingston
illustrated by
Leonard Everett Fisher

Space
is afire
with bursts of bubbling gas,

colliding atoms,
boiling wells
and solar flares

spewing

from a burning star, the sun.

Ninety-three million miles away

this mass,
quaking inferno,
pluming arcs and bridges

roars;

a giant bomb
exploding
hydrogen.

Secrets

by Myra Cohn Livingston
illustrated by Leonard Everett Fisher

Space keeps its secrets
                hidden.
It does not tell.

        Are black holes time machines?
        Where do lost comets go?

        Is Pluto moon or planet?

How many, how vast
  unknown galaxies beyond us?

    Do other creatures
    dwell   on distant spheres?

                Will we ever know?
Space is silent.
It seldom answers.

    But we ask.

The Book That Saved the Earth

by Claire Boiko
illustrated by Dennis Hockerman

Characters

Historian
Great and Mighty Think-Tank
Apprentice Noodle
Captain Omega
Lieutenant Iota
Sergeant Oop
Offstage Voice

Time: 2543 A.D.

Before Rise: *Spotlight shines on* Historian, *who is sitting at table down right, on which there is a movie projector. A sign on an easel beside him reads:* MUSEUM OF ANCIENT HISTORY: DEPARTMENT OF THE TWENTIETH CENTURY. *He stands and bows to audience.*

Historian: Good afternoon. Welcome to our Museum of Ancient History, and to my department—curiosities of the good old, far-off twentieth century. The twentieth century was often called the Era of the Book. In those days, there were books about everything from anteaters to Zulus. Books taught people how to, and when to, and where to, and why to. They illustrated, educated, punctuated and even decorated. But the strangest thing a book ever did was to save the Earth. You haven't heard about the Macronite invasion of 1988? Tsk, tsk. What *do* they teach children nowadays? Well, you know, the invasion never really happened, because a single book stopped it. What was that book, you ask? A noble encyclopedia? A tome about rockets and missiles? A secret file from outer space? No, it was none of these. It

218

was *(Pauses, then points to projector)*——here, let me turn on the historiscope and show you what happened many, many centuries ago, in 1988. *(He turns on projector, and points it left. Spotlight on* Historian *goes out, and comes up down left on* Think-Tank, *who is seated on raised box, arms folded. He has huge, egg-shaped head, and he wears long robe decorated with stars and circles.* Apprentice Noodle *stands beside him at an elaborate switchboard. A sign on an easel reads:* MACRON SPACE CONTROL. GREAT AND MIGHTY THINK-TANK, COMMANDER-IN-CHIEF. BOW LOW BEFORE ENTERING.*)*

Noodle *(Bowing)*: O Great and Mighty Think-Tank, most powerful and intelligent creature in the whole universe, what are your orders?

Think-Tank *(Peevishly)*: You left out part of my salutation, Apprentice Noodle. Go over the whole thing again.

Noodle: It shall be done, sir. *(In singsong)* O Great and Mighty Think-Tank, Ruler of Macron and her two moons, most powerful and intelligent creature in the whole universe——*(Out of breath)* what-are-your-orders?

Think-Tank: That's better, Noodle. I wish to be placed in communication with our manned space probe to the ridiculous little planet we are going to put under our generous rulership. What do they call it again?

Noodle: Earth, Your Intelligence.

Think-Tank: Earth——of course. You see how insignificant the place is? But first, something important. My mirror. I wish to consult my mirror.

Noodle: It shall be done, sir. *(He hands Think-Tank hand mirror.)*

Think-Tank: Mirror, mirror, in my hand, who is the most fantastically intelligently gifted being in the land?

Offstage Voice *(After a pause)*: You, sir.

Think-Tank *(Striking mirror)*: Quicker. Answer quicker next time. I hate a slow mirror. *(He admires himself.)* Ah, there I am. Are we Macronites not a handsome race? So much more attractive than those ugly earthlings with their tiny heads. Noodle, you keep on exercising your mind, and some day you'll have a balloon brain just like mine.

Noodle: I certainly hope so, Mighty Think-Tank.

Think-Tank: Now, contact the space probe. I want to invade that primitive ball of mud called Earth before lunch.

Noodle: It shall be done, sir. *(He twists knobs and adjusts levers on switchboard. Electronic buzzes and beeps are heard. Noodle and Think-Tank remain at controls, as curtain rises.)*

* * *

Setting: *The Centerville Public Library.*

At Rise: Captain Omega *stands at center, opening and closing card catalogue drawers, looking puzzled. Lieutenant Iota is up left, counting books in bookcase. Sergeant Oop is at right, opening and closing book, turning it upside down, shaking it, and then riffling pages and shaking his head.*

Noodle *(Adjusting knobs)*: I have a close sighting of the space crew, sir. (Think-Tank *puts on pair of huge goggles and turns toward stage to watch.)* They seem to have entered some sort of Earth structure.

Think-Tank: Excellent. Make voice contact.

Noodle *(Speaking into a microphone)*: Macron Space Control calling the crew of Probe One. Macron Space Control calling the crew of Probe One. Come in, Captain Omega. Give us your location.

Captain Omega *(Speaking into disc which is on chain around his neck)*: Captain Omega to Macron Space Control. Lieutenant Iota, Sergeant Oop and I have landed on Earth without incident. We have taken shelter in this *(Indicates room)*——this square place. Have you any idea where we are, Lieutenant Iota?

Iota: I can't figure it out, Captain. *(Holding up book)* I've counted two thousand of these peculiar things. This place must be some sort of storage barn. What do you think, Sergeant Oop?

Oop: I haven't a clue. I've been to seven galaxies, but I've never seen anything like this. Maybe they're hats. *(He opens book and puts it on his head.)* Say, maybe this is a haberdasher's store!

Omega *(Bowing low)*: Perhaps the Great and Mighty Think-Tank will give us the benefit of his thought on the matter.

Think-Tank: Elementary, my dear Omega. Hold one of the items up so that I may view it closely. (Omega *holds book on palm of his hand.)* Yes, yes, I understand now. Since Earth

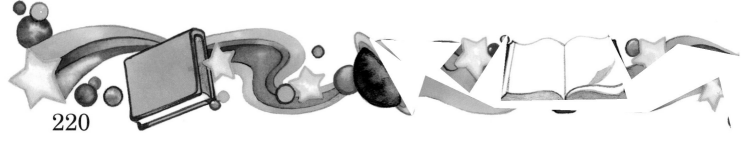

creatures are always eating, the place in which you find yourselves is undoubtedly a crude refreshment stand.

Omega *(To* Iota *and* Oop): He says we're in a refreshment stand.

Oop: The Earthlings certainly do have a strange diet.

Think-Tank: That item in your hand is called a "sandwich."

Omega *(Nodding)*: A sandwich.

Iota *(Nodding)*: A sandwich.

Oop *(Taking book from his head)*: A sandwich?

Think-Tank: Sandwiches are the main staple of Earth diet. Look at it closely. (Omega *squints at book.)* There are two slices of what is called "bread," and between them there is some sort of filling.

Omega: That is correct, sir.

Think-Tank: To confirm my opinion, I order you to eat it.

Omega *(Gulping)*: Eat it?

Think-Tank: Do you doubt the Mighty Think-Tank?

Omega: Oh, no, no. But poor Lieutenant Iota has not had his breakfast. Lieutenant Iota, I order you to eat this——this sandwich.

Iota *(Dubiously)*: Eat it? Oh, Captain! It's a very great honor to be the first Macronite to eat a sandwich, I'm sure, but——but how can I be so impolite as to eat before my Sergeant? *(Handing* Oop *book; brightly)* Sergeant Oop, I order you to eat the sandwich.

Oop *(Making a face)*: Who, sir? Me, sir?

Iota and **Omega** *(Slapping their chests in a salute)*: For the glory of Macron, Oop.

Oop: Yes, sirs. *(Unhappily)* Immediately, sirs. *(He opens his mouth wide.* Omega *and* Iota *watch him breathlessly. He bites down on corner of book, and pantomimes chewing and swallowing, while making terrible faces.)*

Omega: Well, Oop?

Iota: Well, Oop? (Oop *coughs.* Omega *and* Iota *pound him on back.)*

Think-Tank: Was it not delicious, Sergeant Oop?

Oop *(Slapping his chest in salute)*: That is correct, sir. It was *not* delicious. I don't know how the Earthlings can get those sandwiches down without water. They're dry as Macron dust.

Noodle: Sir—O Great and Mighty Think-Tank. I beg your pardon, but an insignificant bit of data floated into my mind about those sandwiches.

Think-Tank: It can't be worth much, but go ahead. Give us your trifling bit of data.

Noodle: Well, sir, I have seen surveyor films of those sandwiches. I noticed that the Earthlings did not *eat* them. They used them as some sort of communication device.

Think-Tank *(Haughtily)*: Naturally. That was my next point. These are actually communication sandwiches. Think-Tank is never wrong. Who is never wrong?

All *(Saluting)*: Great and Mighty Think-Tank is never wrong.

Think-Tank: Therefore, I order you to listen to them.

Omega: Listen to them?

Iota and Oop *(To each other; puzzled)*: Listen to them?

Think-Tank: Do you have marbles in your ears? I said, listen to them. *(Macronites bow very low.)*

Omega: It shall be done, sir. *(They each take two books from case, and hold them to their ears, listening intently.)*

Iota *(Whispering to Omega)*: Do you hear anything?

Omega *(Whispering back)*: Nothing. Do you hear anything, Oop?

Oop *(Loudly)*: Not a thing! (Omega *and* Iota *jump in fright.)*

Omega *and* **Iota:** Sh-h-h! *(They listen intently again.)*

Think-Tank: Well?, Well? Report to me. What do you hear?

Omega: Nothing, sir. Perhaps we are not on the correct frequency.

Iota: Nothing, sir. Perhaps the Earthlings have sharper ears than we do.

Oop: I don't hear a thing. Maybe these sandwiches don't make sounds.

Think-Tank: What? What? Does someone suggest the Mighty Think-Tank has made a mistake?

Omega: Why, no, sir. No, sir. We'll keep listening.

Noodle: Please excuse me, Your Brilliance, but a cloudy piece of information is rolling around in my head.

Think-Tank: Well, roll it out, Noodle, and I will clarify it for you.

Noodle: I seem to recall that the Earthlings did not *listen* to the sandwiches. They opened them, and watched them.

Think-Tank: Yes, that is quite correct. I will clarify that for you, Captain Omega. Those sandwiches are not for ear communication, they are for eye communication. Now, Captain Omega, take that large, bright-colored sand-wich over there. It appears to be important. Tell me what you observe. (Omega *picks up very large copy of "Mother Goose," holding it so that the audience can see title.* Iota *looks over* Omega's *left shoulder, and* Oop *squints over his right shoulder.)*

Omega: It appears to contain pictures of Earthlings.

Iota: There seems to be some sort of code.

Think-Tank *(Sharply interested)*: Code? Code? I told you this was important. Describe the code.

Oop: It's little lines and squiggles and dots. Thousands of them, next to the pictures.

Think-Tank: Code. Perhaps the Earthlings are not so primitive as we have thought. We must break the code. We must.

Noodle: Forgive me, Your Cleverness, but did not the chemical department give our spacemen a supply of Vitamin X to increase their intelligence?

Think-Tank: Stop! A thought of magnificent brilliance has come to me. Spacemen, our chemical department has given you a supply of Vitamin X to increase your intelligence. Take it immediately and then watch the sandwich. The meaning of the code will slowly unfold before you.

Omega: It shall be done, sir. Remove pill. *(Crew take vitamins from boxes on their belts.)* Present Vitamin X. *(They hold vitamins out in front of them, stiffly.)* Swallow. *(They put vitamins into their mouths and gulp simultaneously. They open their eyes wide, shake their heads, and they put their hands to their foreheads.)* The cotangent of a given angle in a right

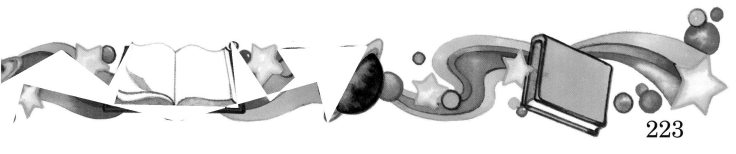

triangle is equal to the adjacent side divided by the hypotenuse.

Iota: *Habeas corpus ad faciendum et recipiendum!*

Oop: There is change of pressure along a radius in curvilinear motion.

Think-Tank: Excellent. Now, decipher that code.

All: It shall be done, sir. *(They frown over book, turning pages.)*

Omega: *(Brightly)*: Aha!

Iota: *(Brightly)*: Oho!

Oop: *(Bursting into laughter)*: Ha, ha, ha!

Think-Tank: What does it say? Tell me this instant. Transcribe, Omega.

Omega: Yes, sir *(He reads with great seriousness.)*

"Mistress Mary, quite contrary,
How does your garden grow?
With cockle shells and silver bells
And pretty maids all in a row."

Oop: Ha, ha, ha. Imagine that. Pretty maids growing in a garden.

Think-Tank: *(Alarmed)*: Stop! This is no time for levity. Don't you realize the seriousness of this discovery? The Earthlings have discovered how to combine agriculture and mining. They can actually *grow* crops of rare metals such as silver. And cockle shells. They can grow high explosives, too. Noodle, contact our invasion fleet.

Noodle: They are ready to go down and take over Earth, sir.

Think-Tank: Tell them to hold. Tell them new information has come to us about Earth. Iota, continue transcribing.

Iota: Yes, sir. *(He reads very gravely.)*

"Hey diddle diddle! The cat and
the fiddle,
The cow jumped over the moon,
The little dog laughed to see
such sport,
And the dish ran away with
the spoon."

Oop *(Laughing)*: The dish ran away with the spoon!

Think-Tank: Cease laughter. Desist. This is more and more alarming. The Earthlings have reached a high level of civilization. Didn't you hear? They have taught their domesticated animals musical culture and space techniques. Even their dogs have a sense of humor. Why, at this very moment, they may be launching an interplanetary

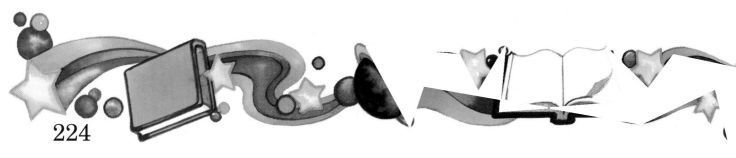

attack of millions of *cows!* Notify the invasion fleet. No invasion today. Oop, transcribe the next code.

Oop: Yes, sir. *(Reading)*

"Humpty Dumpty sat on the wall,
Humpty Dumpty had a great fall;
All the King's horses and all the
   King's men,
Couldn't put Humpty Dumpty
   together again."

Oh, look, sir. Here's a picture of Humpty Dumpty. Why, sir, he looks like——he looks like——*(Turns large picture of Humpty Dumpty toward Think-Tank and audience)*

Think-Tank *(Screaming and holding his head)*: It's me! It's my Great and Mighty Balloon Brain. The Earthlings have seen me. They're after me. "Had a great fall!" That means they plan to capture Macron Central Control and me! It's an invasion of Macron! Noodle, prepare a space capsule for me. I must escape without delay. Spacemen, you must leave Earth at once, but be sure to remove all traces of your visit. The Earthlings must not know that I know——(Omega, Iota *and* Oop *rush about, putting books back on shelves.)*

Noodle: Where shall we go, sir?

Think-Tank: A hundred million miles away from here. Order the invasion fleet to evacuate the entire planet of Macron. We are heading for Alpha Centauri, a hundred million miles away. (Omega, Iota, *and* Oop *run off right, as* Noodle *helps* Think-Tank *off left and curtain closes. Spotlight shines on* Historian *down right.)*

Historian *(Chuckling)*: And that's how one dusty old book of nursery rhymes saved the world from an invasion from Macron. As you all know, in the twenty-fifth century, five hundred years after all this happened, we Earthlings resumed contact with Macron, and we even became very chummy with the Macronites. By that time, Great and Mighty Think-Tank had been replaced by a very clever Macronite——the Wise and Wonderful Noodle! Oh, yes, we taught the Macronites the difference between sandwiches and books. We taught them how to read, too, and we established a model library in their capital city of Macronopolis. But, as you might expect, there is still one book that the Macronites can never bring themselves to read. You've guessed it——*Mother Goose! (He bows and exits right.)*

The End

The Book That Saved the Earth

Meet the Author

Claire Taylor Boiko has worked at many different jobs in theater ever since she was a young woman. While in her twenties, she worked as an actress in Children's Theater. Later, she worked behind-the-scenes on musical shows for soldiers in the Army. Now she writes plays for children. Her plays are found in books such as *Children's Plays for Creative Actors* and *Plays and Programs for Boys and Girls*. Ms. Boiko writes plays about things that interest her, including science, myths, and folk music.

Meet the Illustrator

Dennis Hockerman has been a freelance designer and illustrator for the last 23 years. Besides illustrating children's books, he has done work for the greeting card, gift wrap, and toy industries. In his spare time, Mr. Hockerman enjoys working at his printing press creating limited edition, hand-colored etchings.

Theme Connections

Think About It

With a small group of classmates, talk about the plots of some science fiction programs you have seen.

- Would the play you just read be more realistic if it weren't written as a comedy?
- If intelligent aliens came to Earth, where do you think they should go to learn the most important information about earthlings and our planet?

Check the Concept/Question Board to see if there are any questions there that you can answer now. If the selection or your discussions about the selection have raised any new questions about astronomy, put the questions on the Concept/Question Board.

Record Ideas

 What do you like or dislike about the science fiction genre? Record your notes and ideas in your Writing Journal.

Research Ideas

Write a science fiction story or play based on research you have conducted about astronomy.

Bibliography

Astronomy for Every Kid: 101 Easy Experiments That Really Work

by Janice VanCleve. Try these experiments and learn about the universe.

Comets, Meteors, and Asteroids

by Seymour Simon. Explore the solar system, and spin around with the meteors, asteroids, and comets.

Cosmic Science

by Jim Wiese. Marshmallow constellations, toilet paper planets, and straw rockets are just a few "space-cruising" activities you can enjoy.

Edwin Hubble: American Astronomer

by Mary Virginia Fox. Ever heard of the Hubble telescope? Read about the man for whom the telescope is named.

Flight, Space & Astronomy

by Bob Bonnet and Dan Keen. Try at least one of these fifty-seven projects and experiments and find out how much you can learn about space science.

Tales of the Shimmering Sky

retold by Susan Milord. People everywhere all look at the same sky. Meet people from all over the world through these sky tales.

Voyager: An Adventure to the Edge of the Solar System

by Sally Ride. Take a look at the Voyager spacecraft. Then travel on a mission to Saturn, Uranus, or Neptune.

The Young Astronomer

by Harry Ford. Chart the phases of the moon, watch meteor showers, and read a map of the constellations. This book will teach you how to do those things and more.

A YOUNG ENTHUSIAST'S GUIDE TO ASTRONOMY

Every family has a story. And each of those stories tells of many people and different times and places. Each story tells of the rich heritage that makes up the fabric and texture of the family and out of this fabric and texture, the family members learn their identity.

EP OUR
ARK
EAN.

The Land I Lost:

Adventures of a Boy in Vietnam

from the book by Huynh Quang Nhuong
illustrated by Neil Waldman

I was born on the central highlands of Vietnam in a small hamlet on a riverbank that had a deep jungle on one side and a chain of high mountains on the other. Across the river, rice fields stretched to the slopes of another chain of mountains.

There were fifty houses in our hamlet, scattered along the river or propped against the mountainsides. The houses were made of bamboo and covered with coconut leaves, and each was surrounded by a deep trench to protect it from wild animals or thieves. The only way to enter a house was to walk across a "monkey bridge"—a single bamboo stick that spanned the trench. At night we pulled the bridges into our houses and were safe.

There were no shops or marketplaces in our hamlet. If we needed supplies—medicine, cloth, soaps, or candles—we had to cross over the mountains and travel to a town nearby. We used the river mainly for traveling to distant hamlets, but it also provided us with plenty of fish.

During the six-month rainy season, nearly all of us helped plant and cultivate fields of rice, sweet potatoes, Indian mustard, eggplant, tomatoes, hot peppers, and corn. But during the dry season, we became hunters and turned to the jungle.

Wild animals played a very large part in our lives. There were four animals we feared the most: the tiger, the lone wild hog, the crocodile, and the horse snake. Tigers were always trying to steal cattle. Sometimes, however, when a tiger became old and slow it became a maneater. But a lone wild hog was even more dangerous than a tiger. It attacked every creature in sight, even when it had no need for food. Or it did crazy things, such as charging into the hamlet in broad daylight, ready to kill or to be killed.

The river had different dangers: crocodiles. But of all the animals, the most hated and feared was the huge horse snake. It was sneaky and attacked people and cattle just for the joy of killing. It would either crush its victim to death or poison it with a bite.

Like all farmers' children in the hamlet, I started working at the age of six. My seven sisters helped by working in the kitchen, weeding the garden, gathering eggs, or taking water to the cattle. I looked after the family herd of water buffaloes. Someone always had to be with the herd because no matter how carefully a water buffalo was trained, it always was ready to nibble young rice plants when no one was looking. Sometimes, too, I fished for the family while I guarded the herd, for there were plenty of fish in the flooded rice fields during the rainy season.

I was twelve years old when I made my first trip to the jungle with my father. I learned how to track game, how to recognize useful roots, how to distinguish edible mushrooms from poisonous ones. I learned that if birds, raccoons, squirrels, or monkeys had eaten the fruits of certain trees, then those fruits were not poisonous. Often they were not delicious, but they could calm a man's hunger and thirst.

My father, like most of the villagers, was a farmer and a hunter, depending upon the season. But he also had a college education, so in the evenings he helped to teach other children in our hamlet, for it was too small to afford a professional schoolteacher.

My mother managed the house, but during the harvest season she could be found in the fields, helping my father get the crops home; and as the wife of a hunter she knew how to dress and nurse a wound and took good care of her husband and his hunting dogs.

I went to the lowlands to study for a while because I wanted to follow my father as a teacher when I grew up. I always planned to return to my hamlet to live the rest of my life there. But war disrupted my dreams. The land I love was lost to me forever.

These stories are my memories. . . .

Opera and Karate

When she was eighty years old grandmother was still quite strong. She could use her own teeth to eat corn on the cob or to chew on sugar plants to extract juice from them. Every two days she walked for more than an hour to reach the marketplace, carrying a heavy load of food with her, and then spent another hour walking back home. And even though she was quite old, traces of her beauty still lingered on: Her hands, her feet, her face revealed that she had been an attractive young woman. Nor did time do much damage to the youthful spirit of my grandmother.

One of her great passions was theater, and this passion never diminished with age. No matter how busy she was, she never missed a show when there was a group of actors in town. If no actors visited our hamlet for several months, she would organize her own show in which she was the manager, the producer, and the young leading lady, all at the same time.

My grandmother's own plays were always melodramas inspired by books she had read and by what she had seen on the stage. She always chose her favorite grandson to play the role of the hero, who would, without fail, marry the heroine at the end and live happily ever after. And when my sisters would tell her that she was getting too old to play the role of the young heroine anymore, my grandmother merely replied: "Anybody can play this role if she's young at heart."

When I was a little boy my grandmother often took me to see the opera. She knew Chinese mythology by heart, and the opera was often a dramatization of this mythology. On one special occasion, during the Lunar New Year celebrations——my favorite holiday, because children could do anything they wanted and by tradition no one could scold them——I accompanied my grandmother to the opera.

When we reached the theater I wanted to go in immediately. But my grandmother wanted to linger at the entrance and talk to her friends. She chatted for more than an hour. Finally we entered the theater, and at that moment the "Faithful One" was onstage, singing sadly. The "Faithful One" is a common character in Chinese opera. He could be a good minister, or a valiant general, or someone who loved and served his king faithfully. But in the end he is unjustly persecuted by the king, whose opinion of him has been changed by the lies of the "Flatterer," another standard character.

When my grandmother saw the "Faithful One" onstage she looked upset and gave a great sigh. I was too interested in what was happening to ask her the reason, and we spent the next five hours watching the rest of the opera. Sometimes I cried because my grandmother cried at the pitiful situation of the "Faithful One." Sometimes I became as angry as my grandmother did at the wickedness of the "Flatterer."

When we went home that night my grandmother was quite sad. She told my mother that she would have bad luck in the following year because when we entered the theater, the "Faithful One" was onstage. I was puzzled. I told my grandmother that she was confused. It would be a good year for us because we saw the good guy first. But my mother said, "No, son. The 'Faithful One' always is in trouble and it takes him many years to vindicate himself. Our next year is going to be like one of his bad years."

So, according to my mother's and grandmother's logic, we would have been much better off in the new year if we had been lucky enough to see the villain first!

My grandmother had married a man whom she loved with all her heart, but who was totally different from her. My grandfather was very shy, never laughed loudly, and always spoke very softly. And physically he was not as strong as my grandmother. But he excused his lack of physical strength by saying that he was a "scholar."

About three months after their marriage, my grandparents were in a restaurant and a rascal began to insult my grandfather because he looked weak and had a pretty wife. At first he just made insulting remarks, such as, "Hey! Wet chicken! This is no place for a weakling!"

My grandfather wanted to leave the restaurant even though he and my grandmother had not yet finished their meal. But my grandmother pulled his shirt sleeve and signaled him to remain seated. She continued to eat and looked as if nothing had happened.

Tired of yelling insults without any result, the rascal got up from his table, moved over to my grandparents' table, and grabbed my grandfather's chopsticks. My grandmother immediately wrested the chopsticks from him and struck the rascal on his cheekbone with her elbow. The blow was so quick and powerful that he lost his balance and fell on the floor.

Instead of finishing him off, as any street fighter would do, my grandmother let the rascal recover from the blow. But as soon as he got up again, he kicked over the table between him and my grandmother, making food and drink fly all over the place. Before he could do anything else, my grandmother kicked him on the chin. The kick was so swift that my grandfather didn't even see it. He only heard a heavy thud, and then saw the rascal tumble backward and collapse on the ground.

All the onlookers were surprised and delighted, especially the owner of the restaurant. Apparently the rascal, one of the best karate fighters of our area, came to this restaurant every day and left without paying for his food or drink, but the owner was too afraid to confront him.

While the rascal's friends tried to revive him, everyone else surrounded my grandmother and asked her who had taught her karate. She said, "Who else? My husband!"

After the fight at the restaurant people assumed that my grandfather knew karate very well but refused to use it for fear of killing someone. In reality, my grandmother had received special training in karate from my great-great uncle from the time she was eight years old.

Anyway, after that incident, my grandfather never had to worry again. Anytime he had some business downtown, people treated him very well. And whenever anyone happened to bump into him on the street, they bowed to my grandfather in a very respectful way.

One morning my grandmother wanted me to go outside with her. We climbed a little hill that looked over the whole area, and when we got to the top she looked at the rice field below, the mountain on the horizon, and especially at the river. As a young girl she had often brought her herd of water buffaloes to the river to drink while she swam with the other children of the village. Then we visited the graveyard where her husband and some of her children were buried. She touched her husband's tombstone and said, "Dear, I will join you soon." And then we walked back

to the garden and she gazed at the fruit trees her husband had planted, a new one for each time she had given birth to a child. Finally, before we left the garden my sister joined us, and the two of them fed a few ducks swimming in the pond.

That evening my grandmother did not eat much of her dinner. After dinner she combed her hair and put on her best dress. We thought that she was going to go out again, but instead she went to her bedroom and told us that she didn't want to be disturbed.

The family dog seemed to sense something was amiss, for he kept looking anxiously at everybody and whined from time to time. At midnight my mother went to my grandmother's room and found that she had died, with her eyes shut, as if she were sleeping normally.

It took me a long time to get used to the reality that my grandmother had passed away. Wherever I was, in the house, in the garden, out on the fields, her face always appeared so clearly to me. And even now, many years later, I still have the feeling that my last conversation with her has happened only a few days before.

The Land I Lost:

Adventures of a Boy in Vietnam

Meet the Author

Huynh Quang Nhuong was born in My Tho, Vietnam. He was a first lieutenant in the South Vietnamese Army, and was wounded during the Vietnam War. He came to the United States for medical treatment. Once in the U.S., he became a naturalized citizen. He now makes his home in Columbia, Missouri.

Mr. Nhuong is the first Vietnamese writer to write both fiction and nonfiction in English. He says, "I hope my books will make people from different countries happy. . . " He believes that good literature reaches into the hearts of all those who read it, no matter what country they are from, what age they are, or what they believe.

The Land I Lost was Mr. Nhuong's first book for children. It was published in five different languages and has received awards worldwide.

Meet the Illustrator

Neil Waldman had a painful childhood and art became his outlet. When he was young, he says, "I would retreat to my bedroom, close the door, and sit down with crayons and a sketch pad. As I watched amazing shapes and colors pour from my crayons onto the blank sheets of paper, I could feel the fear and tension dissolve." As an adult, he chose to be a children's book illustrator because it allowed him to earn a living while doing what he loved most. Some of Mr. Waldman's favorite books that he has illustrated are *The Never Ending Greenness, Bayou Lullaby,* and *Quetzal.*

Theme Connections

Think About It

With a small group of classmates, discuss the following questions.

- What were some of the important memories the author had of his childhood?
- Why were these memories so important to him?
- Do you have any memories of friends or family members that are important to you? Why are they important?

Record Ideas

Record in your Writing Journal what you have learned about heritage from this selection. Also note any new questions you have about the unit theme.

Improvise a Scene

The author's grandmother loved the theater so much that, when there were no actors in town, she created plays of her own and recruited people from town to act in them. With a partner, think of a part of the story, "The Land I Lost," that you particularly liked. Together, briefly outline the scene's sequence of events. Then, with your partner, act out the scene for two other people in your class, improvising character roles and dialogue.

Scammon Bay

Anchorage

IN TWO WORLDS:

• A Yup'ik Eskimo Family •

from the book by Aylette Jenness and Alice Rivers
photographs by Aylette Jenness

THE PAST

• *Long Ago* •

Alice and Billy Rivers live with their children in the small town of Scammon Bay, Alaska, on the coast of the Bering Sea. They are Yup'ik Eskimos. Their story really begins long, long ago.

Alice and Billy's parents, grandparents, great-grandparents, great-great-grandparents—all their ancestors for several thousand years—have always lived here. They were part of a small group of Yup'ik Eskimos whose home was this vast area of tidal flats bordering the sea, with inland marshes, ponds, creeks, and rivers lacing the flat treeless tundra, broken only by occasional masses of low hills.

Each year, as the northern part of the earth tilted toward the sun, the long hours of sunlight here melted the snow, melted the sea ice, melted the rivers, melted, even, the frozen land down to the depth of a foot or so. Briefly, for a few months, birds came from the south to lay their eggs and raise their young. The fish spawned, plants grew, berries ripened. And then the earth tilted away from the sun. Days grew shorter, the sun weaker, temperatures fell. The rain turned to snow, plants withered, birds flew south. Ponds, creeks, rivers, and finally even the Bering Sea froze, and layers of snow covered the whole landscape. Fish, sea mammals, and land animals all moved beneath thick blankets of ice and snow.

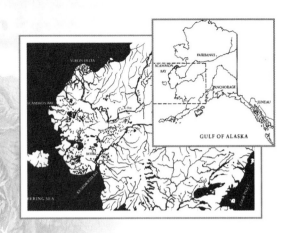

The small, scattered groups of Yup'ik Eskimos knew exactly how to survive here. Living as single families, or in small groups of relatives, they moved with the seasons to catch each kind of fish, bird, or mammal when and where each was most easily available. They harpooned the whales that migrated north along the coast in spring and south in the fall. They shot and snared birds nesting on the tundra, and they gathered the birds' eggs. They netted saltwater fish coming to lay their eggs in the rivers and creeks, and they caught freshwater fish moving beneath the ice of inland creeks. They trapped small mammals on the land for meat and for fur clothing. They knew where to find and how to catch dozens of different fish and animals for food, for clothing, even for light and heat for their small homes.

They had fire, but they didn't know how to use it to make metal. Everything they had they made themselves, with their hands, with stone, bone, or ivory tools—their many intricate snares and nets and traps, their boats and sleds, their homes and their clothing. Life was hard and precarious. Nothing was wasted.

Their mark on the land was light. Today their old sites are nearly part of the earth, not easy to see. These Yup'ik Eskimos didn't build monuments to gods or leaders. They believed that animals had spirits, and that the spirits survived the animals' death to inhabit other animals. After killing a seal, they put water in its mouth to show their caring and respect for it and to ensure that its spirit would return in the form of another seal another time. They made up stories and dances of awe, fear, and pleasure in the animals they knew so well.

They shared with each other, and no one was much better or worse off than anyone else. Families, or groups of families, had rights to certain places for hunting or fishing, but no one owned the land or its resources.

They knew no outsiders, no one different from themselves. During those hundreds and hundreds of years, their way of life changed very little. People followed in the footsteps of their ancestors, children learning from their parents the vast body of knowledge necessary for survival in this environment.

But during the last fifty years, their lives have changed enormously. And these changes are within the memory of the older people living here now.

Listen to Alice Rivers's mother, Mary Ann, describe her childhood. She speaks in Yup'ik, and one of her daughters, Leota, translates into English.

● **Mary Anne Remembers** ●

"I was born, as I was told, in the late fall. My mother delivered me outside in the tundra, out in the open. My mother told me that after I was born I clutched some tundra moss and grass in my hand. I do not know why I was born outside, but it must have been because my mother was out in the tundra.

"When I was first aware of my surroundings, we lived on the other side of the mountains of Scammon Bay. The name of the place where I was born is called Ingeluk, and I think it's called this name because we are surrounded by small hills. We were the only people living in that area. We were secluded away from other people. There was my father, my mother, my two older sisters, and one older brother, and I am the youngest in the family.

"We lived in a sod house. The insides of our house had braided grass hanging on the walls as paneling. We had only one window, which was made out of dried seal guts, and it made a lot of noise when it was windy. Our floor was plain, hard, dried mud. Our beds were dried grass, piled high to keep us warm. We had no blankets. We mostly did with what we had at hand, and we used our parkas to keep us warm. I remember we had one kettle, a small half kerosene tank for our cooking pot, and the plates we had were carved from wood by my father.

"For light, we used seal oil when we had the oil, and it smoked a lot. Other times we had no light because we had no oil. I remember my mother cooked whitefish, and she carefully skimmed off the oil from the pot we had, and what she took out of the cooking pot we used in our oil lamp. The oil from the fish made pretty good light; it never smoked like the seal oil did. There were lots of stories being told, that's what we did during the evenings.

"Our main diet was fish, caught in my father's traps. There were times that we were really hungry. We were very poor. Sometimes when we woke up in the morning, we had nothing at all to eat.

"We didn't have any kind of bread. We did not know what coffee and tea were.

"I saw my first white man when we were traveling by our skin boat. I did not know who he was, but later on I was told that the white man was trading goods for fur or skins. Maybe I was fifteen years old when I saw an airplane.

"We lived in a sod house. The insides of our house had braided grass hanging on the walls as paneling. We had only one window, which was made out of dried seal guts, and it made a lot of noise when it was windy."

"I liked the life we used to live a long time ago, but we were always in need of something. I would say we live in comfort now. I don't go in hunger now. I say both lives I led were good, and I like both."

Mary Ann grew up and married a man who lived nearby, Teddy Sundown. They began to raise their family in Keggatmiut, as Scammon Bay is known in Yup'ik. It was a good site, and a number of families settled there. They built their small log houses on the lower slope of a range of hills that rose out of the flat tundra. A clear stream, racing down the hillside, flowed into the river that wound along the base of the hills, and finally emptied into a wide, shallow bay of the Bering Sea. Mary Ann and Teddy still moved to seasonal camps to fish, trap, and hunt, but as the village grew, they began to spend more and more of the year there.

The United States government set up a school in Scammon Bay and hired a Yup'ik teacher. All of the children were expected to attend school.

Missionaries had come to convert the people from their traditional religion, and the village was divided between Catholics and Protestants. Two churches were built.

Alice was the fourth child born to Mary Ann and Teddy. She is shown at the age of ten, standing on the far right of her family. She speaks of growing up in Scammon Bay.

"Our home was a one-room building. Our beds were together——Mom and Dad's bed and our bed. All of us kids slept together in one bed. No table——the tables came later on. We used to eat sitting on the floor, Eskimo way. Mom used to cook bread on top of the stove, 'cause there was no oven. To me it used to be the best bread I've eaten. Then as I grew older, we got a stove and oven, and she started baking bread.

"We ate bread, birds, dried herrings, clams, mussels, fish——boiled and frozen——seals, mink, muskrats. There were two stores. We bought shortening, flour, tea, coffee——just what we needed.

"We were always together. We'd go to church every morning. Mom would wake us up early, we'd go to Mass. We never used to be lazy, we used to just go, get up and go, get up to a real cold morning, and by the time we were home, the house would be nice and warm.

"Right after church we used to go straight to school, all of us. I remember that learning to write my name was the hardest thing. I was maybe about six. We had Eskimo teachers. It was one room, and everything was there.

"After school, we'd have lots of things to do—— bringing some wood in, dishes to wash, house to clean, babies to watch, water to pack. We had aluminum pails with handles. We used to run over to the stream and pack water until we had what we needed. In the winter we had to keep one hole in the ice open the whole winter. This was one of the things I used to do with my sisters, not only me.

"Planes came in maybe once a week with mail. We didn't know about telephones. We had a radio, just for listening. I think we listened to one station all the time. No TV.

"The teachers had a short-wave radio. If someone got sick, they would report us to the hospital. They would give us medication or send us to the hospital in Bethel."

● Alice Grown Up ●

By the time Alice was an adult, Scammon Bay was a village of a hundred and fifty people, with twenty-five log and frame homes. For transportation, each family had a dog sled and team, and a boat for use in summer.

The government began to take a larger role in the Yup'ik villages. A new school was built, with living quarters for non-Eskimo teachers from outside of Alaska. Children were taught a standard public elementary school curriculum, which had little reference either to their own lives or to what they knew and didn't know about life outside Scammon Bay. They were forbidden to speak Yup'ik in school, in the belief that this would help them to learn English, and that learning English was very important.

A postmaster was hired from among the village men, and a custodian for the school. A health aide was trained, and a small clinic built and stocked. More planes came to Scammon Bay, and it became easier to fly someone needing hospital care out——as long as the weather was good.

Government money became available for low-income families and for the elderly and disabled. There were few opportunities to earn cash, but almost all of the men in Scammon Bay were able to earn some money by hunting or trapping seals, mink, muskrats, and beaver and selling the skins to be made into luxury fur coats outside of Alaska. In summer they netted salmon in the river mouths north of Scammon Bay and sold this valuable fish to processors, who marketed it throughout the United States as smoked fish, or lox.

Each summer a freighter came up the coast from Seattle, Washington, with supplies for the villages. Everyone began to buy more factory-made goods. Some families bought stoves that burned fuel oil instead of relying on brush wood they cut nearby. Some bought windmills, which produced enough electricity for one or two light bulbs in their homes. Some bought snowmobiles, which enabled them to travel farther than they could by dog team to hunt and trap, but which, unlike dogs, required money for fuel and new parts.

And for the first time in the long history of the Yup'ik Eskimos, some people began to travel away from their homeland. Some teenagers went to boarding school in the state of Washington. Some men went to National Guard training, and some families moved away permanently, settling in Alaskan towns and cities, or even as far away as Oregon and California.

But most remained in Scammon Bay, and some new Yup'ik people came to live there from other towns.

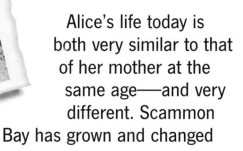

Alice's life today is both very similar to that of her mother at the same age—and very different. Scammon Bay has grown and changed in many ways.

There are three hundred and fifty people in Scammon Bay now, living in fifty-six houses. Most of the old log homes are now used for storage, and many people, like the Riverses, have new houses provided by the government at low cost. A dish antenna relays television to all the homes. Satellite transmission enables families to make telephone calls anywhere in the world. Huge storage tanks hold fuel to run an electric generator that provides enough power for each home to have all the lights that people want. A water and sewage disposal system required building a water treatment plant and a lagoon on the tundra for waste water. The dump, full of cans, plastic, fuel drums, and broken machinery, is a reminder of the difficulty of disposing of modern trash.

For some years the state government made a great deal of money from taxes on oil found in Alaska, and this money paid for many of the modern conveniences in Scammon Bay and other rural towns. An airstrip was built so that planes could land more easily at all times of the year; it is regularly plowed in winter. Three small planes a day fly into Scammon Bay, bringing everything from cases of soft drinks to boxes of disposable diapers and, of course, the mail. A huge new gym has been built, and

Satellite transmission enables families to make telephone calls anywhere in the world.

a new clinic, a preschool center, town offices, and a post office. The school is now run by the state, not the federal government, and goes all the way through the twelfth grade.

In spite of the changes, the traditional pattern of living from the land is still powerful. This can be seen most clearly as people move to seasonal camps during the summer months.

●   School   ●

During the school year the family's life falls into very different patterns from those of summer. Billy begins his winter rounds of hunting and fishing, going out by snowmobile nearly every day to get food or firewood for the family. Alice goes to work as the school cook, and the Rivers children go to their classrooms each morning.

Billy Junior, in the second grade, is learning to type. He says proudly, "I've already finished typing one book, and now I'm on another. We can read any kind of books. Now I'm on a hard one."

In Sarah and Isaac's combined third and fourth grade class, Clifford Kaganak teaches Yup'ik. Here he writes words in Yup'ik on the chalkboard, and the class practices reading and translating. They want to be fluent in both of their languages—English and Yup'ik.

Down the hall, Jennifer Allison Keim works with the older Rivers boys—Oscar, Jacob and Abraham. Jacob enjoys using the computers, but generally the boys would rather be out hunting and fishing—or using the school skis. Jennifer says, "My goals are for the kids to be educated to the point where they can protect themselves from outsiders, so if something comes their way that they have to deal with, they'll know how to weigh and measure and make decisions."

The teachers all know that the school has a great responsibility to prepare the kids for the outside world, and they also want to encourage a sense of pride in Yup'ik Eskimo culture. Some students want to go on to college after graduating from high school in Scammon Bay, and the teachers work hard to make this happen.

During the school year, traditional ways of life are practiced mostly on the weekends. The end of each school week marks the beginning of two days of hunting and fishing for the whole Rivers family.

Alice says, "On the weekends, we get to go traveling with Billy. Usually we decide what we're going to do ahead of time, what's going to happen. Like if we want to go fishing, we go fishing, or hunting ptarmigans. We're out most of the day Saturday doing this and that."

This is where Billy becomes the teacher, training the kids in both the oldest methods of hunting and fishing, and the newest. Since the children spend so much time in school, this is an important time for them to learn how to survive as Eskimos.

"I teach my boys the way I've been taught, the way my dad taught me. What I think that's wrong, I try to do it better than my dad. And when I make a mistake, I try to correct it to my boys, so they'll do it better than I did.

"I start taking them out as soon as they're old enough——like in the boat, when they're old enough to sit down and take care of themselves. I tell them little things like taking the anchor out, putting the anchor back up. As soon as they understand our words, we teach them from there. If they show you something that they know, you'll know they learned it——and then they can start doing it by themselves.

"Each one of them that goes with me, I talk to them, I tell them about little things——what's dangerous, what's not dangerous. I tell them about melting ice——even though it looks good on the surface, some places you can't see when it's covered with snow, it's thin. That's where they fall through. I teach them what thin ice looks like, and how it looks when it's safe.

"Oscar's been going with me first, 'cause he's the oldest one, then Jacob. One of them will know more, the one that pays attention more, just like in school. The one that doesn't listen, or doesn't pay attention, he'll make more mistakes or get more scolding.

"Oscar was about seven or eight when I first let him shoot a gun. He got his first seal when he was maybe eight or nine. In the boat I did the driving, and I had him do the shooting. He got a young mukluk that was a baby in springtime. He shot it, and after he shot it, he looked at me, looked back, and he smiled. 'I catch it.' "

Oscar remembers this very clearly. He says, "My grandpa divided the seal up in circles and gave it to the old people." This is the traditional Yup'ik way of sharing a boy's first catch with the elders, still carried on, though motorboats have replaced kayaks, and rifles are used in place of thrown harpoons.

THE FUTURE

Alice and Billy know very well that life is changing fast here in Scammon Bay, and they want their children to be prepared for this.

Alice says, "When I was a kid, I used to do things with my mom. I used to watch her sew. Now I try to have Mattie knit, crochet, make things, but she thinks it's too boring. She knows how to do it, but she can't sit and look at one thing for a long time. I can't even teach her how to sew a skin. She doesn't have any patience.

"Now there's so many other things going on. In our time there was no basketball, no Igloo [community center], hardly any dances."

Billy says, "When I was Billy Junior's age, I used to run maybe twenty or thirty times around a pond with my little wooden boat. Just run around, play with it, put mud inside of it, and run around. I'd never think of TV, it wasn't in my mind.

"Everything is not the same here in Alaska, not like before. Things are changing. Things are getting more expensive. Most of the people are depending on more jobs. I mean working, you have to have a job.

"I talk to the kids, I just say what we'd like them to do. I tell them, 'If you go to school, and be smart over there, and try to learn what you're taught, you guys will have good jobs, and good-paying jobs. I want you to have good-paying jobs, so we'll have the things that we need, anything we need'; like this I talk to them.

"I'd be happy to have them travel to see other countries, to have them learning something that's Outside—*if* they have a job. 'Cause Outside there's many people without jobs, no home. Here it's okay, as we help each other here in the villages.

"We get after the kids for not doing their homework. We want them to be more educated, more than us. I mean, learn more. I only went up to the fifth grade."

Alice agrees. She adds "I want them to learn other ways—Outside ways. And I want them to learn our ways, too—hunting for our kind of foods. We can't have store-bought food all the time. I want them to learn both ways."

Looking down on Scammon Bay from the hill, it seems like a very small settlement, nearly lost in the huge expanse of tundra around it. From this distance it doesn't look so different from the Scammon Bay of Alice's childhood. Yet it is invisibly connected to the whole world now. And so is the Rivers family.

Now there's so many other things going on. In our time there was no basketball, no Igloo [community center], hardly any dances.

IN TWO WORLDS:

Meet the Authors

Aylette Jenness, a writer and photographer, met **Alice Rivers** when they were both young women. At the time, Aylette had moved to Alaska to write books about the people of Scammon Bay. While writing *Gussuk Boy* and *Dwellers of the Tundra*, she met Alice Rivers. After finishing the books, Aylette left Alaska. When she returned to Alaska for a visit more than twenty years later, she met up with her old friend, Alice Rivers. Alice told her about how different things were in Scammon Bay since she had lived there twenty years ago. The two decided to work together on the story of how Alice's family had grown and changed, and how the little community on the Bering Sea had changed as well. Rivers's mother, Mary Ann Sundown, also contributed to the book by telling about the way people lived during the years she herself was growing up near Scammon Bay.

Theme Connections

Think About It

With a small group of classmates, discuss the following questions.

- What are the differences between Scammon Bay and where you live?
- How does the place in which people live affect their culture?
- Why is it important for families to tell their stories? What purpose does it serve?
- Is heritage important to the Yup'iks? Have their feelings about their heritage changed over time?

Record Ideas

Think about the ways the Yup'ik tribe's community has changed over the generations, and then try to predict what other changes may come in the future. Write a paragraph in your Writing Journal about what you think their community will be like in another twenty years.

Make a Chart

Draw a straight line across a piece of paper, then divide the line into three sections. Label the first section "The 1940s," the second section "The 1970s," and the third section "Present Day." The object is to find out what kinds of work and play activities children took part in during each of the years on your chart. You may get this information by interviewing friends or family members that were children during those years, or you may get your information from books, movies, television, or personal experience. List the activities below the chart date during which they occurred.

Compare and contrast the information for each date. Have the activities changed over three generations? Did they change as much over the years as the Yup'ik's culture did? Why or why not?

History *of the* Tunrit

collected by Knud Rasmussen
a traditional Netsilik Eskimo Legend
translated by Edward Field
illustrated by Pudlo

When our Netsilik forefathers came to these hunting grounds
the Tunrit people already lived here.
It was the Tunrit who first learned
how to survive in this difficult country.
They showed us the caribou crossing places
and taught us the special way to fish in the rivers.

Our people came from inland
so we love caribou hunting more than anything else,
but the Tunrit were sea people
and preferred to hunt seal.
They actually went out on the salt sea in their kayaks,
hunting seal in open water. That takes nerve.
We only hunt them through the ice at breathing holes.
They also caught whales and walruses as they swam by:

The bones of these creatures are still lying around
in the wrecks of the Tunrit houses.
And they hunted bear and wore their skins for clothes.
We wear caribou.

The Tunrit were strong, but easily frightened.
In a fight they would rather run than kill. Anyway,
you never heard of them killing anyone.
And we lived among the Tunrit in those days peacefully,
for they let us come and share their land:
Until once by accident some of them killed one of our dogs
and ran away scared, leaving their homeland.

All of the Tunrit fled finally from their villages here,
although we cannot remember why anymore:
They just ran away or the land was taken from them.
And on parting from us they cried:
"We followed the caribou and hunted them down;
now it is your turn to follow them and do the hunting."

And so we do to this day.

The Night We Started Dancing

by Ann Cameron
illustrated by Carlos Caban

I am named after my dad, Luis, but everybody calls me Luisito. I live with my grandfather and grandmother; my four uncles; my two aunts; my cousin, Diego; a girl named Maria who helps my grandmother; our two dogs, Chubby and Pilot; our two cats, Stripes and Hunter; and our big green parrot, Bright Star, that my grandmother always says she is going to bake and serve for dinner someday.

We live in a town called Santa Cruz, in Guatemala, Central America. Santa Cruz has a park where there are great band concerts, free, every week. It has a public school, and a big college for army cadets, and it has an electronics store where you could special-order a computer, but it doesn't have paved streets, it has only dirt streets that turn to dust in the winter when it's dry, and to mud in the summer when it rains.

I like dirt streets. It goes with the special thing about Santa Cruz, which is that it's a very old town. It was a town before Columbus discovered America, and before the Spaniards came from Spain to steal our land and our gold and make slaves of people, because they said their religion was the true one, and God liked them better than us.

On the edge of Santa Cruz there is a high hill covered with old pine trees and the ruins of pyramids and an ancient fortress. That's where the headquarters of our people was, the headquarters of the kingdom of the Quichés, where our ancestors fought the Spaniards harder than anybody in Guatemala, before they lost for good.

Once, when I was six, a real Spaniard from Spain came to our house for dinner. He was going to do some business with my grandfather, so my grandmother invited him.

The whole dinner I kept watching my grandfather and the Spaniard all the time, and looking at my grandfather's big machete knife that he keeps by the front door.

Finally, I couldn't stand it, I said, "*Con permiso,* excuse me," and got up from the table and followed my grandmother into the kitchen when she went to get more food, and I even ducked under Bright Star's perch to get there faster.

"When?" I asked my grandmother. "When is he going to do it?"

"Who?" my grandmother said. "Do what?"

"When is Grandpa going to kill the Spaniard?" I whispered, and Bright Star hissed in his loudest voice, "Kill the Spaniard!" and the Spaniard looked around fast and dropped his fork.

My grandfather stopped munching his tortilla. "Don't be concerned," he said to the Spaniard, "we just have a crazy parrot," and my grandmother said, "One day I am going to bake you, Bright Star!"

Then she took me into one of the bedrooms and closed the door.

"What is this all about?" she said. "Why would Grandpa kill the Spaniard?"

"For being a Spaniard," I said.

"Are you crazy?" my grandmother said. "How can the Spaniard help being a Spaniard? He was born one, just like you were born a Guatemalan and a Quiché. Don't you know the battles with the Spaniards were over hundreds of years ago? We have to judge people by what they do, not by where they come from. And we have to fight our own battles, too, not the ones our ancestors fought."

So that was when I first found out that we'd never get our kingdom back—at least not the way it used to be.

My grandfather was born poor, and he never went to school. He worked from the time he was six years old, out in the wheat fields and the cornfields, hoeing. Every day when he finished work and went home, he would pass by his own dad in the street, drinking and spending all the family money. My great-granddad never helped my granddad at all. But my granddad just kept working, and when he was twenty, he started buying land—pieces nobody thought were good for anything—and on the land he planted apple orchards, and when the apples grew all over, big and beautiful, he got rich. He built a big house for my grandmother and our family, with five big bedrooms, and a patio in the middle full of flowers, and a living room where he and my grandmother put up all the pictures of both their families, except my grandfather never put up a picture of his dad. Then, last year, he must have finally started feeling sorry for his father, because he got his picture out of a drawer, and dusted it off, and put it up in the living room, only not with the rest of the pictures.

So now my great-grandfather is staring out at the rest of the family, kind of ashamed-looking, from behind a fern.

My grandmother only learned to read four years ago, but she made my aunts and uncles study hard in school, and now she's making me do it, too. When I asked her why I had to study so hard, she said, "So that you aren't working with a hoe in the fields all your life, with the sun beating down on your head like a hammer."

When my grandparents' kids got to be old enough to study in the capital, my grandparents bought a house there for them to live in. So most of the year my aunts and uncles are there, studying architecture, and economics, and dentistry, and law, and accounting, and psychology. Only my youngest aunt, Celia, who is sixteen, is still living in Santa Cruz all the time. But next year she's going to the capital, too. She says she's going to study to be a doctor. My grandparents are very proud of all their children. The sad thing is, their oldest son, the only one who was studying agriculture and who loved the land the way my grandfather does, was my father, and he died. My mother died with him.

My mother was teaching grade school and my dad was in the last year of his agriculture studies when they died. I was four years old.

It happened four years ago, when my mom and dad and I and Uncle Ricardo were taking a bus from the capital to go back to my grandparents' house for Christmas. The bus terminal was full of dust and people trying to sell ice cream and coconuts and last-minute Christmas presents. Lots of people were going back to their hometowns for the holidays, and there weren't enough buses. Everybody was pushing and shoving to get on the ones there were.

My mom had a suitcase, and my dad had me on his back because he figured I couldn't run fast enough, and Uncle Ricardo was staring toward the sun with his hand shading his eyes, trying to see the bus that goes to Santa Cruz.

"Santa Cruz! That's it! Run!" he shouted, and my mom and dad raced for the front door of the bus, and Uncle Ricardo raced for the back, and they did flying dives over the top of a bunch of other people. My mom and dad got seats right behind the driver, and I sat on my mom's lap. Uncle Ricardo got stuck at the back, standing up.

Everybody pushed the windows down to get more air, and the driver put the bus in gear, but it didn't move, and his helper, the ticket taker, got out a hammer and a wrench and raised the hood on the bus and hammered on something for a while, and then the driver tried to move the bus again, and it went, and Uncle Ricardo heard my mother say, "A miracle! What a miraculous miracle!" and the ticket taker ran after the moving bus and jumped in the open door with the hammer and the wrench in his hand, and we were off.

Uncle Ricardo settled in and tried to take his elbow out of the stomach of the person on his right, and get his feet out from under the feet of the person on his left. My mom and dad were probably about the only ones who could see out the window, and who knew how the driver was driving.

The bus didn't go very fast, because it couldn't with so many people on it, but after a while Uncle Ricardo felt the bus lurch, and he heard my dad say to the driver, "Be careful, brother!" so he figured that the bus driver must have been taking a chance passing on a mountain curve.

A little while later he felt the bus twist again, and he heard my father say to the driver, "A man who foresees trouble and prevents it, is worth two men." But it seemed like the driver didn't feel like listening, because a little while later Uncle Ricardo heard my father say, "No matter where you are going, you don't have to get there first. The thing is, to get there."

And after that he heard my mother say, "Driver, there is more time than life."

And that was all he heard, except for my mother's voice just once more, shouting, "Luisito!" just before my father grabbed me with one hand and threw me out the window.

The bus driver went head-on into another bus. And my mother was right, because time just keeps going on and on and on, but she and my dad and the bus driver and the ticket taker and a lot of other people ran out of life completely.

Uncle Ricardo was okay because he was at the back, and I was okay.

The only part I remember begins with the grip of my father's hand, and how it hurt when he shoved me through the window frame. But I don't like to remember. I like to think about daytime things, my aunts and uncles, and things that are happening now.

But sometimes I still dream about it, being thrown out the window. In the dream I am little again, the same age I was then, and I land down a hillside in a freshly hoed field, just the way I really landed, but it is not daytime, it is almost completely dark, and I get up and go back to the wrecked bus, to find my mom and dad, but it gets darker and darker, and I never can find them.

Uncle Ricardo says one day I won't have the dream anymore. He says that my parents loved me a lot, and that I will always have them in my heart. He says one day my dream self will understand that, too. It will know that my parents are always with me when I remember them. It won't have to go back to the wrecked bus to look for them anymore.

And really I am okay, and Uncle Ricardo is okay, and my grandmother also is okay, because she loves all her children very much, but equally. The only one who has not been okay is my grandfather, because he loved my dad more than anybody. My dad wasn't only his son, he was his best friend.

The first Christmas after the accident we didn't celebrate, because nobody wanted to. But the next Christmas we didn't celebrate either, because Grandpa didn't want to. On the anniversary of the accident, he cut a lot of white roses and put them in front of my parents' wedding picture that hangs in the living room, and we visited their graves at the cemetery, so that was all there was of Christmas that year, too.

And from the beginning my grandmother said we shouldn't mention my mom and dad in front of my grandfather because it might upset him too much. She said we should just wait, and in time he would get better.

But it got to be September of the third year after my father died, and my grandfather still wasn't any better. My aunt Patricia, who had been leaving my cousin Diego with us a lot in Santa Cruz, decided to take Diego to the city. She said it was because she didn't have so many courses and she would have more time to spend with him, but Uncle Ricardo told me it was really because she thought it was too gloomy for Diego around our house.

The only reason I liked being in the house is that I like my grandmother and Celia a lot, my grandmother because she never yells at anybody, and Celia because she treats me like a grown-up. She got me to help her with a lot of projects, especially her Laugh Development Project, in which she said she needed the opinion of a man.

She wanted to develop four new laughs, even though my grandmother said it was a waste of time, and she couldn't see what was wrong with the laugh Celia was born with.

Celia said these are modern times, and a person should have five of everything. She said her original laugh was for when she really felt like laughing, and the other four would be for when she couldn't afford to be serious. She wanted my

opinion because she wanted to make sure the four new laughs would be good enough to impress boyfriends.

So when Grandpa wasn't around, she practiced in front of the big cracked mirror on the patio.

"Ha, ha, HAH, HAH, hah," went the first laugh, which is a rapid one where she tosses her long black hair back behind her shoulders. That is her Rio de Janeiro laugh.

"Ho ho ho," she laughs slowly, and rubs her chin thoughtfully with the finger of one hand. That's her Paris laugh.

"Hee hee hee," she giggles, and covers her eyes with her hands. That's her Tahiti laugh.

"Hoo, hoo, hoo, hoo," she laughs, and raises her eyebrows very high. That's her Mexico City laugh.

She got all the ideas for the laughs from TV and from fashion magazines. After she got them all worked out, I told her they were all good, except the Tahiti laugh, which looked like she was just waking up in the morning, so she decided to rename it a waking-up laugh, to throw a stretch into it.

So she did. But just when she had them all perfect, Bright Star got them perfect, too. He sang them all off in a row, and then he said, in my voice, "Laugh Development Project."

"Now I can't bring any boyfriend home!" Celia said. "Either I can't bring one home, or I can't use my laughs."

"Not only that," I said, "Grandpa is going to know about this for sure."

Celia shrugged. "Maybe he'll borrow a laugh," she said. "He doesn't seem to have one of his own. Anyway, what more can he do? We already don't have Christmas anymore."

Sure enough, when Grandpa came home, Bright Star talked. He laughed all four laughs, and then imitated me, saying "Laugh Development Project."

It happened at dinner. My grandfather looked at Bright Star, and he looked at Celia, and he looked at me, but all he said was, "After school tomorrow, I want to take you out to the orchards, Luisito."

So I said okay, and the next afternoon we hiked out to the orchards.

"You are around your Aunt Celia too much," my grandfather said, but not unkindly. "You need the influence of a man."

"I am a man," I said.

"You are?" my grandfather said. "How do you know?"

"Celia said so."

He looked at me and said it took more than Celia's saying so to make somebody a man, and then he started telling me about the trees, and what you had to do to take care of them, and how many different kinds of apples there were, and how you could tell them apart.

But a bad thing happened, because the orchards are right next to the pyramids and the forts of the old kingdom, and I kept thinking about them and wanting to go over there, instead of listening to my grandfather.

"Luisito," he said suddenly, "how many kinds of apples do I have?"

And I couldn't tell him.

"You're not listening! Your father understood and remembered everything when he was your age!" he shouted. "Go on home to your grandmother!"

So I left, and instead of going straight home, I went over to the pyramids and ran up to the top of the biggest and stood there listening to the branches of the pine trees in the wind. It didn't help anything. And then I walked home alone.

When I told my grandma what happened, she said, "Your dad did understand and remember very well when he was your age. But when he was your age, he also played with matches once and set a whole cornfield on fire. It took us, the neighbors and the whole fire department to put it out."

"Tell Grandpa that!" I said. "Remind him about it!"

"I will sometime," my grandmother said, "but not now."

"When?" I asked. "You said Grandpa would get better and we just had to be patient. He used to make jokes, Celia says. He used to take everybody on trips. Now he never does, and he never gets any better."

"You are right," my grandmother said.

"Besides," I said, "Christmas is coming, and I am tired of not having Christmas, and so is Celia."

"You're probably right," my grandmother said. "We should celebrate Christmas."

And she actually used the telephone, which she never uses, to call up Ricardo and talk to him about it.

And that night at dinner, she told my grandfather, "It's time we started to celebrate Christmas again."

"I would rather not," my grandfather said.

"The children say they won't come home for Christmas, unless we celebrate, like the old days. Luisito and Celia say they would rather go into the city to be with Ricardo and everybody if we don't celebrate Christmas."

"Um," my grandfather said.

"I might go, too," my grandmother said.

"*You* might go?" my grandfather said.

"Yes, I probably will go," my grandmother said.

"You would *leave* me?" my grandfather said.

"Just for Christmas," my grandmother said.

"It wouldn't be good," my grandfather said. "We've been together thirty-one years. You've never been away. Not one day!"

"Times change," my grandmother said.

"Well," my grandfather said, "we had better celebrate Christmas. But I won't dance."

"You don't have to dance," my grandmother said. "Nobody has to dance. But at least we will have dance music, anyway."

Celia and I made a beautiful golden Christmas tree out of corn husks that we cut to fasten on

wires and make the shape of branches. When we were done, the tree went all the way to the ceiling, and we draped it with red chains of tinsel. And my grandmother stood in front of the stove all Christmas Eve day making the tamales for the midnight dinner—corn stuffed with chicken and meat and olives and raisins and hot chili sauce, and wrapped in banana leaves to cook. And everybody arrived from the city about six-thirty at night, just in time for the supper we were going to have to tide us over to the real dinner at midnight.

Uncle Ricardo brought Diego and me about sixty firecrackers to set off at midnight, when all the kids in town go outside to set off firecrackers, so we were feeling good. And my grandfather had dressed up in his best and happiest clothes, new pants, and a cap that makes him look as young as my uncles.

Everybody hugged, and we all sat down to eat, but nobody talked much until we were almost finished, when Aunt Patricia said, "All the same, it's sad anyway."

And my Uncle Pedro, who had been an exchange student in the U.S. for one year of high school, said, "If the roads had shoulders, the way the highways do in the U.S., they never would have died."

And Celia said, "So in the great U.S.A. there are no traffic accidents?"

And before Pedro could answer her, my grandfather got up out of his chair and went out on the patio, and we all stopped talking.

"Luisito," my grandmother said, "go be with your grandfather."

So I went out on the patio and stood by my grandfather, who was looking up at the sky and wouldn't look down.

I just stood there by him, looking up, too.

There was a full moon, shining down on the patio and on the papery violet leaves of the bougainvillea, and my grandfather spoke, in a choked voice.

"See the leaves? There are so many you can't see the branch, and all different.

"And we are like them, all different, but holding on to an invisible branch——but two of us are missing!

"Why do they have to talk about it? Don't they know I've cried enough? What do they think I do out in the orchard, but cry?"

"You should cry with us," I said, and I saw my grandfather's eyes drop tears, and we stood there a long time.

Everybody else had gone into the living room, and while we were standing there, the dance music started, very slowly, low music, soft like smoke, winding into the moonlight.

"Oh, Luisito," my grandfather said. "What can we do? What can anybody do? Luisito, we should dance."

And so my granddad and I danced, around the cage of Bright Star, who was sleeping under a new Christmas blanket, and past the cracked mirror and the bougainvillea vine, and then, very slowly, into the living room. And then I danced with Celia, and my grandfather put his arms around my grandmother and danced with her, and everybody danced with everybody, straight through until midnight when the fireworks started going off in huge booms all over town, and we all held hands, and everyone of us kissed every other one, and I noticed for the first time in a long time that in the photo of my mom and dad, above Grandpa's white roses, they were smiling.

The Night We Started Dancing

Meet the Author

Ann Cameron grew up filled with curiosity about other people and read to satisfy that curiosity. After graduating from Harvard, she became an editor so she could read books for a living. After two years of that, however, she knew she would rather be writing them. Today, Ann Cameron is an author who writes about the people who interest her.

Her friends and neighbors are always sources of inspiration. A South African friend, who told stories about his childhood, inspired her first children's book, *The Stories Julian Tells*. She also writes about the people that live around her. Her life is guided by her belief that, "when I do what really matters to me, I'm happy, and my friends are real friends who like me for what I really am."

Meet the Illustrator

Carlos Caban teaches painting and drawing at the Art Institute in San Miguel de Allende, Mexico. This is a small colonial city famous for its art. He grew up in New York but he became interested in Indian cultures while working for the Peace Corps in Colombia, South America. He says, "The story was especially exciting for me because I love the Mayan culture and people and my paintings have been influenced by them."

Theme Connections

Think About It

With a small group of classmates, discuss the following questions.

- What does this story tell you about the importance of family and traditions?
- When Luisito's grandfather began to dance with him, what do you think it meant?
- What might have happened to Luisito's grandfather if the family had not insisted on celebrating the Christmas holiday?
- Are there any traditions in your family? If so, do you know how they were developed?

Record Ideas

Think of something you might say to a person who is sad to make them feel better, and write it in your Writing Journal. Then make a list of activities you and your classmates can take part in together, to make people in your community happier.

Do a Character Sketch

Work with a partner and write a description of the characters in this story. Remember to include enough information to let someone who didn't read the story understand what each character is like. As you work, follow these guidelines.

- Plan with your partner what information to include.
- Share your plans with another pair of students.
- Revise your plan, as you see fit.
- Write your character description.

The West Side

from *How Juan Got Home*
by Peggy Mann
illustrated by Bob Dorsey

*Juan Morales has come from Puerto Rico to New York
City to live with his Uncle Esteban. Juan's mother believes
that he will receive a better education in New York than in
Puerto Rico. When the plane lands and his uncle's arrival at
the airport is delayed, Juan is told that the airline will give
him a free flight back to Puerto Rico if his uncle does not
arrive to pick him up. Juan misunderstands and believes he
will be able to return to Puerto Rico any time he decides to
do so. After a few days in his uncle's apartment and some
unsuccessful attempts to make friends with the English-
speaking boys who live on his street, Juan is unhappy and
is determined to return to Puerto Rico. In the meantime,
however, he agrees to go on a shopping expedition for Puerto
Rican food in a neighborhood on the West Side of New York.*

Juan stepped off the bus at Columbus Avenue. It was
as though he had stepped off the bus into Puerto
Rico. The street was alive with children and Spanish
music. Some of the children, barefoot and wet, played
around the water gushing from a fire hydrant, ran in
and out screaming laughter and Spanish words. Latin
music came blaring from radios on windowsills . . .
from a young man who sat on a box in front of Bodega
Rivera strumming a guitar and singing a Spanish love
song . . . from a bongo band on the corner playing hard
rock with a loud Latin beat.

Women leaned out of windows shrilling in Spanish to children on the street. A group of men sat around a bridge table on the sidewalk, playing dominoes. Women in bright cotton dresses sat on the front steps gossiping in Spanish. And the stores! At home the stores often had *americano* names: the Blue Moon Bar Restaurant . . . Joe's Shop . . . the Cooperative . . . Mercado's Barbershop . . . . But here: everything Spanish! Farmacia Flores . . . Tienda La Favorita . . . Zapatería El Quijote . . . Repostería Borinquén. . . .

All crowded together like this, the store signs, the music, the look and the sound of the Spanish people, it seemed somehow *more* Puerto Rican than anything he had seen in Puerto Rico. He was no longer a stranger. He didn't even need to ask directions. With a smile on his face he strode into Bodega Rivera.

He *was* home. The small crowded grocery store was just like the one on his street in Barranquitas. The same small, sweet *niños* bananas hung in clumps in the dusty window; and the long, green *plátanos* hung next to them on iron hooks. The same bins of tropical fruits and vegetables. The same cans and bottles on the shelves: guava juice, papaya juice, *asopao de jueyes*, red beans, pink beans, white beans, pinto beans, chick peas, *Doraditos, Florecitas, coco rico* and *chinita*. Even the same penny candy machine. And the same packets of ladies' panty hose on the rack behind the counter.

The shopkeeper, who wore a large black mustache and a dirty white apron, was arguing with a customer about the price of his *batatas*. Loudly Señor Rivera informed her that he had to import the *batatas* from the island. If she could not pay for special Spanish food she should eat American.

When, grumbling, she counted out her money and left, a boy about Juan's age stood on tiptoe in front of the counter and asked in a loud voice whether Señor Rivera would sell him some boxes.

"Boxes of *what?*" Señor Rivera said.

"Empty boxes," the boy said. "We're having a stickball game on the street tomorrow afternoon and we already sold twenty box seats to people who want to watch from the sidewalk. Now we gotta get the boxes."

"Get out of here, Carlos," Señor Rivera said. "I'm busy."

"But Señor Rivera!" Carlos persisted. "I'm willing to pay for the boxes. Usually you give them out free to customers. I'm going to *pay!*"

"Yes?" Señor Rivera said. "And how are my customers going to carry home their groceries if I got no more boxes?"

"Listen," Carlos said, "I'll make you a deal. If you let us have the boxes, I'll let your son Willie umpire the game."

Señor Rivera said nothing. He scowled.

"As you know," Carlos said, "your boy Willie is kind of a pain-in-the-neck kid. That's why he gets beat up so much. But nobody beats up an umpire. You got to respect an umpire."

"How much did you sell the box seats for?" said Señor Rivera.

"Five cents a box for cardboard, ten cents for wood. I told them they could take the seats home with them."

"And how much are you planning to pay me, Carlos, for every box I give you?"

"Well," Carlos said, "a penny for cardboard. Two cents for wood."

Señor Rivera laughed. "Carlos," he said, "you're going to grow up to be the president of the First National Bank. Listen," he added, "go down in my cellar and haul yourself up twenty boxes. You can have them for free."

Carlos grinned and started for the flight of steps leading down to the cellar.

"Save a box seat for me," Señor Rivera called after him. "I want to come watch my son Willie be umpire."

Juan then stood on tiptoe in front of the greasy glass counter. He ordered twelve *plátanos verdes*, two pounds of *gandules* and one ounce of *ajíes*. But when he paid his money, and held the three paper bags in his hands, he still did not want to leave.

If only his uncle had the job of maintenance engineer on Columbus Avenue! Then he, Juan, might not even want to go home. If he lived over here, then he could go to school over here. Maybe here they even had Spanish schools and he'd never need to learn English at all!

But Uncle Esteban had explained that a boy must go to school in the district where he lived. He would have to go to school on the rich East Side of Manhattan; a school which would, no doubt, be filled up tight with *americanos*.

He noticed the boy called Carlos who came staggering up from the cellar with an armload of cardboard boxes. "Hey!" He walked over to Carlos. "You want me to help you carry those boxes to wherever you're going?"

"Sure," Carlos said in English. "Matter of fact, I was going to ask you to give me a hand." He smiled.

Juan didn't understand the English, but a smile was the same in any language.

He smiled back.

They made two trips from the Bodega Rivera to the basement of the brownstone rooming house where Carlos lived. Juan kept talking almost nonstop all the way. He had so much talk inside him it seemed he just couldn't get it all said.

Carlos spoke very little. When they had finished piling the boxes in a corner of the basement, Carlos explained why he always answered Juan in such short sentences. He knew very little Spanish.

Juan stared at him through the basement gloom, astounded. A *puertorriqueño* who didn't know Spanish?

Carlos shrugged and explained that they'd come from the mainland when he was three years old to live with his grandmother. He'd been brought up on English, in the streets and in school. In fact, the only Spanish he knew came from talking to his grandmother.

Juan nodded. He felt he had found a friend—only to lose him. What was worse, he felt like a fool. Here he'd been jabbering away to this boy all about Barranquitas and his house and his mother and sisters and friends and his miniature car collection and the Piñonas River and his school and the TV programs he watched at home. And all the time Carlos had hardly understood a single word!

"As a matter of fact," Carlos said in English as he started up the basement stairs, "you'll find that most of the Spanish kids on this street don't speak Spanish. At least, their Spanish is nothing to speak of!" Then, having made a kind of pun, Carlos laughed.

But Juan trudging up the stairs behind him did not laugh. He had not understood a word Carlos said.

Carlos turned then and repeated the sentences in a stiff and inaccurate Spanish.

Juan nodded glumly. He felt betrayed. Even if he took the bus over here every day to play with the *puertorriqueño* kids on Columbus Avenue, it would be no good. He would still be a stranger—among his own people. Only they weren't his own people anymore. They were *americanos*.

When they reached the street Carlos said, in Spanish, "Well, thanks for helping me out."

And, in Spanish, Juan replied. "That's okay." Then he added, "I better say good-bye now. I'll be going back home at the end of the week."

"To the island?" Carlos said, in some surprise.

Juan nodded.

"You must be pretty rich," Carlos said, "to come hopping all the way over here just for one week. How much is the plane fare?"

Juan explained that the trip home wouldn't cost him anything. The airline would fly him home free.

Carlos frowned. He did not understand. "Free? How could that be?"

Juan, speaking in slow careful Spanish as though he were addressing a very small child, explained how the airline had promised to send him home free the night he arrived. So since he hadn't taken them up on their offer then, he would do so at the end of the week.

"Listen, you stupid kid," Carlos said. "Sure they were going to send you home free when your uncle didn't show up. I mean they can't let a little kid like you just be hanging around the airport at night all alone. But your uncle *did* show up. So the offer's over. Now you're *his* worry. Not theirs. How could they ever make any money if they kept dealing out free tickets to anyone wanting to make a trip back home?"

He spoke now in English. Juan kept nodding. Then he said, "*No entiendo.* I not onnerstan'."

So, with some effort, Carlos repeated it all in Spanish. Juan nodded again. This time he understood all too well, and knew with certainty that Carlos was correct. In fact, this very thought had been lurking in the back of his mind. But he hadn't allowed it to come forward before. Because he didn't want to know the truth. The truth that he *could* not go home.

"Listen, kid," Carlos said suddenly, in Spanish, "since you helped me with the boxes, how'd you like a free box seat for the game tomorrow afternoon?"

"What kind of game?" Juan asked.

"Stickball."

"What's stickball?"

"Stickball's what it says it is," Carlos said. "You hit a ball with a stick. Want me to show you?"

Juan nodded.

"C'mon," Carlos said. "I got my equipment upstairs." He shoved open the front door and Juan followed him into the hallway. The place smelled strongly of cats and rancid cooking oil and the garbage which sat outside each doorway in overflowing pails or paper bags.

Juan felt like holding his breath and holding his nose. Who would want to live in such a place when they could be back in the fresh mountain air of Barranquitas where the only smell one noticed was that of flowers?

When they reached the third floor Carlos took a ring of keys from his pocket and started unlocking one of the doors. "We got three different locks," he explained to Juan, "because we have been robbed five times."

Juan was impressed. Carlos must live in a pretty big place with some valuable things in it for anyone to bother robbing his apartment five times. After all, even though the hallways smelled, that didn't mean the apartments weren't beautiful inside.

But inside there was nothing much either. Just one room with a flowered curtain drawn across the middle. The whole place was not much bigger than the bedroom he shared at home with his two sisters. There was a wooden table and four wooden chairs all painted bright green. There was a picture of the Virgin Mary tacked to the wall. And in the corner a small stove and large sink, stacked with dishes. Sunlight fell in through the open window and lay in a long oblong pattern across the worn green linoleum on the floor. There was a flower box on the windowsill with some geraniums in it.

Not a bad place, Juan thought. At least it looked friendly. He'd a lot rather live here than in Uncle Esteban's fine basement apartment where all the windows had bars like a jail.

Carlos meanwhile had gone behind the curtain. He came back with a small rubber ball and a broom. "Of course," he said, "the bat we play with is a mop handle without the mop. But our captain keeps that in his house. I'm the manager of the team," he added, with an edge of pride in his voice. "That means I set up the games and arrange everything. The big game we got on tomorrow is against the Young Princes. Come on. I'll show you how we play."

Juan followed Carlos into the hallway again, waited while his new friend locked the door with three different keys, and went down the stairs after him, taking two at a time as Carlos did.

In the street Carlos waited until a few cars had gone by. Then, when there was a lull in the traffic, he stepped out, threw the ball into the air, swung the broom handle hard. And missed.

Shamefaced, he picked up the ball. "Well, I myself am not so hot at this game," he said in English. "I'm better at organizing than playing. But the idea is, if you hit the ball past the first sewer that's pretty good. If you hit it past the second sewer, that's sensational. And if you hit it past the third sewer, that's impossible. The third sewer's right down at the end of the street. You can hardly even see it from here."

Juan nodded. He had barely understood a word that Carlos said. But he was embarrassed to ask his friend to repeat it all over again in Spanish. So he asked instead, "I try?"

"Sure," Carlos said and threw him the broom which Juan caught in one hand. Then Carlos threw the ball which Juan caught in the other hand. And stepped out into the street.

"Hey! *Watch it!*" Carlos screamed in English.

Juan stepped back just as a yellow taxi sped by his toes. He'd been so intent about showing Carlos that he could hit this ball with the broom that he forgot about everything else——including getting run over. His heart now started thudding with fear at his narrow escape.

"Listen!" Carlos said sternly. "They got such things as cars in this city and don't you ever forget that!"

Juan nodded. He looked carefully up and down the street.

"It's okay now," Carlos said. "Nothing coming."

But still Juan felt afraid.

"Hurry up! *Avanza!*" Carlos said. "Take your chance while you got it."

So Juan, his heart still pounding, stepped out into the street, threw the rubber ball into the air, and hit it with the broom handle. Hard.

He watched the ball proudly as it sped through the air.

Carlos screamed again. And again Juan rushed back to the safety of the sidewalk. But this time there were no cars coming. This time Carlos screamed for another reason. "You hit three sewers!" he kept screaming. "Man, don't you understand, you hit *three sewers!*"

"Yes," said Juan. "I onnerstan'." He did not know what "three sewers" meant. But he did understand that Carlos was impressed at how he had hit the ball.

"Listen," Carlos said. "You must be puttin' me on, man. Telling me you never played stickball before." He repeated the question in Spanish. The words were charged with suspicion. "You sure you never played stickball before?"

Juan shook his head. "No," he said. "I have never played stickball before." He saw no reason to explain that he had been playing stick-stone ever since he was seven years old. Hitting a stone with a stick across the Piñonas River in the Contest game he had invented.

"Listen, kid," Carlos said suddenly. "How'd you like to play on our team tomorrow afternoon?" Then, slowly, carefully he tried the words in Spanish. "*¿Vas a jugar con nosotros mañana?*"

Juan grinned. "Sure, man," he said in English. "Hokay!"

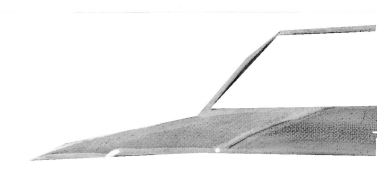

The West Side

Meet the Author

Peggy Mann is a native New Yorker. She has based a lot of her writing on childhood experiences that she had when her family restored a brownstone building on a slum street in Manhattan. Her first book, called *The Street of the Flower Boxes*, was about her years in the brownstone. It was made into a children's television special. Other books in the series include *The Clubhouse, When Carlos Closed the Street, How Juan Got Home*, and *The Secret Dog of Little Luis*.

Today, the slum block she lived on as a little girl is a showplace. Families from the area got together and fixed up all the old brownstones as part of an urban renewal project. Now, that block stands as an example to other urban renewal projects around the country. Peggy Mann started, and became the president of, one of the committees that makes these projects possible.

Meet the Illustrator

Bob Dorsey has been a professional illustrator for 17 years, working with a wide range of media and a variety of subject matter. Some of his favorite subjects include portraits, wildlife, children, and sports. Mr. Dorsey is well known for the numerous portraits that he has done for the National Baseball Hall of Fame in Cooperstown, New York. His paintings have been exhibited throughout the country.

Theme Connections

Think About It

In small groups, share the experience of someone you know who has had to move from another place. Have you had the experience of moving to a new place? If so, consider sharing that experience with your group members.

Record Ideas

In your Writing Journal, write about a time when you had to move and how the move affected you. If you have never moved, try to imagine what it would be like if you did, and record this in your Writing Journal.

Share a Story

Think of a book you have read, a movie you have seen, or a story you have heard about someone who has left his or her home to live in a new place. Share the story with a small group of classmates. Be sure to explain how the person felt when he or she had to move. What are some things that that person worried about? What kinds of things did they need to figure out about the place where they moved? Did the person move to a place with new traditions and customs? If so, did the person continue to practice his or her customs, or leave them behind?

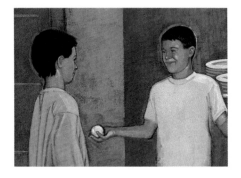

Family Greeting. 1962. **Eli Tikeayak.** Canadian Inuit, Rankin Inlet. Light green-grey stone. Art Gallery of Ontario, Toronto. Gift of Robert C. Williamson, C.M., 1989.

Mother and Child. 1922. **Pablo Picasso.** Oil on canvas. 100 × 81 cm. The Baltimore Museum of Art: The Cone Collection formed by Dr. Claribel Cone and Miss Etta Cone of Baltimore, Maryland. ©1998 Estate of Pablo Picasso/Artist Rights Society (ARS), New York.

Naranjas (Oranges). 1988. **Carmen Lomas Garza.** Gouache. 20 × 14 in. Collection of Mr. and Mrs. Ira Schneider, Scottsdale, Arizona. Photo by Wolfgang Dietze.

Chinatown

from *Child of the Owl*
by Laurence Yep
illustrated by Yoriko Ito

*In the time since her mother, Jeanie, died, Casey
Young has traveled around California with her
father, Barney. But when he becomes sick and has
to be hospitalized, Casey goes to live with her
grandmother, Paw-Paw, in San Francisco's
Chinatown. Here she begins to learn more about
her Chinese heritage and about her mother.*

I lay in bed thinking for a long time after Paw-Paw
had finished her story. I'd never asked her about
Jeanie before this, I suppose, because Barney had
taught me not to talk about her. Finally I rolled over
on my side to face her. "When did Jeanie feel lonely?"

Paw-Paw picked up a deck of cards and began to
play a game of solitaire. She could play even while
she talked. A three on the four of one column. A
jack on the queen of another column. Flip. Flip. Flip.
Like her fingers had eyes and brains so Paw-Paw
didn't even have to look down. Her hands could do
everything. "Maybe I should let your daddy tell you."

I turned so I lay on my stomach, hugging a pillow
under my chin. "Barney won't talk much about her.
Was she lonely when she was my age?"

Paw-Paw must have sensed the longing in my
voice. "Oh, no. Your mommy always had lots of
friends. She was very pretty. And very sweet. She

was always a big help to me." Paw-Paw finished her game and began to sweep the cards into the middle of the table so she could gather them into a deck. "And your daddy was thought to be a very good-looking boy so they were always a natural couple. From grammar school on."

"Grammar school?"

"They both went to Commodore Stockton just a little way from here. And then they went through junior high and high school together." Paw-Paw began to shuffle her cards to get them ready for the next time she wanted to play.

"Were they very popular?"

"Oh, yes. Very popular. You'd always see them together at all the dances in Chinatown. Your momma liked dancing."

Paw-Paw went to the bureau and opened a middle drawer, rummaging around till she took out an old, worn brown bag and drew a small pile of photos out of it. She set them down on the table and sorted through them. "That's your momma. She was going to a dance that night." Paw-Paw tapped one photo of a pretty girl of about sixteen in bobby sox and a long skirt like all the American girls used to wear—or at least that's what Barney and some of the older people used to tell me when we had watched late-night movies in different hotel lobbies. "I used to sew all your momma's clothes but only with the best material." She glanced at me briefly and then went through some of the other old photos of Jeanie, who had a different outfit in each one. And while I didn't much care about the clothes, somehow talking with Paw-Paw about Jeanie made me feel less lonely.

"But she couldn't have always gone out with Barney. What did she do with you for fun? I mean, besides playing cards."

"We went to see Chinese movies." Paw-Paw put her cards down in a neat stack by the little cup that held her toothpicks. They were cinnamon-flavored and each was wrapped in a little paper envelope. "Would you like to see a movie like your mommy and I used to see?"

I wasn't doing much of anything so I figured why not. "I've got money for myself."

"Why spend your money? I can sew some extra shirts this week."

"Are you sure it's okay?" I asked.

"Of course, it's okay," she snapped and I could see there would be no arguing with her.

Paw-Paw bundled up as usual, putting on a blouse over her pajama top and then a sweater and a heavy silk jacket over the sweater so that by the time she had on her heavy cloth coat, she looked twice as round. Over her head she put her favorite vermilion chiffon scarf with the roses embroidered on it with gold thread.

Paw-Paw seemed very comfortable within the small world of Chinatown; I wondered if Jeanie had been too. It didn't cover more than half a square mile or so then, and within those boundaries, as I was to find out, it is a very small, tightly knit world where everyone knows your business and you know theirs. To the west lay the souvenir shops and on the east, delicatessens and grocery stores and meat markets, some of which had fish tanks in the bottom half of their windows in which a hundred fish would be squeezed, all staring out at you with cold, black eyes, or even turtles, or sometimes cages of snakes, all to be sold and eaten.

To the north was Stockton Street, where my school was. Mostly it was sewing-machine shops up that way: plain storefronts sometimes with wallpaper covering the windows or old, sun-bleached curtains. From within would come the steady whir and whine of the machines of the ladies sewing dresses, shirts, even jeans and expensive wedding outfits for American stores. A lot of ladies with no English could only do that. Just above Stockton Street was the public grammar school, Commodore Stockton, or "Commodore" to the kids. Across from it lay the YWCA and Cameron House, a kind of club for Chinese kids. Above that, where Paw-Paw never went, were the cable-car lines and the apartment houses for Americans, including the fancy hotels and limousines of Nob Hill.

But at that moment I was thinking mainly about the movies we were going to see. I had my doubts because all I had seen up to then were Charlie Chan movies or silly houseboys on TV shows or funny laundrymen in westerns. But even so, one of those kinds of movies was better than nothing because I knew Paw-Paw never left Chinatown to see any of the Hollywood movies just a few blocks away.

We went to the Chinese Globe that had a bright neon sign outside in front and looked like a regular theater except for the fact that there was a guy selling newspapers by the ticket booth. He had about a dozen different Chinese newspapers laid in neat piles on a board that he laid over some boxes. But I saw a dozen portable newsstands like that set

up all over Chinatown——in doorways or in corners or in front of busy stores. He nodded familiarly to Paw-Paw as she bought our tickets at the booth.

When I finally got to see the movies, they were completely different than I thought. I could see why Jeanie had liked them. For one thing, the Chinese were actually people who could be brave or sad. They had subtitles in English, too, which was good. It was something to see Chinese do more than be the sidekick to some white guy in a fight, or see the Chinese actually win. I mean, I almost felt like crying when I saw it: a kind of bubbling feeling deep down inside that had me almost cheering and crying while this Chinese mother led her three sons in beating up the bad guys. And it was even better when I saw the Chinese girls fighting.

The second feature, you see, was *Princess of the Streets,* which is about this girl who grows up in the back streets of Hong Kong. She gets friendly with this other girl who does juggling and fighting displays in a medicine show. And together she and her friend wipe out the big crime boss. I don't think I ever saw anyone jump as high in the air to kick someone.

It must have rained while we were inside the theater because when we came out later, the streets were slick and black, like they were made of shining crystal. I saw a Chinatown I'd never seen before. It was the Chinatown Jeanie must have seen. Suddenly all the gaudy neon signs were no longer a bunch of words but were like snakes of colored lights crawling up the faces of the buildings and their reflections smashed themselves on the streets, looking like broken stars sliding back and forth and trying to put themselves back together. Funny, but it seemed, right then, like I'd just come home.

A radio store had begun playing music over an outside loudspeaker. Some of the stuff, especially the opera, sounded terrible to me—a high whiny kind of noise—but this sounded different. Some people might have thought there was too much of a clutter of sound with the cymbals crashing and the drums beating and everybody playing like mad, but there was something inside of me that liked it—like it synchronized right with the pulsing of my blood through my body. And the sound wound its way through the chatter of the nighttime crowds.

Humming with the tune, Paw-Paw took my arm for support as we made our way along the slippery

pavements of Grant Avenue. We passed by the
delicatessens, where Paw-Paw pointed to the dark-
brown, roasted ducks dangling from hooks in the
windows. "That's what I like," she said. "Jeanie too."

"I've never had duck in my life," I said.

She patted my arm, the one she was holding on
to. "Maybe I'll sew some extra shirts and dresses
someday and we'll buy half of one so you can try it."

We went about two blocks before the rain started
to fall again. It was falling pretty hard so we stopped
under the awning of this one souvenir shop.
Paw-Paw acted like the window display had been
put there just to entertain us. "Look at that whirly
thing." She pointed at one of those little solar
windmills that rotate whenever they're near a source
of light like the light bulb illuminating the window.

There was something wrong about the window. At first I couldn't figure it out but as Paw-Paw went on mentioning things in the window, I realized she hadn't talked about one Chinese thing yet. I started to study the window then. There didn't seem to be anything as beautiful or as old as the owl charm Paw-Paw wore about her neck. There was just a lot of silly stuff like two-headed back-scratchers. Paw-Paw didn't point at any of those or at some of the things that were downright nasty——like pellet guns and various types of knives, from simple pocket- and hunting knives to switchblades and gravity blades that snap out with a flick of a wrist. The only thing vaguely Oriental that I saw at first in the window were the Japanese kimonos and geisha dolls they sold.

"It doesn't seem right somehow," I said. "I mean, if it's a Chinatown souvenir shop, shouldn't it be selling Chinese stuff?"

"The Americans won't let us bring in things from China." She shrugged. "And the Taiwan government's too busy to bother with souvenirs. You have to sell the Americans something."

"But we're selling things as if they're Chinese when it's really . . . well, I don't know . . . this stuff just seems like junk compared to your owl charm. There's no story behind most of this stuff. There's no meaning to this stuff. This junk is probably not even much fun."

"They do have a few real Chinese things. See?" She moved a little to the side and bent down, pointing to one dark corner of the window. "See down there in the back?"

I leaned forward slightly and looked where her finger was pointing and saw a bunch of dusty statues crowded together like they were making a last stand. "They've got some of the stuff you've got on your bureau. Look, there's that pretty lady with the flower."

Paw-Paw studied me. I hadn't laughed about the owl story and I had even liked the Chinese movies so I guess she decided to go ahead. "That lady is the Listener. She could have gone to heaven, but when she was just about to enter the gate, she could hear all the poor souls back on earth groaning and she turned her back on heaven, saying she could not enter until everyone else had gone before her, so she spends all her time trying to help the rest of us to heaven."

Though it was a cold, rainy night outside, I felt warm inside now that Paw-Paw was finally explaining things to me. "Hey, there's the guy with the big head."

"He's the spirit of long life," Paw-Paw corrected me. "His head swelled up because he's so full of life. He helps keep the record of your life and sometimes with special people he juggles his books and they live longer, so maybe someone dies when they're ninety-one instead of nineteen. He's got a magic peach in his hand, grown in heaven for the gods. A person eats that peach and that person lives forever."

And she told me the eight statues—not as small as hers—were the Eight Immortals who had once been simple men and women but had gained the secret of immortality. One of them had meditated so long and let his dream-soul wander so far away that his body died in the meantime and his dream-soul had to take the bony body of a crippled beggar when it got back.

She told me about a few more of the statues and when she stopped, I asked her a new question I'd been thinking about. "What would it be like if we were in China, Paw-Paw?"

Paw-Paw shut her eyes but kept her face turned toward the window as if she were trying to picture it herself. "It'd be very noisy and you'd have much less time to yourself than here. You have to go through the rain to the village lavatory. Or maybe you have to empty out a . . . a . . . what is the word? . . . a chamber pot."

"Ugh."

"No heat except the stuff in the stove so you

have to go and look for every leaf and every bit
of grass and all your neighbors would be doing
the same thing."

"Would you have a whole bunch of families
together in the same big house? Like Uncle Phil
and Uncle Chester would live with you?" Uncle
Chester was a year younger than Jeanie and
lived down in L.A.

Paw-Paw shook her head. "Only if we were rich,
but we'd probably be poor farmers if we had stayed
back in China. Each of them would have their own
little house and you and I would be crowded in
somehow into one of those two."

I drew my finger down the glass slowly. Rain dribbled down from the awning overhead. "But still, would you like that better than the way you live now? I mean if we were in China, you'd really be in charge, like the mother was in the first movie, bossing all her grown-up sons around."

Paw-Paw sighed. "I don't know. It's too easy to worry about the way things might have been. I'd rather live with the way things are now. That's what the Owl Spirit did after all."

"Well, why don't you live with one of your children now?"

"I could live with your Uncle Phil anytime I want, but they always get this rotten chicken meat from the freezer, when chickens should be fresh. But no, the feathers make too much mess and they don't like it when I take out the blood and guts. And I say, 'What do you think's inside of you?' Or they give me steak in a huge chunk and they hand me a knife and that thing with the four sharp points."

"A fork?"

"Yes, and I say, 'When I come to the dinner table, I come to eat, not to cook. Meat should be cut up and cooked properly in the kitchen before dinner.'"

"They'd probably let you make your own meals," I said.

"Well, I guess I could make my peace with them on that, but there are other things." Her eyes glanced at the statues in the window. "They tell me those things are only for stupid, old people."

I realized that it all depended on how I looked around myself—if there were invisible walls around Chinatown for Paw-Paw, they were like the walls of

a turtle, walls behind which you could remain warm and alive, and for someone like me, those walls didn't have to be any more of a trap than I let them. They could be like something to give me shape and form and when I couldn't grow anymore inside them, I could break out of those invisible walls.

Paw-Paw began to retie her scarf but her fingers had begun to stiffen in the cold and the wet. I reached my hands out. "Here, Paw-Paw, let me help you." So Paw-Paw leaned forward, waiting patiently until I had retied her scarf. She checked the knot under the chin of her reflection in the window, smoothing her hand over it.

She smiled, pleased. "You did that very well. Such strong young fingers."

She gripped my fingers tightly in her hand for a moment with what seemed like an immense strength. "Now help an old lady up the hills. It's wet and I'm afraid I'm going to fall."

I let her take my arm then and once again she was just a little old lady and we climbed slowly up the steeply slanting hillside, like two small owls clawing their way along a branch that twisted upward into the night sky.

Chinatown

Meet the Author

Laurence Yep was born in San Francisco, California. His Chinese-American family lived in an African-American section of the city, so he had to commute to a bilingual school in Chinatown. Yep says he never encountered white culture in America until high school, and always felt like an outsider. Growing up, he found few books that dealt with being a Chinese-American. Because of this, he used his own writing to fight racial stereotypes. He likes to write about this feeling of being an outsider and believes this is the reason he is so popular with young adult readers.

Meet the Illustrator

Yoriko Ito was raised in Japan, but moved to the United States when she was about 21 years old. Says Yoriko Ito, "Even when I was little, I knew I wanted to paint, but my parents would say, 'What are you talking about?' I dreamed about pursuing art in high school, but it was when I came to the United States that I actually decided to pursue art."

She now works painting backgrounds for animated films. Some of the movies she has worked on are "The Prince of Egypt" and "El Dorado." She advises other aspiring artists, "You have to do your best always—don't doubt your ability. Trust yourself, especially if you enjoy art." She especially encourages trying new, fun ways to test one's artistic abilities.

Theme Connections

Think About It

A visit to Chinatown helped Casey to become more aware of her Chinese heritage. With a small group of students, discuss the following questions.

- What traditional figures did Paw-Paw describe?
- What did the figures mean to Paw-Paw?
- Did they mean the same to other people?
- What family traditions did Paw-Paw describe?
- What did Casey's experiences with her grandmother teach her?

Record Ideas

Do you own an object that means something special to you? If not, can you think of a friend or a family member that owns or carries an object that is of some significance to him or her? Describe that object in your Writing Journal, and tell why it is meaningful or important.

Draw a Special Family Object

Draw a picture of the object described in your Writing Journal, and then give your drawing a title or caption. Prepare a final draft of the object's description and attach it with your drawing. Share your drawing and description with other students, and post it on the Concept/Question Board for possible use in your unit activity.

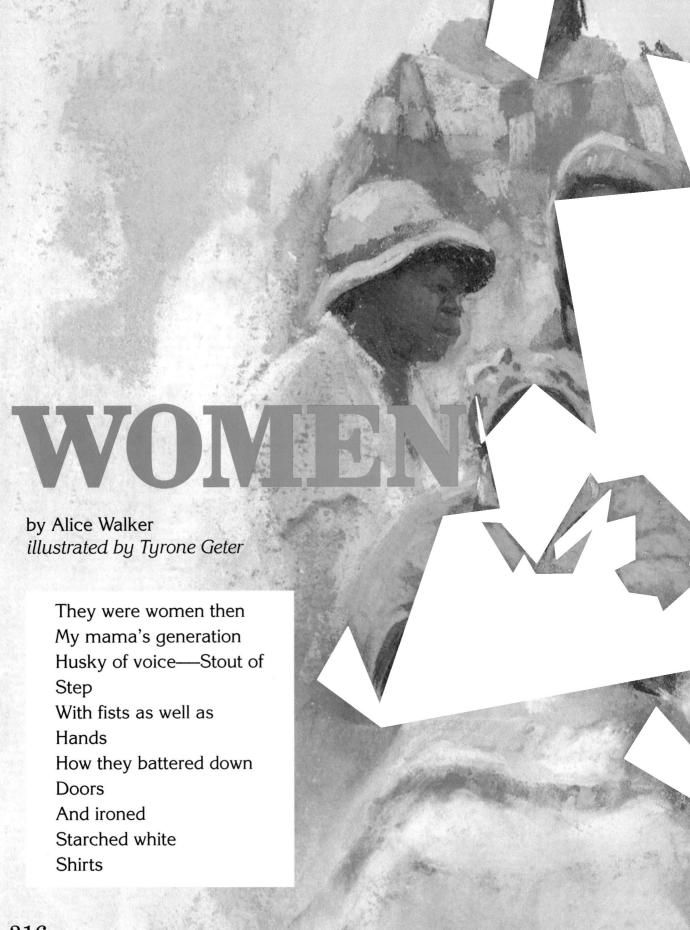

WOMEN

by Alice Walker
illustrated by Tyrone Geter

They were women then
My mama's generation
Husky of voice—Stout of
Step
With fists as well as
Hands
How they battered down
Doors
And ironed
Starched white
Shirts

316

How they led
Armies
Headragged Generals
Across mined
Fields
Booby-trapped
Ditches
To discover books
Desks
A place for us
How they knew what we
Must know
Without knowing a page
Of it
Themselves.

317

The Night Journey

from the book by Kathryn Lasky
illustrated by Trina Schart Hyman

Rache lives with her parents, Ed and Leah; her grandmother, Rose; and her great-grandmother, Sashie. Rache's parents and grandmother warn her not to upset Nana Sashie by asking about tsarist Russia and the persecution Jewish people were subjected to there. However, Rache is fascinated by the story Nana Sashie has begun to tell about her family's dangerous escape from that country.

In an old trunk Rache finds a piece of the brass samovar, or tea urn, that figures largely in Nana Sashie's story. The samovar was the one thing that Sashie's mother, Ida, chose to take with her from Russia. The selection begins on the evening when Rache's father surprises the family with a rebuilt samovar. That night, Nana Sashie continues her story for Rache after the others have gone to bed.

"I have one last gift," said Ed.
"Oh, Ed, enough already!"
"This is actually a gift for the whole family."
"Oooooh!" Rache, Leah, and the nanas exclaimed in unison.

"Just one minute while I get it." Ed went to the pantry and returned with something large and fairly tall wrapped in cloth. "It was too big to wrap in paper so I just put this cloth around it." As he set it on the table he asked, "Who wants to unwrap it?"

Rache was puzzled. There were not the usual hesitations, the if-you-don't-like-it statements.

"Rache, why don't you unwrap it?"

"Well, okay," said Rache with slight apprehension. She leaned forwards and gave a light tug. The cloth fell off. There was a sharp gusty sound as each of the women sucked in her breath in shock. Then silence. A samovar——polished and bright——stood before them. Rache heard Nana Sashie whisper something in Yiddish. The top piece——the crown, Ida's crown——flickered unquenchably in the candlelight. The good soldier was back! Rache sat stunned as conversation bubbled up around her.

"It's a samovar!"

Even the babies liked a glass of tea from the samovar.

"Ed, however did you do it?"

From my bed I could see the samovar.

"Well, the part that Rache found started me off."

"Were you here that day?"

Like a polished good soldier.

The words floated back to Rache through the din.

"So I started hunting in antique shops and got some leads from the museum——you know, just to find the other brass parts."

Its brass catching the glow of the gas lamp in the street outside.

"I'll tell you who was really incredibly helpful and who did most of the rebuilding when we got the parts was . . ."

I used to pretend it was a good soldier . . .

"Bo Andersen of Andersen's Jewelry. You know, the son, the kid . . ."

"You mean the one who's about forty?"

"Yes. Well, he just loved working on this."

"Nana Sashie?" Leah suddenly looked worried. "Ed, I hope this doesn't . . . Nana Sashie, are you all right?"

A sentry in the darkness standing watch over us.

There were two small pockets of loud silence in the happy din——one was Nana Sashie, whose face seemed lost in a gentle reverie, and the other was Rache, who, now over her initial astonishment, felt a confusing mixture of emotions. When she had first discovered the samovar part, Rache had been disgusted by Leah's and Nana Rose's ignorance of Sashie's Russia. But now she felt a real apprehension, as if the gulf between the two worlds had closed too quickly and the one world that she had explored with Sashie would no longer be just theirs alone. Sashie! Funny, she had never thought of her as just Sashie before. She had always been Nana Sashie. It was odd. Odder still was her father. Did he know about the meetings with Nana Sashie? Had he seen her go into Nana's room that night?

"Rache! Come back to the world of the living. Thank you."

"Oh, sorry!"

"Nana Sashie asked you a question."

"Oh! What? What, Nana?"

"Would you kindly fetch the toolbox. There are a few bolts that need tightening if we are going to use this for making tea——which we are!"

After tightening several bolts, Nana Sashie declared the samovar fit for a trial run and insisted that they bring it to her bedroom.

"I don't like the idea of her sleeping with that thing burning in her room," said Nana Rose to Ed and Leah.

"What do you mean? I slept with 'that thing' burning every night in my room for my first nine years!"

"Sparks could fly."

"No, it's very well designed," said Ed. "It's probably safer than our electric toaster."

"Well, I don't like the idea."

"Well, I do," Nana Sashie said bluntly.

"I thought it was supposed to be for the whole family?" Nana Rose persisted.

"It is. You can come up to my room for tea any time. It's easier for you to come upstairs than for me to come down."

That seemed to settle it; the samovar went to Nana Sashie's room. If people wanted a cup of tea, they had to go to her bedroom, which consequently became quite socially active.

But that first night the samovar would belong to Nana Sashie and Rache alone. At least, that was the thought in Rache's mind as she moved across the hall carpeting to Sashie's room. It was 2:30 in the morning and Rache had not even needed the alarm to wake her for this short hike toward the long journey through time, through Nana Sashie's time, to the world that might not be strictly their preserve for much longer. She stepped into the bedroom. The polished good soldier loomed before her in the night. The street lights were lawns away in the suburbs, and yet the samovar seemed lambent and luminous, as if catching the reflections from a distant mirror.

"I knew you'd come tonight."

Rache jumped in surprise. The voice sounded so young.

"Nana Sashie!"

"Who else?"

"You're awake?"

"Yes."

"How's your stomach?"

"What about my stomach?"

"The garlic didn't upset it?"

"Of course not! Stop with the stomach already! Come sit down here beside me." She patted the covers. "Quite remarkable, isn't it? With just one piece to start with, your father did an amazing job! And now he's back, the good soldier." Nana Sashie gave Rache's hand a squeeze.

Like iron filings pulled to a magnet, Rache's and Sashie's eyes were drawn to the glow of the samovar. The old eyes flickered with new color. Time melted. A century bent. There was a young voice.

"We're going with him?"

A strange waxy face with dreadful eyes had melted out of the mist of the cobbler's alley. Sashie felt a stinging cuff on her ear as soon as she asked the question.

"Be quiet!" Her father's voice was sharp. He leaned forward and greeted Wolf warmly.

As Sashie saw her father's hand actually touch the other man's flesh, she felt her stomach turn, and she recoiled in horror. She sought her mother's hand, but Ida was like a statue, rigid, her eyes unseeing sockets. Through the fog came the disembodied cluckings of chickens. Sounds, even the strangest ones, took on a peculiar intimacy in the thickness of a fog, and Sashie shivered as she heard these.

"Wolf Levinson," said Joe. "My family——Sashie; my wife, Ida; my sister, Ghisa; and my father, Sol."

Wolf nodded and touched his hand to his hat in his first social gesture in twenty-five years.

"We have no time to waste, Joe." Sashie felt her mother wince at hearing her husband's name spoken by this man. "So if you will follow me, the wagon's right here. I have arranged the coops so you can get in and lie flat. Then I'm afraid after you're settled I must put them back to cover you."

"Yes. Yes, Wolf, we understand," said Joe.

"Well then, this way and we can lay out the bedclothes to make it more comfortable." There was a bustling as bundles were taken off backs and rearranged in the wagon. Sashie was busy untying her own, but she suddenly was aware of a stony, inexorable stillness directly behind her. It was as if Ida were not even breathing. Joe put down his toolbox and moved quickly to

her side. He spoke gently. "Come on now, Ida." He began to untie her bundle quickly. "It's going to be all right."

"The chickens are one thing, but the devil is something else!"

"Don't be silly, Ida." But Ida did not answer.

Crawling down a temporary center aisle Wolf had made, Sashie was helping Ghisa spread the bedclothes on the floor of the wagon. As long as she kept helping Ghisa she did not have to look at or really think about the strange face with the awful eyes. But now there was trouble. She could sense it. Ida was not moving and Joe was desperate. Sashie peeked around a coop. Her mother's bedrock stance shocked her. She felt the real possibility that the escape might never begin, that they were doomed to stand here until morning, when they would be discovered. And then what? She had absolutely no idea how her father could ever move her mother onto the wagon. It would take a miracle. Sashie suddenly thought of Moses standing by the Red Sea before it parted. Next to Ida, the Red Sea was a puddle to jump. Sashie had never seen anything as unmovable as Ida. Partially hidden by the coop, Sashie listened to the drama taking place between her parents.

"Ida, you must!" pleaded Joe.

"Who is this man?"

"Ida, he is our only chance."

"What hell has he been to?"

"Ida!" Joe swallowed hard and brought his face close to hers. "For the love of our children, get in that wagon!" What in the world was he going to do, Sashie wondered. Carry her?

"Ida, say this with me." And Joe began a soft chant: *"She'ma Y'Isoreal! Adonai Aloujanou! Adonai Echod!* Hear, O Israel! The Lord our God! The Lord is One!"

Sashie's eyes widened as she saw her mother lean on her father's arm and begin to move. As she took these first steps on the longest journey, Sashie could hear her mother whispering softly the words of the *Shema*, the Jewish statement of faith.

The blankets had been spread. Ida and Sashie stretched out in the most forward part of the wagon, each with a baby tucked in at her side. The space left between them was for Joe. At their toes were the tops of Ghisa's and Zayde Sol's heads, who were stretched out from the midsection of the wagon to the back end. Ida and Sashie settled in as best they could. With a small pillow under their heads, they had about twelve or fifteen inches clearance between their faces and the chicken coops. This seemed much more ample than Sashie had imagined. There was plenty of room to place a tier of the samovar over her face as a shield.

"This isn't bad, Mama," said Sashie, trying on the samovar face mask. "Here, try it." Sashie turned toward her mother to hand her the brass piece.

"No, I want to see," Ida said emphatically.

"So much for the samovar!" muttered Ghisa, whose voice floated up from Sashie's feet. There was no way that Sashie could see Ghisa's or Zayde Sol's face, and she found that she missed the smirk that must have punctuated her aunt's remark. She could just see her mother's face by turning her head to the side, and she could see Louie's chubby face, tucked in under her own arm and sleeping for now. Cecile's face was mostly buried under her mother's blouse, but Sashie listened hard and through the clucking gale of the chickens above could hear the deep, throaty sucking noises of the infant as she nursed, a sound she had heard a thousand times but which thrilled her in a new way. Her father had arranged himself between Ida and Sashie. His head was a little forward of theirs, so he did not block their view of each other, and in order to see Joe, Ida and

Sashie needed only to crane their necks and look up a bit. He quickly put a hand on each of their shoulders.

"Well, is everything as comfortable as possible here? You know, you don't need to be on your backs; you can turn over on your stomachs. Everyone all right?" Joe asked. "Ida?"

"All right." She replied flatly.

"Sashie?"

"Fine, Papa."

"Ghisa?"

"Lovely!" Darn, Sashie thought. She wished she could see Ghisa's face.

"Papa?" Joe asked.

There was a slight pause, then, "I'm alive?"

"All ready?" Wolf's face loomed at the end of the aisle.

"All set," Joe answered. His voice seemed tinged with excitement that bordered more on joy than fear.

"All right, I'll put on the last coops."

There was a great clatter and clacking as Joe dropped the first coop into the center aisle where it rested on the edges of the flanking coops. A little chunk of white night disappeared, and Sashie felt her heart beat faster. More clatter and clucks, and another piece of the night vanished. One by one the coops were dropped, and piece by piece the world above Sashie and her family was eaten up. The clucking of chickens choked the air around her, and Sashie found herself gulping for breath. Terrified of inhaling one of the white feathers that tumbled crazily through the air, she tried to screen her mouth with her scarf, but then it was harder to breathe.

"Sashie!" Her father's voice came through strong and gentle. "Look at me, Sashela." She craned her neck towards her father. "You breathe like me now. Do just what I do. First in through the nose, not too deep, then out through the mouth blowing softly. Slowly. Take your time, Sashela. There's plenty of air. And you think of nice things, like the smell of bread baking and kites flying and the first leaves of May and lighting Hanukkah candles."

"Harruh!" They heard Wolf grunt and slap the reins on the horse's back. The wagon groaned and lurched forwards, the wheels creaking, and they were on their way. Sashie thought she could count every cobblestone as the wagon rolled down the cobbler's alley. But she kept breathing just as her father had told her to and tried to think of nice things——things that now seemed rare and wondrous, like an open window on a starry summer night, a raindrop's path on glass, April branches with leaves curled tight as babies' fists.

They must be on Vaskeyevka Street. She would try and guess their route as they went. But she certainly could not see, and at this hour there were no sounds except the blizzard of cluckings that raged inches above them. She wondered if they would go by the park. And then after the park, what? She had never gone beyond the park. The Alexandra Gate of the park was the farthest perimeter of her life. Some chicken droppings splattered on her cheek, but just as disgust welled up inside Sashie a new noise split the cluckings——iron spikes hitting stone. The world above was laced with the rhythmic strikes.

"Whoa! Whoa!" She felt the wagon stop. Ghisa slid forwards a bit, her head pressing on Sashie's feet, and Sashie's head pressed against her father's arm. Louie's eyes flew open. Sashie opened her eyes as wide as she could and, staring directly into the little boy's, commanded his silence with an unblinking and fierce gaze that was intended to freeze his tongue. Quickly she reached up her sleeve for a sugar stick and popped it into his mouth. It worked, this time. Outside she could hear Wolf conversing in Russian with some men. The street was being repaired and impassable for a four-wheel vehicle. They must turn around and take Zolodievka Street. There followed a great deal of jangling and jolting shot through with Wolf's grunts and barks at the horse. Sashie felt the wagon roll backwards a few feet, then forwards. There were more barks. From the noise Sashie thought that Wolf must be off the wagon and guiding the horse around by pushing and pulling on the harness. Louie cried out once, but the sound was drowned by the tumult of the horse whinnying in protest, chickens clucking, harness jangling, wheels creaking, not to mention the string of curses and barks emanating from Wolf.

"Old man!" said one of the street workers jovially. "Watch your tongue. You know there are not just roosters aboard your wagon. I see some hens!"

The swirl of feathers seemed to freeze in the air above Sashie. She felt Ghisa grab her foot and her father's hand bite into her shoulder.

"Just joking!" She heard the man protest innocently. "Can't you take a joke, old man?"

Sashie had not heard Wolf say anything to the street worker, but she had a sense that Wolf need not say much to fill another with dread. The wagon was finally turned around. The street worker stood just by Sashie's side of the wagon now. With only the boards between them, she could hear him mutter nervously to the other, "Queer eyes!" Sashie could feel Wolf climbing into the driver's seat.

"Harruh!" he yelled. The wagon lurched forwards and clattered out of the street.

If they had to take Zolodievka Street instead of this one, it must be fairly near, and if it were fairly near, reasoned Sashie, the Alexandra Gate of the park was not that far away. Approaching the edge of her known world, Sashie felt a ripple of excitement run through her body. She remembered suddenly a book her father had shown her that had a picture of a map from long long ago, from before Columbus had discovered the new world. The map showed a world with the continents and oceans known in the early fifteenth century. At a certain distance from the land, sea serpents were drawn riding through the crests of waves, with the legend Here Beginneth the Region of the Dragons. Except, thought Sashie, in Russia the dragons live everywhere, and she and her family were supposed to be escaping from them to the tsarless region of what angels? She was not sure. Although she herself had not dealt directly with the dragons, Sashie never once doubted their existence. One did not have to have tea with the tsar and tsarina to have his life sabotaged by them, or their ministers, or the notorious Black Hundreds, who were nothing but street thugs glorified by the tsar and given a license to kill Jews. She remembered her father's stories of the army and she had the feeling that that was not the half of it. And she would never forget the night the news came of her grandparents. She had been only three years old at the time, but she would never forget it——the hollow, stunned voice of her mother repeating over and over, "Both of them?" No, Sashie believed in these dragons, and something deep, deep inside told her that the dragon's fire had scorched Wolf. His eyes were queer because he had looked straight down the fiery throat. She wondered what it was he had seen. She would probably never know, Sashie thought, and she could certainly never ask.

Louie had finished his sugar stick and was demanding more. Sashie felt the wagon turn another corner. They must be near the Alexandra Gate. Had Columbus been forced to begin the region of the dragons with a baby wailing for more and twisting his nose, as Louie was now twisting Sashie's? "Hush, hush!" commanded everyone, but Louie would not be quiet.

"Give him another one!" hissed Ghisa from Sashie's feet. Sashie groped up her sleeve for another sugar stick. "Here," she huffed, "what do I care if you grow up to have rotten teeth!"

Ida prayed a strange prayer——that her baby boy would grow old enough to have rotten teeth. And Joe, buoyed by Sashie's relentless optimism, smiled quietly to himself and patted his daughter on the shoulder.

Sashie had fifteen sugar sticks. At this rate, she calculated, they would not last the day. "We might need the b-o-t-t-l-e." Ida and Joe weren't overjoyed at the prospect of drugging babies, but such a possibility had had to be planned for on this trip and a bottle of milk with a light sleeping draught had been prepared. Just then Sashie heard a torrent of water from a slop bucket being thrown out a high window. The chickens on the left side of the wagon forward of her sent up a loud cackle. They must have caught some of it, and then under the layer of cackles was another noise——a steamy hiss of curses from Ghisa. There seemed to be more street noises now——shutters being opened, dogs barking, more wheels creaking, fragments of early morning talk drifting out of doorways as shopkeepers readied for trade. But where were they? It sounded nothing like the noises one would hear around the Alexandra Gate. There were not any buildings near the gate from whose windows slop buckets would be emptied. They must be beyond the gate and near the outskirts of Nikolayev, Sashie thought. As if to answer her question, there was suddenly a new sound and a new motion as the wheels of the wagon rolled from cobblestones to wood. The bass tones of the wooden planks rumbled beneath the wheels and the rush of coursing spring waters muted the manic cluckings. Even Louie, who had managed to sit up, stopped sucking on his sugar stick.

"What dat?" the baby demanded softly.

"It's the river." Sashie whispered. "We're leaving Nikolayev now."

"Oh."

"Be a good boy, Louie!" Sashie patted his knee. Louie was now starting to crawl around, exploring under the chicken coops. It seemed to keep him quiet and drain off some of his energy, so nobody tried to stop him. There wasn't far he could go.

As the wagon moved from the bridge to the dirt road, the clucks and cackles rolled up once more in a suffocating swarm. Oh, to hear water again! thought Sashie. But the liquid resonance of the flowing river was soon a memory obliterated by the cackles that seemed to bristle right inside Sashie's brain. She would go mad if she listened to the chickens another minute! She would think of a song. But she could not think of one. She would try to hear the road under the wheels. But she could not hear it. The road did, however, feel different from the cobblestone streets. It was softer. The speed seemed slower—not just slower, but thicker, Sashie thought. How can motion feel thick? It was not a bad feeling. And the noise, it wasn't noise. She caught herself. How can I hear noise, Sashie thought, above the cackles? But she did. And it was different. It wasn't noise that was reflected from hard surfaces like cobblestones, wood, and granite. It came from a deep quiet center. They were soft and sucking sounds; the sound of things being absorbed, soaked up. It's mud sounds, thought Sashie, ecstatically. "I am listening to spring mud." It was like beautiful music to Sashie.

Just above the mud but not as high as the wagon top she heard another sound. It was the whispering of a south wind blowing through winter grass. Sashie had never in her life been outside the city. She had never known the sound of the vast quietness of the country, which absorbed noise to make new sound. She lay perfectly still, listening as the country sounds bloomed around her like huge flowers.

Through the minutes and in and out of hours they slept, whispered, ate a hunk of bread or piece of potato. The babies were doing tolerably well and the sleeping draught had not yet been needed. A huge baked potato kept Louie busy for twenty minutes. A medley of whispered nursery rhymes delivered by Sashie and her father averted a near tantrum.

Sashie had just finished drawing tiny faces on both her thumb and index finger for a puppet finger show to entertain Louie when she felt Wolf slow the horse.

"Whoa!" he said.

The horse and the wagon stopped. Just as Wolf had begun to speak to the horse, Sashie had heard distant rapid beats, like small explosions in the earth.

"Trouble!" Wolf's voice was tight with fear. "Everybody must be quiet! It's soldiers." He paused, and Sashie thought she could hear the breath catch in his throat. "My God, it's an imperial regiment!"

Then there was a timpani of cold metal as sabers and spurs jangled in the air. Sashie had managed to grab Louie and press him flat on the floor. Her father lay his leg over the little boy's kicking ones and Sashie clapped her hand over his mouth.

"Hail! In the name of their imperial majesties, the Tsar Nicholas and the Tsarina Alexandra!"

Wolf mumbled something conciliatory, but Sashie could not hear the exact words, for the only noise was that of metal clanging, leather squeaking, hooves striking the ground, animals panting, and occasional coughs. The chickens' clucking was eclipsed by the noises that accompanied the tsar's regiment of twenty on an exercise in the countryside. And beneath the chicken coops the human cargo lay in frozen terror.

"You carry chickens, I see . . ." The commander spoke. "And where are you bound for?"

"Oh, just to Borisov to deliver them for my boss to a client."

"How generous of your boss. I am sure he would not begrudge a few chickens for the tsar's regiment, and the client will never miss them."

"Lieutenant, if you please, two or three coops." Sashie heard a man jump from a horse.

"Aaaaagggg!" screamed Wolf. "Hold it!"

" 'Hold it!' You old Zhidi!" The last word hung in the air like a dagger dripping blood. "Zhidi," the abusive word for "Jew," had become quite popular with the latest wave of pogroms. Sashie trembled all over. She pressed her hand harder on Louie's mouth.

The commander spoke slowly. "You deny one of the tsar's most loyal and favored regiments a few chickens? To deny the tsar's officers is to deny the tsar, and to deny the tsar is to deny God!" the voice thundered.

"No! No! I do not deny anything to you, your . . . your excellency. It's just that the coops are in bad repair and if you carry them with you they are bound to come apart and the chickens escape. Better you take the chickens slaughtered."

"Fine. Lieutenant, skewer a few chickens then, if you will."

There was a bright flash and Sashie's breath suddenly locked in her throat. Her eyes widened in terror as she saw the tip of a thin silver blade slice through the mesh and come within three inches of her face. Time stopped as her eyes focused on the glinting sliver of death that played above her. She could even see the scarlet sleeve of the officer's jacket. The three gold buttons blazed through a small flurry of white feathers, and the black decorative braid at the cuff was like four coiled snakes ready to strike. The silvery death dance went on raging above her face and throat. The moist still air from her half-open mouth fogged the blade tip.

"Here! I find you a fat one. Those are all skinny." The blade stilled. The silver death retreated through the slashed mesh to the world above, and Sashie fainted.

A few seconds later she came to and heard Wolf talking rapidly.

"Those are the scrawny ones. Good breeders, but no good eating. Now over here we have your scratchers."

"Scratchers?" asked the commander.

"Yeah, scratchers. They have to scratch for their food. Makes 'em tough. Stringy. They're big chickens, mind you. Weighty, but quite tough. No flavor. But here. Here in the middle we have our plumpsters——we call them plumpsters." Wolf prattled on faster than a runaway cart down Kliminsky Street on the science and technology of poultry. "With the plumpsters you get more meat per cubic centimeter than any other kind of chicken. Succulent! Juicy! You see, the plumpsters are not required to scratch for their food. And what food it is! Whole-grain bread soaked in gravy, pumpkin seeds, kasha. We Zhidi should only eat like that! The plumpsters' main job in life is eating, with an occasional stroll in a very small area. A chicken, one might say, truly fit for a tsar. Please sire, your sword. I will fetch you the plumpest of the plumpsters. Yes, a rare bird indeed!"

Sashie felt the wagon shake as Wolf pulled himself up on the side. "Kosher is quick!" She heard Wolf mutter to himself in Yiddish. In less than three minutes he had slaughtered

ten chickens. Blood dripped down the center aisle onto the bedclothes.

"Your chickens, your excellency. May you and your officers eat them in good health!"

"Your client will never miss them," came the reply.

As the spurs dug into flanks, whinnies mixed with leathery squeaks and metallic janglings filled the air. The command finally came——"Forward!"——and then the rapid explosive noises of eighty hooves striking the earth as they moved off with their imperial load.

Zhidi, Sashie thought, when at last she could think again. Wolf called himself a Zhidi. How very strange that he could do this——abuse himself with this foul word even though it was done to ingratiate himself with the commander. For the first hours after the encounter with the regiment, Sashie lay in a state of total exhaustion. It was as if her nerves, her brain, and each muscle in her body had used every bit of energy available. Gradually, however, she began to realize that she was alive. It was a miracle. It was as if she were a newborn baby with an older mind that could appreciate the wonder of its own birth—— of being born a whole, complete human being. She tingled all over with the sheer excitement of her own living body. She touched her throat and face. She traced the gullies and curves of her ears. She pressed hard through all the layers of clothing and felt a rib. She took a joyous inventory of her body. Then after the miracle of survival was confirmed, she thought of Wolf and the word he had used in reference to himself. How absolutely confounding and unfathomable it was. She could not imagine ever calling herself by this horrible name, no matter what the danger was.

Sashie had stared unblinkingly as Death sliced the air just inches from her face and throat. She was sure Wolf had seen something worse, but what was it? The haunted man contained a death riddle. Sashie had been brought to the edge, but Wolf in some way had crossed over.

The fog had long ago burned off and slants of sunlight had pierced through the mesh and feather storm into the netherworld of the coops. But now the sun was at too low an angle to light the wagon, and Sashie felt a twilight chill. If she could only move more, she would feel warmer. Louie was warm as a puppy from crawling around under the coops, and though he was now sleeping, his short little body could curl up into a nice ball perfect for conserving energy. Sashie tucked him in closer to her own body to steal a little heat. Soon she drifted in and out of a troubled sleep that jolted and lurched and flashed with silver blades dripping blood. Then everything stopped and she woke up into a night-still world with her own hand fast at her throat.

"All right!" Wolf shouted. She felt him jump down from the driver's seat. "We're here."

"My God!"

"Thank God!"

"Am I dead or alive?"

"Or a chicken!"

"It's all right, Ida, we're here!"

"Oh, Joe!"

"Hang on, folks. I'll get the coops off in half a second." Sashie felt Wolf climb on the back end of the wagon. She heard the clatter of the first coop being removed.

"Ah!" exclaimed Ghisa with wonder as she saw the first piece of the world above. Another two coops were removed and

Sashie heard Zayde Sol recite a *broche*, a prayer, upon seeing the evening again. Then another coop was removed and a square of night sky reappeared, black velvet chinked with stars. Piece by piece the sky came back and the wind, with the smell of winter grass and earth, blew across Sashie's face.

Each person had to be helped off the wagon by Wolf and, except for Louie, walked around a few feet by him until their legs and back regained their strength. Sashie needed Wolf's arm only for a couple of steps. Almost immediately she was off on her own trying out her new legs. First she tried walking a few meters, but the night was so warm, the air so gentle, and the field so vast that Sashie felt she must dance, leap, fly through this startling country. Under the starry dome of the Russian night Sashie whirled and jumped. Her head thrown back, she watched the stars spin and smelled the thawing earth and listened to the wind songs in the grass.

Ghisa too was soon running and skipping in jerky little circles around a moonlit tree stump. The babies squealed and Ida and Joe said soft prayers of thanksgiving and laughed gently with each other in the night. And Zayde Sol said more *broches*——*broches* for seeing stars again, *broches* for seeing the moon, *broches* for seeing a baby walk, and *broches* for seeing a granddaughter dance.

The Night Journey

Meet the Author

Kathryn Lasky says she has always been a "compulsive story maker" and today writes books for children, teenagers, and adults. She enjoys being her own boss, setting her own hours, and being able to wear anything she wants to work.

Her book *The Night Journey* won the Association of Jewish Libraries Sydney Taylor Book Award and was named a Notable Book by the American Library Association.

Other works by Lasky include *Sugaring Time*, *The Weaver's Gift*, *Puppeteer*, *Beyond the Divide*, *Prank*, and *Pageant*.

Meet the Illustrator

Trina Schart Hyman started drawing at a very young age but attended five art schools and rode her bike 3,000 miles through the Netherlands and England before she started taking her art portfolio to publishers. They rejected her work for three years, but today she is a Caldecott Award-winning artist for children's books.

Hyman says her illustrations are full of her friends, family, and neighbors. In *Snow White*, some of the dwarfs are people she knows!

Theme Connections

Think About It

With a small group of students, discuss the following questions.

- How did Nana Sashie feel about the samovar? Why?
- Why did Nana Sashie get to keep the samovar in her room?
- Why did Rache visit Nana Sashie's room in the middle of the night, just after they got the samovar?
- Why did Rache visit Nana Sashie's room on other nights as well?
- Why did Rache want to hear Nana Sashie's stories?

Record Ideas

What have you learned about heritage from this story? What do you want to learn about your own heritage? Write your thoughts in your Writing Journal.

Draw a Family Tree

To help you remember the characters in "The Night Journey," and the generations to which they belong, make a family tree. Whose names should go on the roots? Whose names should be written on the biggest branches? Whose names should be written on the smaller branches?

Parmele

from *Childtimes: A Three-Generation Memoir*

by Eloise Greenfield and Lessie Jones Little

Every summer we took a trip down home. Down home was Parmele.

To get ready for our trip, Daddy would spend days working on our old car, putting it in shape to go on the road, and Mama would wash and iron all of our clothes. Then everything would be packed in the tan leather suitcase and the black cardboard suitcase, and we'd be ready to go.

Mama and Daddy would sit in the front with Vedie in Mama's lap, and Wilbur, Gerald, and I sat in the back with our legs on top of the suitcases. This was before cars had trunks. Or radios. Or air conditioners or heaters. And there were no superhighways. The speed limit was forty-five miles an hour, and we went thirty-five to keep from straining the car.

It was an eight-hour trip to Norfolk, Virginia, where we always went first. Grandma Pattie Ridley Jones and Grandpa had moved there by that time, and we'd spend about a week with them, then go on to Parmele for another week.

On the road, I played peek-a-boo with Vedie between her naps. Or my brothers and I would count all the cars on the road. We'd say, "There go one! That's twenty-two. There go another one!" And we'd read out loud the rhymes on the red signs advertising Burma shaving cream, and wave at people sitting on their porches, and argue with each other until one of us got real mad and real loud and Mama told us we were giving her the jimjams and to be quiet.

One thing that we saw on the road frightened me. Chain gangs. We saw them often, the lines of black men in their black-and-white-striped jail suits, chained by their ankles and watched over, as they repaired the roads, by white men with guns.

Eloise Greenfield stands at the far right of this photograph taken at Parmele in 1941. With her are her grandfather, her mother, her grandmother, Wilbur, Vedie, and Gerald.

I wasn't afraid of the men, and I didn't think about maybe getting shot. But for a reason I didn't understand, I was afraid of the whole thing. Those bent-over striped backs, the sharp points of the picks the men swung, the sound of the picks hitting the concrete, the sight of men with long guns, pacing. It scared me.

After a few miles, that scared feeling would fade away, and I'd start to have fun again, or I might take a nap, and it always seemed as if days had passed before we finally crossed the line into Parmele.

By the time of my visits there, only a few trains were still passing through. My Parmele wasn't a train town or a mill town. It was a quiet town. Chinaberry trees and pump water and tree swings and figs and fat, pulpy grapes on the vine. People saying, "hey" instead of "hi," the way they did in Washington, *hey-ey*, sending their voices up, then down, softly, singing it through their noses. Parmele was me running from the chickens when I was little, riding around the yard in a goat-pulled cart, sitting on the porch and letting people going by in their cars wave at me, reading in the rocking chair, taking long walks to the gas station for soda pop with the children of Mama's and Daddy's childtime friends. Parmele was uncles and aunts and cousins. And Granny. And Pa.

Mack and Williamann Little, 1890s.

They were Daddy's parents, Mack and Williamann Little. Black people in Parmele called them Mr. Mack and Miss Williamann. White people called them Uncle Mack and Ain' Williamann.

Granny was thin and whitehaired. She kept snuff tucked inside her bottom lip and wore aprons over her long dresses. I remember her most bending over the collards in her garden or feeding the chickens. She used to sew leftover material from my dresses into her patchwork quilts. She used to make apple jelly and green tomato pickles. Anything her grandchildren wanted, she wanted them to have.

And so did Pa.

"Leave the children alone," he used to tell mamas and daddies. "They ain't doing nothing."

Pa was a sharecropper. He worked in the fields, farming the land for the white man who owned it, and got paid in a share of the crops he raised. Along with that, he had almost always had some kind of little business going, even when Daddy was a boy——a meat market, an icehouse, a cleaner's, a grocery store.

Long before I was born, Pa had been a member of the Marcus Garvey group that used to meet in Parmele on Sunday afternoons. It was one of thousands of branches of the United Negro Improvement Association headed by Marcus Garvey. They met to talk about the beauty and strength of blackness, and to plan the return of black people to Africa.

I didn't think my grandfather was afraid of anything except the frogs that came out of the

Eloise Little, 1932

345

mud-filled ditches at night and flopped across the yard, and he knew plenty of names to call them. The thumb on his right hand looked like a little baldheaded man. The top joint had been cut off in a farm accident, and he had put it in a jar of preserving liquid that stayed on the front-room mantel. I never got tired of looking at it.

Children hung around Pa, nieces and nephews and neighbors, listening to his stories, giggling at his jokes. Some nights there would be just us——Wilbur, Gerald, and me, with our grandfather——sitting on the porch where the only light was that of the stars and the nearest house was a long way down the road. He'd tell scary stories, and get really tickled when we got scared. He swore his ghost stories were true.

"One night," he'd say, "me and my brother John was coming 'cross that field over yonder." He'd make his arm tremble and point toward the woods across the highway. "And we commence to hearing this strange sound. Ummmmm-*umph!* Ummmmm-*umph!* And we looked up and saw this . . . this *haint!*"

He'd twist his face and narrow his eyes in horror as he stared out into the darkness, and I could just feel all those haints hovering behind us, daring us to turn around and run for the door.

Sometimes Pa would stop right in the middle of a story.

"Then what happened, Pa?" one of us would ask.

"Oh, I left after that," he'd say, and he'd laugh. Then we'd laugh, small nervous laughs, wanting to believe that it had all been just a joke.

Every year when it was time for us to leave, a sudden change would come over Pa. One minute he'd be challenging

Eloise Little and Bobby Greenfield, 1948

Vera and Vedie Little, Langston Terrace, 1949

Daddy to a foot race that never took place, and the next minute he was weak and sick, trying to get us to stay. He didn't think he would live to see us the following summer, he'd say. At breakfast he'd begin the blessing with, "Lord, I sure do thank You for allowing me to see my family one last time before You call me home," and he'd pray a long, sad prayer that brought tears to our eyes.

But finally, when nothing worked, Pa would give up and help Daddy load the car with suitcases and with sacks of fresh corn and peanuts. There'd be hugs and kisses and more tears, and then we'd drive away, leaving him and Granny standing on the side of the road, waving, waving, waving, getting smaller and smaller, until they blended into one and disappeared.

Pa never liked to leave home. Granny came to visit us a few times over the years, but Pa always made an excuse. He couldn't get away right then, he had too much work to do, or something. One year, though, he had to come. He'd had a stroke, and Mama and Daddy brought him to Washington to take care of him. The stroke had damaged his body and his mind, so that he didn't understand much of what was going on around him, but he knew he wasn't where he wanted to be. Mama would take him for a walk and he'd ask people on the street, "Which way is Parmele?"

My grandfather never got back to Parmele. He lived in Washington for eighteen months, and then, in 1951, at the age of seventy-eight, he died.

Parmele

Meet the Authors

Eloise Greenfield was born during the Great Depression in Parmele, North Carolina. However, she did most of her growing up in Washington, DC. Her father used to pile the family into the car once a week to visit the library for a supply of books. She says she found far too few books that told the truth about African-Americans, and she wanted to change that.

Today she is a member of the African-American Writers Guild. She uses grant money to teach creative writing to elementary and junior high students, and has written many award-winning books.

Lessie Jones Little was born in Parmele, North Carolina, and spent most of her childhood there. Like many of the people in her town, she and her family made their money working on farms. The work was very hard and tiring, and didn't pay well. The money she earned went toward buying schoolbooks and cloth for her dresses.

When she graduated from high school, she was awarded a pin that signified she had earned the best grades. She went on to work as a teacher and then a clerk at the Office of the Surgeon General. It wasn't until she was sixty-seven years old that she began writing children's books. She collaborated on two books with her daughter, Eloise Greenfield, and also wrote an award-winning book of poems.

Theme Connections

Think About It

With a small group of students, discuss the following questions.

- What did the author enjoy about visiting her grandparents?
- What heritage was passed on during the author's visits?
- What do you enjoy about visiting your grandparents and older family friends?
- During these visits, how do they pass on pieces of their own heritage to you?

Record Ideas

What have you learned about heritage from your group discussion? Record your thoughts and ideas in your Writing Journal.

Write a Critique

Write a critique of the selection "Parmele." Give examples of what you liked and didn't like about the story, what you learned from it, and what characters you particularly liked or disliked. Share your critique with other students, comparing and contrasting your ideas.

Bibliography

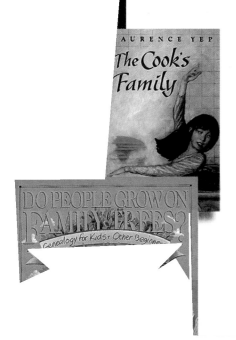

The Cook's Family

by Laurence Yep. What happens when you pretend to be someone's long-lost granddaughter? You might become part of the cook's family!

Do People Grow on Family Trees? Genealogy for Kids and Other Beginners

by Ira Wolfman. Learning something about your ancestors' lives means learning something about yourself. This fascinating guidebook shows you the steps to discovering your genealogy.

Going Back Home: An Artist Returns to the South

by Michele Wood and Toyomi Igus. Michele Wood goes home to learn about the place and people of her origin. She shares her story through her paintings.

The Great Ancestor Hunt: The Fun of Finding Out Who You Are

by Lila Perl. If you want to search for your roots, this is the book that will help you get started.

In My Family: En Mi Familia

by Carmen Lomas Garza. Share this Mexican American's family activities and fun. Learn how family history has shaped their lives.

Journey to Ellis Island

by Carol Bierman. Imagine leaving your home in Russia and traveling to America with your mother and sister with only what you can carry in a suitcase. That's what Julius Weinstein did when he was 12 years old in 1922. Julius grew up to become a great storyteller, and this book captures these fascinating and often funny tales about Europe, Ellis Island, and America.

Secret of the Andes

by Ann Nolan Clard. Without a past or a family, an Incan boy lives in a hidden valley high in the mountains of Peru. What are the secrets of his Inca ancestors that he must discover to understand his destiny?

This Land is My Land

by George Littlechild. Through his art and words George Littlechild shares his feelings about being Native American in this time and place.

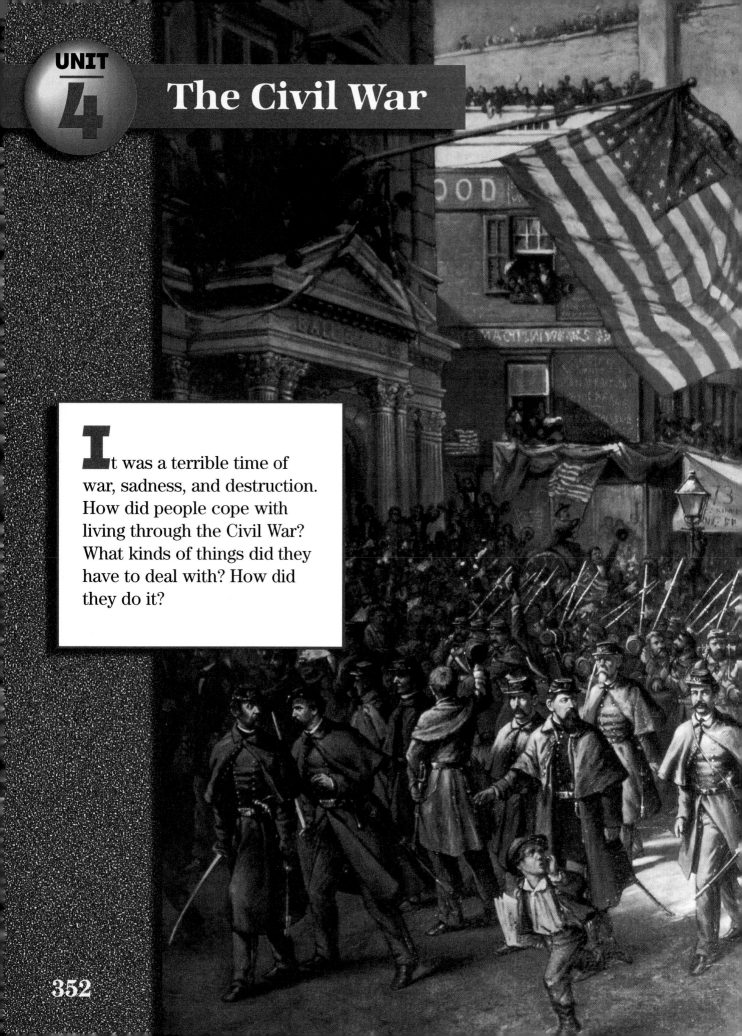

UNIT
4
The Civil War

It was a terrible time of war, sadness, and destruction. How did people cope with living through the Civil War? What kinds of things did they have to deal with? How did they do it?

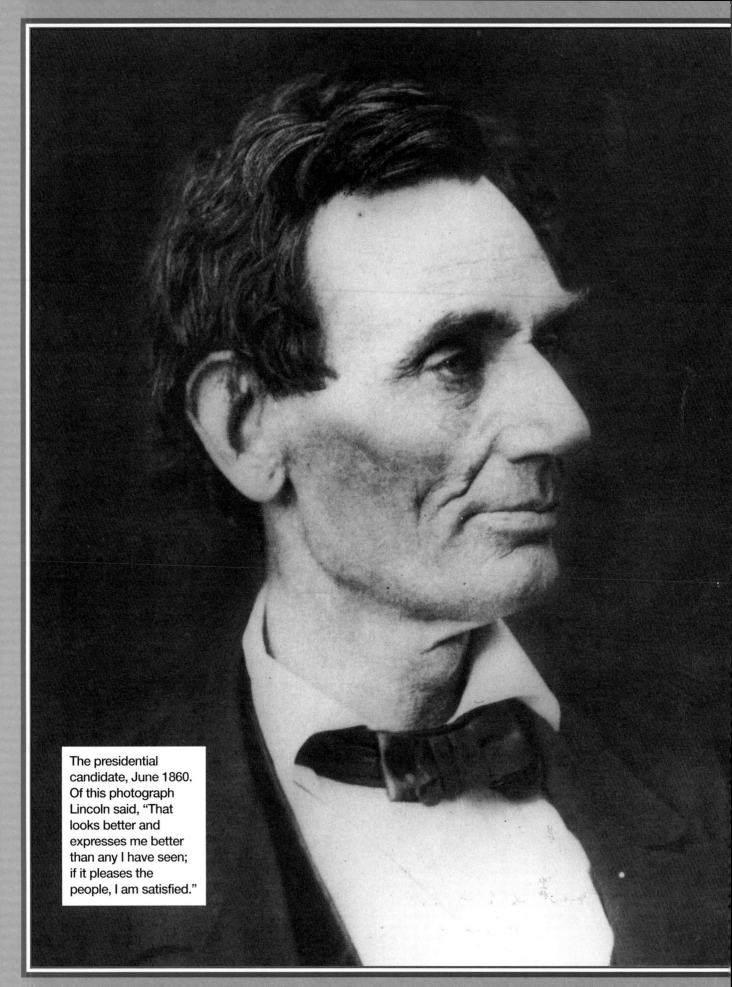

The presidential candidate, June 1860. Of this photograph Lincoln said, "That looks better and expresses me better than any I have seen; if it pleases the people, I am satisfied."

Half Slave and Half Free

from *Lincoln: A Photobiography*
by Russell Freedman

"If slavery is not wrong, nothing is wrong. I cannot remember when I did not so think, and feel."
—ABRAHAM LINCOLN

When Abraham Lincoln took his seat in Congress in 1847, Washington was a sprawling town of 34,000 people, including several thousand slaves. From the windows of the Capitol, Lincoln could see crowded slave pens where manacled blacks waited to be shipped south.

Southern planters had built a cotton kingdom on the shoulders of enslaved blacks, and they meant to preserve their way of life. Many white Southerners claimed a "sacred" right to own Negroes as slaves. Slavery was a blessing for blacks and whites alike, they said, "a good—a positive good," according to Senator John C. Calhoun of South Carolina.

Slave uprisings and rebellions had resulted in tough measures to control blacks and silence white critics of slavery. Throughout the South, antislavery writings and societies were suppressed or banned.

Slavery had never prospered in the North and had been outlawed there. Some Northerners wanted to abolish slavery everywhere in the land, but abolitionists were still a small and embattled minority. Most people in the North were willing to leave slavery alone, as long as it was confined to the South.

Downtown Springfield, where Lincoln practiced law, as it appeared in the 1850s. The street is paved with split logs laid flat side up, and the sidewalk is built of wooden planks.

While the North was free soil, it was hardly a paradise for blacks. Racial prejudice was a fact of everyday life. Most Yankee states had enacted strict "black laws." In Illinois, Lincoln's home state, blacks paid taxes but could not vote, hold political office, serve on juries, testify in court, or attend schools. They had a hard time finding jobs. Often they sold themselves as "indentures" for a period of twenty years——a form of voluntary slavery——just to eat and have a place to live.

Even in northern Illinois, where antislavery feelings ran strong, whites feared that emancipation of the slaves would send thousands of jobless blacks swarming into the North. Abolitionists were considered dangerous fanatics in Illinois. Lincoln knew that to be branded an abolitionist in his home state would be political suicide.

Early in his career, Lincoln made few public statements about slavery. But he did take a stand. As a twenty-eight-year-old state legislator, he recorded his belief that slavery was "founded on both injustice and bad policy." Ten years later, as a congressman, he voted with his party to stop the spread of slavery, and he introduced his bill to outlaw slavery in the nation's capital. But he did not become an antislavery crusader. For the most part, he sat silently in the background as Congress rang with angry debates over slavery's future.

Lincoln always said that he hated slavery. He claimed he hated it as much as any abolitionist, but he feared that efforts to force abolition on the South would only lead to violence. He felt that Congress had no power to interfere with slavery in states where it already existed.

He wanted to see slavery done away with altogether, but that would take time, he believed. He hoped it could be legislated out of existence, with some sort of compensation given to the slaveholders in exchange for their property. As long as Congress kept slavery from spreading, Lincoln felt certain that it would gradually die a "natural death."

When his congressional term ended in 1849, Lincoln decided to withdraw from public life. For the next five years he concentrated on his law practice and stayed out of politics. As he traveled the Illinois circuit, arguing cases in country courthouses, slavery was becoming an explosive issue that threatened to tear the nation apart.

Vast new territories were opening up in the West, bringing the North and South into conflict. Each section wanted to control the western territories. The South needed new lands for the large-scale cultivation of cotton and other crops with slave labor. The North demanded that the western territories be reserved for the free labor of independent farmers and workers. Meanwhile, as the territories reached statehood and gained votes in Congress, they would hold the balance of political power in Washington. The admission of each new state raised a crucial question: Would it enter the Union as a free state or a slave state?

Below: $100 Reward Poster to apprehend fugitive slave. Riply County, Mo., March 2, 1860.

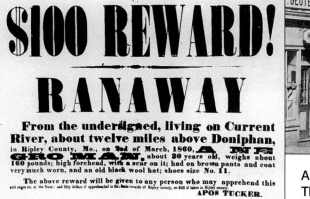

Above: Slave market in Atlanta. The slaves were held in pens until they were auctioned off.

So far, Congress had managed to hold the country together through a series of uneasy compromises, such as the Missouri Compromise of 1820. These agreements permitted slavery in some western territories and barred it in others. But attitudes were hardening. Growing numbers of Northerners had come to regard slavery as a moral evil, an issue that could no longer be avoided. Southerners, meanwhile, were more determined than ever to protect their way of life.

The issue came to a head in 1854, when Congress passed the bitterly debated Kansas-Nebraska Act. Under the Missouri Compromise, the region that included the territories of Kansas and Nebraska had been declared off-limits to slavery. Under the new Act, however, the future of slavery in those territories would be determined by the people who settled there. They would decide for themselves whether to enter the Union as free states or slave states.

Five generations of a slave family on a South Carolina plantation.

The Kansas-Nebraska Act had been introduced by Lincoln's old political rival, Stephen Douglas, now a U.S. Senator from Illinois. Douglas's policy of "popular sovereignty" caused a storm of protest in the North. By opening new territories to slavery, his measure overturned the Missouri Compromise, which had held slavery in check. With the passage of Douglas's Act, Lincoln ended his long political silence. "I was losing interest in politics," he said, "when the repeal of the Missouri Compromise aroused me again."

He was "thunderstruck and stunned," aroused as he had "never been before." Douglas and his followers had opened the gates for slavery to expand and grow and establish itself permanently. Now it would never die the "natural death" Lincoln had expected. He felt compelled to speak out. For the first time in five years he neglected his law practice. He traveled across Illinois, campaigning for antislavery Whig candidates and speaking in reply to Senator Douglas, who had returned home to defend his policies.

Lincoln told his audiences that slavery was a "monstrous injustice." It was a "cancer" threatening to grow out of control "in a nation originally dedicated to the inalienable rights of man." And it was not only wrong, it threatened the rights of everyone. If slavery was permitted to spread, free white workers would be forced to compete for a living with enslaved blacks. In the end, slavery would undermine

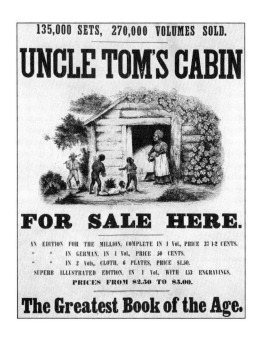

Published as a book in 1852, *Uncle Tom's Cabin* became an international best seller that for hundreds of thousands of readers dramatized the horrors of slavery.

the very foundations of democracy. "As I would not be a slave, so I would not be a master," Lincoln declared. "This expresses my idea of democracy. Whatever differs from this, to the extent of the difference, is not democracy."

He had been studying the history of the nation, pondering the words and ideals of the Founding Fathers. He believed that the cornerstone of the American experiment in democracy was the Declaration of Independence, which states that "all men are created equal," and that all are entitled to "Life, Liberty, and the pursuit of Happiness." Lincoln took this declaration personally. It meant that every poor man's son deserved the opportunities for advancement he had enjoyed. He felt that the Declaration of Independence expressed the highest political truths in history, and that blacks and whites alike were entitled to the rights it spelled out.

Although Lincoln was determined to oppose the spread of slavery, he admitted that he didn't know what to do about those states where slavery was already established, where it was protected by a complex web of state and national laws. "I have no prejudice against the Southern people," he said. "They are just what we would be in their situation. If slavery did not now exist amongst them, they would not introduce it. If it did now exist amongst us, we should not instantly give it up. . . . I surely will not blame them for not doing what I should not know how to do myself. If all earthly power were given me, I should not know what to do, as to the existing institution."

By 1856, open warfare had broken out in Kansas. Antislavery Northerners and proslavery Southerners had both recruited settlers to move into the territory. "Bleeding Kansas" became a battleground of rigged elections, burnings, lynchings, and assassinations as the rival forces fought for control of the territory.

Violence reached even to the floor of Congress. After delivering an impassioned anti-Southern speech on "The Crime Against Kansas," Senator Charles Sumner of Massachusetts was beaten with a cane and almost killed by Congressman Preston Brooks of South Carolina.

Then the U.S. Supreme Court handed down a decision that shocked antislavery forces everywhere. In 1857, the court ruled in the *Dred Scott* case that Congress had no power to prohibit slavery in any of the nation's territories, because that would violate property rights guaranteed by the Constitution. Scott was a slave who sued for his freedom on grounds that his master had twice taken him onto free soil in the North. The court declared that as a black man, Scott was not and never had been a citizen. He was not entitled to the rights spelled out by the Declaration of Independence. Slaves were private property, the court said, and Congress could not pass laws depriving white citizens of "the right of property in a slave."

The *Dred Scott* decision was a stunning setback for the opponents of slavery. But it also helped mobilize antislavery opinion. Lincoln spent two weeks studying the decision so he could prepare an

Right: Charles Sumner, the ardent antislavery senator from Massachusetts.

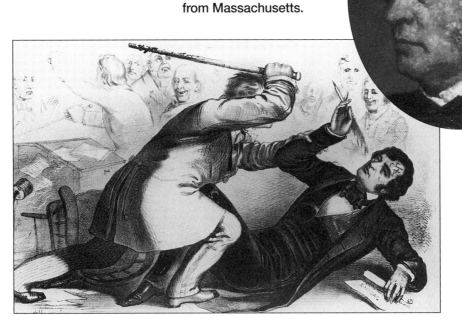

A newspaper drawing shows Representative Preston Brooks attacking Senator Charles Sumner on the Senate floor.

Purchased for fifteen hundred dollars, this house at Eighth and Jackson streets in Springfield was the only home that Lincoln ever owned. In this 1860 photograph, Lincoln and his son Willie are standing on the terrace, just inside the picket fence.

argument against it. Speaking in Springfield, he pointed to the "plain unmistakable language" of the Declaration of Independence. When its authors declared that all men have equal rights, "This they said, and this they meant," Lincoln argued. He urged respect for the courts, but he added: "We think the *Dred Scott* decision is erroneous. We know the court that made it has often overruled its own decisions, and we shall do what we can to have it overrule this."

By now, Lincoln had become a leading antislavery spokesman in Illinois. And he had switched his political allegiance. Since entering politics he had been a Whig, but the Whigs had not been able to unite in opposition to slavery, and now the party was splintered and dying. Thousands of Whigs had gone over to the Republicans, a new party founded in 1854 to oppose the spread of slavery. Lincoln remained loyal to the Whigs until 1856, when he made up his mind to leave his "mummy of a party" and join the Republicans himself.

He wanted to be in office again so he could influence public policy, and this time he was after Stephen Douglas's Senate seat. The two men had been rivals for twenty years now. Douglas had risen to national prominence. He had been a judge of the Illinois Supreme Court, a congressman and a senator, an outstanding leader of the Democratic party. Lincoln's political career had floundered after his solitary term in Congress. "With *me*, the race of ambition has been a failure——a flat failure," he remarked. "With *him* [Douglas] it has been one of splendid success. His name fills the nation and is not unknown, even, in foreign lands."

Lincoln had made an unsuccessful bid for the Senate as a Whig, in 1855. As a Republican he tried again, and in 1858 he won his new party's nomination. He launched his campaign on a sweltering June evening with a rousing speech before twelve hundred shirt-sleeved delegates at the state Republican Convention in Springfield.

Where was the nation headed? Lincoln asked them. More than four years had passed since the passage of the Kansas-Nebraska Act, yet agitation over slavery had not ceased. "In my opinion," he sang out, "it *will* not cease, until a *crisis* shall have been reached, and passed.

"A house divided against itself cannot stand.

"I believe this government cannot endure, permanently half *slave* and half *free*.

"I do not expect the Union to be *dissolved*——I do not expect the house to *fall*, but I *do* expect it will cease to be divided.

"It will become *all* one thing, or *all* the other."

Lincoln warned that the opponents of slavery must stop its westward expansion. They must put slavery back on the "course of ultimate extinction." Otherwise slavery would spread its grip across the entire nation, "till it shall become lawful in *all* the States, *old* as well as *new*——*North* as well as *South*."

There could be no fair fight between slavery and freedom, because one was morally wrong and the other morally right. Senator Douglas and the Democrats did not care about the advance of slavery, said Lincoln. The Republicans did care. The issue facing the country was the spread of slavery across the nation and into the future.

Some Republicans felt that the speech was too extreme, too much "ahead of its time." But most of the delegates in Lincoln's audience cheered him on. It was the strongest statement he had ever made about slavery. And it set the stage for his dramatic confrontation with Stephen Douglas.

The campaign between them during the summer of 1858 was to capture the attention of the entire nation. In July, Lincoln challenged Douglas to a series of public debates. Douglas accepted the challenge, agreeing to seven three-hour debates in small Illinois towns.

At least twelve thousand people were on hand for the first debate at Ottawa on August 21. More than fifteen thousand showed up at Freeport a week later, even though it rained. At every stop, people came from miles around in wagons and buggies, on horseback and on foot, to see and hear the candidates and decide who was the better man. Town squares were festooned with banners and flags. Peddlers hawked Lincoln and Douglas badges, bands played, cannons roared, and marshals on horseback tried to maintain order among huge crowds as the candidates arrived in town.

With his opponent, Douglas, seated to his right, Lincoln addresses the crowd at Charleston, Illinois, on September 18, 1858. Lincoln and Douglas held seven debates, each lasting three hours.

Douglas traveled in high style, riding from town to town in a private railroad car, sipping brandy and smoking cigars, surrounded by friends and advisors and accompanied by his beautiful wife. Lincoln traveled more modestly, as an ordinary passenger on the regular trains. His wife Mary stayed home with their sons Willie and Tad. She heard her husband speak only once, at the final debate in Alton.

Newspaper reporters trailed the candidates, taking down their speeches in shorthand and telegraphing stories to their newspapers back east. What the debaters said in remote Illinois towns could be read the next day in Boston or Atlanta.

The striking contrast between Douglas and Lincoln——The Little Giant and Long Abe, as reporters called them——added color and excitement to the contests. Douglas was Lincoln's opposite in every way. Barely five feet four inches tall, he had a huge round head planted on massive shoulders, a booming voice, and an aggressive,

self-confident manner. He appeared on the speakers' platform dressed "plantation style"——a navy coat and light trousers, a ruffled shirt, a wide-brimmed felt hat. Lincoln, tall and gangly, seemed plain in his rumpled suit, carrying his notes and speeches in an old carpetbag, sitting on the platform with his bony knees jutting into the air.

Left: Six feet four— A. Lincoln, also known as Long Abe or The Tall Sucker. His eventual victory over Douglas earned him another nickname—The Giant Killer.

Right: Five feet four— Senator Stephen A. Douglas, nicknamed The Little Giant. His booming voice and confident manner made up for his small stature.

The give and take between them held audiences spellbound. Douglas defended his doctrine of popular sovereignty. The nation could endure half slave and half free, he argued. Each state had the right to decide for itself the question of slavery.

Lincoln replied that popular sovereignty was just a smoke screen to allow the spread of slavery. The country had endured for decades half slave and half free only because most people believed that slavery would die out. Besides, slavery wasn't just a matter of states' rights. It was a moral issue that affected the whole country. "This government was instituted to secure the blessings of freedom," said Lincoln. "Slavery is an unqualified evil to the Negro, to the white man, to the soil, and to the State."

Douglas argued that the constitutional guarantee of equality applied only to white citizens, not to blacks. The Supreme Court had ruled that blacks weren't citizens at all. "I am opposed to Negro equality," said Douglas. "I believe this government was made by the white man for the white man to be administered by the white man."

Douglas pressed the issue of white supremacy. Was Lincoln in favor of Negro equality? Did he advocate a mixing of the races? In Illinois, where many voters opposed equal rights for blacks, these were touchy questions. Across the state, Douglas kept race-baiting Lincoln, warning white crowds that he was a "Black Republican" who wanted to liberate the slaves so they could stampede into Illinois to work, vote, and marry with white people.

Lincoln complained bitterly that Douglas was twisting and distorting the issue through a "fantastic arrangement of words, by which a man can prove a horse chestnut to be a chestnut horse." The issue was not the social or political equality of the races, he protested defensively. He had never advocated that Negroes should be voters or office holders, or that they should marry whites. The real issue was whether slavery would spread and become permanent in America, or whether it would be confined to the South and allowed to die out gradually.

Lincoln appealed to the voters to "discard all this quibbling about this man and the other man——this race and that race and the other race as being inferior." And he added: "There is no reason in the world why the Negro is not entitled to all the natural rights enumerated in the Declaration of Independence, the right to life, liberty, and the pursuit of happiness. I hold that he is as much entitled to these as the white man."

At the time, senators were elected by state legislatures, not by popular vote. When the returns came in, the Republicans had not won enough seats in the legislature to send Lincoln to the Senate. Douglas was reelected by a narrow margin. "The fight must go on," Lincoln told a friend. "The cause of civil liberty must not be surrendered at the end of one or even one hundred defeats." Even so, the defeat hurt. "I feel like the boy who stumped his toe," he said. "I am too big to cry and too badly hurt to laugh."

Lincoln lost the election, but the debates had catapulted him to national prominence. He continued to speak out on the issues in Illinois and throughout the North, and by 1860, he was being mentioned as a possible candidate for president. At first he doubted that he could win. "I must, in all candor, say I do not think myself fit for the presidency," he told an Illinois newspaper editor. But powerful Republican leaders felt that Lincoln had a good chance to carry the party banner to victory. As they began to work for his nomination, he did not interfere. "The taste *is* in my mouth a little," he admitted.

When Illinois Republicans held their state convention on May 9, 1860, Lincoln was chosen unanimously as their favorite-son candidate. The cheering delegates lifted his long frame overhead and passed him hand-by-hand down to the speaker's platform.

A week later, the national convention of the Republican party met in Chicago. Several prominent Republicans were competing for the presidency, and Lincoln was not the first choice of many delegates. But he was acceptable to all

Mary Lincoln with her sons
Willie (left) and Tad (right) in 1860.

factions of the party, and after some backstage maneuvering, he was nominated on the third ballot. He had spent the day quietly down in Springfield, waiting for news from the convention, and passing the time playing handball.

Meanwhile, the Democratic party had split in two. Northern Democrats meeting in Baltimore nominated Stephen Douglas for president. Southern Democrats, unwilling to accept any Northerner, held their own convention in Richmond, Virginia, and nominated John C. Breckinridge of Kentucky. Another group, the Constitutional Union party, also entered the contest with John Bell of Tennessee as their candidate.

It wasn't customary in those days for a presidential candidate to campaign on his own behalf. Lincoln didn't even leave Springfield until after Election Day. But his supporters carried on a spirited campaign, playing up Lincoln's humble background. At Republican rallies and parades all over the North, he was hailed as Honest Abe, the homespun rail-splitter from Illinois, a man of the people who was born in a log cabin and was headed for the White House.

Shortly before the election, Lincoln received a letter from Grace Bedell, an eleven-year-old girl in Westfield, New York, suggesting that he grow a beard. " . . . you would look a great deal better for your face is so thin," she wrote. "All the ladies like whiskers and they would tease their husbands to vote for you." As he waited for the nation to vote, Lincoln took her advice.

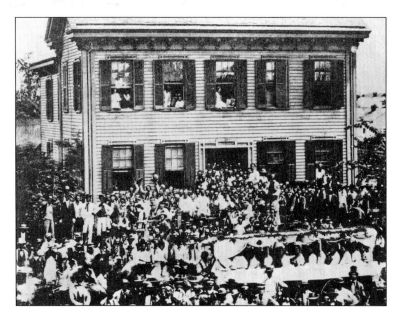

A crowd of well-wishers gathers in front of Lincoln's home at a campaign rally in 1860. Lincoln is standing to the right of the doorway in a white summer suit.

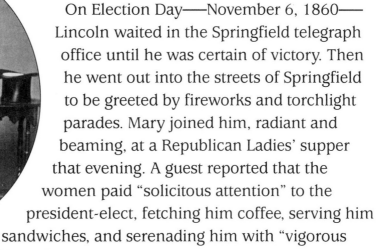

The new president.

On Election Day——November 6, 1860——Lincoln waited in the Springfield telegraph office until he was certain of victory. Then he went out into the streets of Springfield to be greeted by fireworks and torchlight parades. Mary joined him, radiant and beaming, at a Republican Ladies' supper that evening. A guest reported that the women paid "solicitous attention" to the president-elect, fetching him coffee, serving him sandwiches, and serenading him with "vigorous Republican choruses."

Lincoln received 1,866,000 votes and carried every Northern state. Douglas had 1,377,000 votes, and Breckinridge, the candidate of the Southern Democrats, 850,000 votes. The North had swept Lincoln into office. In the South, his name hadn't even appeared on the ballot.

Douglas had warned that a Republican victory would bring on "a war of sections, a war of the North against the South, of the free states against the slave states——a war of extermination." Southern leaders were saying that they would never accept this "Black Republican" as president. They were already threatening to withdraw from the Union and form an independent slave nation. An Atlanta newspaper declared: "Let the consequences be what they may . . . the South will never submit to such humiliation and degradation as the inauguration of Abraham Lincoln."

In December——three months before Lincoln took his oath of office——South Carolina led the way. The state announced that it had seceded from the Union. It was now a sovereign nation, dedicated to the preservation of slavery.

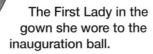

The First Lady in the gown she wore to the inauguration ball.

Half Slave and Half Free

Meet the Author

Russell Freedman grew up in San Francisco. His parents were good friends with several authors. Many of the authors came over to discuss the news of the day with the Freedmans. The ideas that were discussed by these authors in his home helped Russell learn to develop his own thoughts. It was a skill he would use well as an author. The idea for his first book was taken from an article in *The New York Times*. It was about teenagers who had already done amazing things in their lives. He called it *Teenagers Who Made History*.

Theme Connections

Think About It

With a small group of classmates, consider how the United States would be different if Abraham Lincoln had not been president. Discuss the following questions.

- Why was the Declaration of Independence especially meaningful to Abraham Lincoln?
- What did you learn about Lincoln's personal thoughts from his role in politics leading up to the Civil War?

Check the Concept/Question Board to see if there are any questions there that you can answer now. If the selection or your discussions about the selection have raised any new questions about the Civil War, put the questions on the Concept/Question Board.

Record Ideas

Why is Abraham Lincoln still celebrated as one of the United States' greatest presidents? Record your notes and ideas in your Writing Journal.

Research Ideas

- Find out more about Abraham Lincoln's ideals and how he was personally affected by the war.
- Explore the many reasons why the South wanted to withdraw from the Union.

Battle Hymn of the Republic

by Julia Ward Howe

illustrated by Steve Haskamp

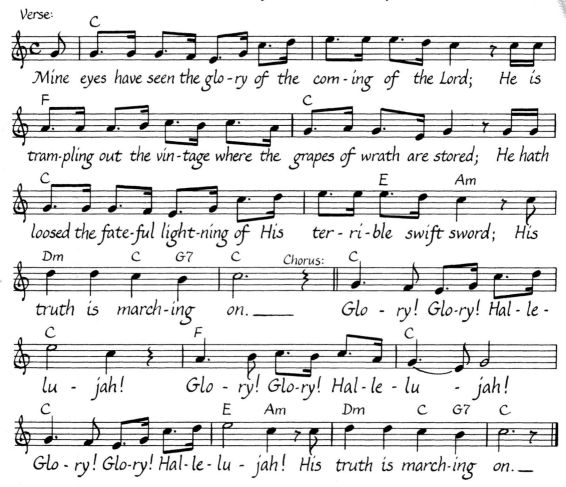

Verse:

Mine eyes have seen the glo-ry of the com-ing of the Lord; He is
tram-pling out the vin-tage where the grapes of wrath are stored; He hath
loosed the fate-ful light-ning of His ter-ri-ble swift sword; His
truth is march-ing on.___ Glo-ry! Glo-ry! Hal-le-
lu-jah! Glo-ry! Glo-ry! Hal-le-lu-jah!
Glo-ry! Glo-ry! Hal-le-lu-jah! His truth is march-ing on.___

by Daniel Decatur Emmett
illustrated by Steve Haskamp

Verse:
I __ wish I was in the land of cot-ton, Old times there are
not for-got-ten, Look a-way, Look a-way! Look a-way! Dix-ie
Land. In __ Dix-ie Land __ where __ I was born in, Ear-ly on one
frost-y morn-in, Look a-way! Look a-way! Look a-way! Dix-ie
Land. **Chorus:** Then I wish I was in Dix-ie, Hoo-ray! Hoo-ray! In
Dix-ie Land I'll take my stand, To live and die in Dix-ie, A-
way, __ A-way, __ A-way down south in Dix-ie, __ A-
way, __ A-way, __ A-way down south in Dix-ie. __

Carrying the Running-Aways

from *The People Could Fly*
by Virginia Hamilton
illustrated by Leo and Diane Dillon

Never had any idea of carryin the runnin-away slaves over the river. Even though I was right there on the plantation, right by that big river, it never got in my mind to do somethin like that. But one night the woman whose house I had gone courtin to said she knew a pretty girl wanted to cross the river and would I take her. Well, I met the girl and she was awful pretty. And soon the woman was tellin me how to get across, how to go, and when to leave.

Well, I had to think about it. But each day, that girl or the woman would come around, ask me would I row the girl across the river to a place called Ripley. Well, I finally said I would. And one night I went over to the woman's house. My owner trusted me and let me come and go as I pleased, long as I didn't try to read or write anythin. For writin and readin was forbidden to slaves.

Now, I had heard about the other side of the river from the other slaves. But I thought it was just like the side where we lived on the plantation. I thought there were slaves and masters over there, too, and overseers and rawhide whips they used on us. That's why I was so scared. I thought I'd land the girl over there and some overseer didn't know us would beat us for bein out at night. They could do that, you know.

Well, I did it. Oh, it was a long rowin time in the cold, with me worryin. But pretty soon I see a light way up high. Then I remembered the woman told me to watch for a light. Told me to row to the light, which is what I did. And when I got to it, there were two men. They reached down and grabbed the girl. Then one of the men took me by the arm. Said, "You about hungry?" And if he hadn't been holdin me, I would of fell out of that rowboat.

Well, that was my first trip. I was scared for a long time after that. But pretty soon I got over it, as other folks asked me to take them across the river. Two and three at a time, I'd take them. I got used to makin three or four trips every month.

Now it was funny. I never saw my passengers after that first girl. Because I took them on the nights when the moon was not showin, was cloudy. And I always met them in the open or in a house with no light. So I never saw them, couldn't recognize them, and couldn't describe them. But I would say to them, "What you say?" And they would say the password. Sounded like "Menare." Seemed the word came from the Bible somewhere, but I don't know. And they would have to say that word before I took them across.

Well, there in Ripley was a man named Mr. Rankins, the rest was John, I think. He had a "station" there for escaping slaves. Ohio was a free state, I found out, so once they got across, Mr. Rankins would see to them. We went at night so we could continue back for more and to be sure no slave catchers would follow us there.

Mr. Rankins had a big light about thirty feet high up and it burned all night. It meant freedom for slaves if they could get to that bright flame.

I worked hard and almost got caught. I'd been rowin fugitives for almost four years. It was in 1863 and it was a night I carried twelve runnin-aways across the river to Mr. Rankins'. I stepped out of the boat back in Kentucky and they were after me. Don't know how they found out. But the slave catchers, didn't know them, were on my trail. I ran away from the plantation and all who I knew there. I lived in the fields and in the woods. Even in caves. Sometimes I slept up in the tree branches. Or in a hay pile. I couldn't get across the river now, it was watched so closely.

Finally, I did get across. Late one night me and my wife went. I had gone back to the plantation to get her. Mr. Rankins had him a bell by this time, along with the light. We were rowin and rowin. We could see the light and hear that bell, but it seemed we weren't gettin any closer. It took forever, it seemed. That was because we were so scared and it was so dark and we knew we could get caught and never get gone.

Well, we did get there. We pulled up there and went on to freedom. It was only a few months before all the slaves was freed.

We didn't stay on at Ripley. We went on to Detroit because I wasn't takin any chances. I have children and grandchildren now. Well, you know, the bigger ones don't care so much to hear about those times. But the little ones, well, they never get tired of hearin how their grandpa brought emancipation to loads of slaves he could touch and feel in the dark but never ever see.

Carrying the Running-Aways

Meet the Author

Virginia Hamilton was deeply influenced by her family and its history. Her mother's family descended from a fugitive slave, Levi Perry. Her father played the mandolin and was an outlander from the west. From her relatives she learned to use storytelling as a way of thinking and dealing with problems. Today, family is the most prominent theme in her own writing.

Meet the Illustrators

Leo and Diane Dillon met in a New York art school. At first their artwork was a source of competition between them. Today they work together and refer to themselves as "the artist, Leo and Diane Dillon."

The Dillons always pass their work back and forth several times. In the final piece it is impossible to know how the work was divided. Over the years they have created art for children's books, advertisements, posters, album covers, magazines, soap packaging, and fine paintings.

Theme Connections

Think About It

With a small group of classmates, consider what life must have been like for slaves who were escaping to the North.

- Why did the narrator return to his owner's plantation time after time instead of escaping with the slaves he rowed across the river?
- Why did the narrator think it was important to tell his children and grandchildren about how he helped slaves escape to freedom?

Check the Concept/Question Board to see if there are any questions there that you can answer now. If the selection or your discussions about the selection have raised any new questions about the Civil War, put the questions on the Concept/Question Board. Maybe the next selection will help answer the questions.

Record Ideas

Why do you think slaves were forbidden to read and write? Use your Writing Journal to record your notes and ideas.

Research Ideas

- Find out more about the routes and conductors of the Underground Railroad.
- Explore the oral storytelling tradition of the African-American culture.

Harriet Tubman Series, #10. c. 1939–40. Jacob Lawrence.

Casein tempera on gessoed hardboard. Hampton University Museum, Hampton, Virginia.

Harriet Tubman

by Eloise Greenfield

Harriet Tubman didn't take no stuff
Wasn't scared of nothing neither
Didn't come in this world to be no slave
And wasn't going to stay one either

"Farewell!" she sang to her friends one night
She was mighty sad to leave 'em
But she ran away that dark hot night
Ran looking for her freedom

She ran to the woods and she ran through the woods
With the slave catchers right behind her
And she kept on going till she got to the North
Where those mean men couldn't find her

Nineteen times she went back South
To get three hundred others
She ran for her freedom nineteen times
To save Black sisters and brothers

Harriet Tubman didn't take no stuff
Wasn't scared of nothing neither
Didn't come in this world to be no slave
And didn't stay one either

And didn't stay one either

The Drinking Gourd

musical notation by Christina T. Davidson
illustrated by Andy Levine

"The Drinking Gourd" sounded like a simple folk song but was really a map to freedom. Hidden in its lyrics were directions along the Underground Railroad. The "drinking gourd" refers to the constellation called the Big Dipper, which points to the North Star. "When the sun comes back and the first quail calls" meant spring, when travel was safest. The "old man" was Peg Leg Joe, who left tracks of "left foot, peg foot," along the riverbank and who carved signs in dead trees. The river that "ends between two hills" was the Tombigbee River, and the "great big river" was the Ohio River, where Peg Leg Joe waited to carry the escaped slaves across to the free states on the other side.

Chorus:
Fol-low ___ the drink-ing gourd! ___ Fol-low ___ the drink-ing gourd. ___ For the old man is a-wait-ing for to car-ry you to free-dom If you fol-low the drink-ing gourd. When the sun comes back, and the first quail calls, ___ Fol-low ___ the

drink-ing gourd. — For the old man is a-wait-ing for to

car-ry you to free-dom If you fol-low the drink-ing gourd.—

Chorus: Follow the drinking gourd! etc.

The riverbank makes a very good road,
The dead trees will show you the way.
Left foot, peg foot, traveling on,
  Follow the drinking gourd.

Chorus: Follow the drinking gourd! etc.

The river ends between two hills,
Follow the drinking gourd.
There's another river on the other side,
  Follow the drinking gourd.

Chorus: Follow the drinking gourd! etc.

When the great big river meets the little river
Follow the drinking gourd.
For the old man is a-waiting for to carry you to freedom,
  If you follow the drinking gourd.

So I Became a Soldier

from *The Boys' War* by Jim Murphy

On April 12, 1861, thousands of Confederate troops were assembled in the still darkness of early morning, looking out toward the mouth of Charleston Harbor. The object of their attention was a squat brick structure sitting on an island one mile away: Fort Sumter. Inside, Robert Anderson, a major in the Union army, along with sixty-eight soldiers, braced for the attack.

"Then the batteries opened on all sides [of Sumter] as if an army of devils were swooping around it."

Slowly, darkness lifted and Sumter's shape became more and more distinct. Confederate gunners adjusted the firing angle of their weapons, torches poised near the fuses. At exactly 4:30 A.M., General P. G. T. Beauregard gave the command, and the bombardment——and with it the Civil War——began.

An officer inside Fort Sumter described the war's opening shot:

"The eyes of the watchers easily detected and followed the shell as it mounted among the stars, and then descended with ever-increasing velocity, until it landed inside the fort and burst. It was a capital shot. Then the batteries opened on all sides [of Sumter] as if an army of devils were swooping around it."

Thirty-four hours and over four thousand shot and shells later, Sumter's forty-foot-high walls were battered and crumbling. Fires consumed portions of the interior and were moving closer to the powder magazine. No one inside the fort had been seriously injured in the bombardment, but the outcome of the fight was inevitable. The battle for Fort Sumter ended with the surrender of Union forces on April 14.

Before leaving the fort, Union troops were allowed a brief flag-lowering ceremony accompanied by a cannon salute of fifty guns. (Oddly enough, a freak accident during this ceremony caused an explosion that killed two men——the first victims of the Civil War.) Then, with banners flying and the drums beating the rhythm to "Yankee Doodle," Anderson's small force marched aboard the steamship *Baltic* and headed for New York. Beauregard's soldiers entered the burning fort triumphantly and raised the Confederate Stars and Bars. Even before the smoke had a chance to clear, the nation——including its boys——was ready to go off to war.

When word of Fort Sumter's fall reached him in Washington, President Abraham Lincoln acted quickly, issuing a call for seventy-five thousand volunteers to put down the insurrection. News of the president's call to arms spread with surprising speed——by telegraph, newspaper headlines, and word of mouth. Thomas Galway was fifteen years old and living in Cleveland, Ohio, when he heard.

"As I was coming from Mass this morning," Galway wrote in his journal, "I saw bulletins posted everywhere announcing the bombardment of Fort Sumter. Large crowds were gathered in front of each bulletin board, people peering over one another's heads to catch a bit of the news. All seemed of one mind. Everyone talked of war."

Over in Indiana, fourteen-year-old Theodore Upson was working in the cornfield with his father when a neighbor came by. "William Cory came across the field (he had been to town after the Mail). He was excited and said, 'the Rebs have fired upon and taken Fort Sumpter.' Father got white and couldn't say a word.

"William said, 'The President will soon fix them. He has called for 75,000 men and is going to blocade their ports, and just as soon as those fellows find out that the North means business they will get down off their high horse.' "

Much the same was happening in the South. Newspapers hailed the victory at Sumter and predicted that the North would not risk any sort of military action. Public meetings were held to whip up support for the Confederate government.

T. G. Barker, then just thirteen, was attending a small private school in South Carolina. "We were in class," Barker remembered, "all bent over our books, when Headmaster

A regiment of young Confederate soldiers drills under the walls of Castle Pinkney, South Carolina, 1861.

Hammond entered. He did not knock to announce himself, which was unusual, and he did not speak to our teacher either. This was also unusual. He went instead to the middle of the room and said in a serious voice: 'We have had word this morning. Fort Sumter has surrendered and is now a part of the Confederate States of America.' Then he smiled. A second passed and not a sound. Then, as if shot from a cannon, the class stood as one and cheered Hooray! Hooray!"

The political and social causes of the war were numerous and complex, and still produce arguments among historians. Certainly, the profound cultural differences between the North and South were a factor, as were their opposing views on the issue of states' rights. And there is little doubt that an important element of the split was the institution of slavery. Many in the North saw slavery as evil and wanted it abolished completely. Others would accept slavery if it could be confined to the South or if the South agreed to phase it out over a number of years.

For its part, the South viewed slavery as vital to its economic survival. Agriculture, especially the growing of cotton, was its most important business. Slavery provided the cheap labor needed to bring in crops at a profit. Without slavery, Southerners argued, their entire way of life would crumble and be destroyed.

Intensifying matters was the fact that Southern interests were trying to introduce slavery in the newly settled western regions. Many in the North felt that slavery had to be stopped before it had a chance to spread and take hold in the West. As far as Southerners were concerned, the federal government was nothing more than an interfering bully trying to force its views on them.

The slavery question was not a new one at all. It had been discussed and debated, argued and fumed over for nearly fifty years. Tempers were frayed to the point of exploding, and fights had even taken place on the floor of the Senate. When war actually broke out, it was like a pressure-release valve. At last, the country seemed to sigh with relief, something concrete was finally going to settle the dispute.

The result on both sides was an enthusiastic rush to enlist. Men crowded the recruitment centers in the nearest cities or signed on with locally organized units. Emotions ran so high that everywhere enlistment quotas were being met and surpassed easily. Caught up in all of this were boys.

Generally, boys from the North did not join the army because they felt a burning desire to stamp out slavery. One boy's comment about slavery is fairly typical: "I do not know anything about it, whether it is a good thing or a bad thing," he wrote in a letter, "and when talk gets around to it I say very little." Many joined because they wanted to take the defiant South and "set them straight." But most signed up for a simpler reason——to escape the boring routine of farm life and take part in an exciting adventure.

The same spirit of adventure and glory motivated Southern boys as well. A Mississippi recruit said he had joined "to fight the Yankies——all fun and frolic." But underneath the festive attitude was another, deeply felt reason for serving——to defend their homes from a large invading army. One Southern boy made his feelings clear, "I reather die then be com a Slave to the North."

Each side had recruitment rules that expressly banned boys from joining and fighting. At the start of the war, for instance, the Union held that a recruit had to be at least eighteen years old. In spite of this, a tall fourteen- or fifteen-year-old could easily blend into a crowd of men and slip through in the hurry to form a unit. Those questioned about their

A Union drummer boy in full uniform.

age might be able to bluff their way past a wary recruiting sergeant. Anyway, how would a recruiter check on an applicant's facts? The standard forms of identification we have today, such as driver's license, social security number, and credit cards, did not exist back then. There were no computers or telephones either, so verifying someone's birthday was nearly impossible.

By far the easiest way for a boy to slip into the army was as a musician, especially as a drummer or bugler. These were considered nonfighting positions, so recruiters often allowed a boy to sign on without worrying about his age. The Union army alone had need of over forty thousand musicians, while an estimated twenty thousand served for the South.

Many boys found it surprisingly simple to enlist for duty that would take them into the thick of the fighting. Thomas Galway did. The day after the surrender of Fort Sumter, Galway visited a nearby armory run by a group called the Cleveland Grays. "But they did not seem to me to be the sort of stuff that soldiers are made of, so I went away." That evening, "I went to the armory of the Hibernian Guards.

Sixteen-year-old Edwin Francis Jennison was killed at Malvern Hill, Virginia, in July 1862.

They seemed to like me, and I liked them. So together with Jim Butler and Jim O'Reilly, I enlisted with them. My name was the first on the company's roll to enlist. I didn't tell them that I was only fifteen. So I became a soldier."

On occasion, a boy would enter with the blessings of one or both parents. Ned Hutter went to join the Confederate army near his hometown in Mississippi. When the recruitment officer asked his age, Ned told him the truth: " 'I am sixteen next June,' I said. . . . The officer ordered me out of line and my father, who was behind me, stepped to the table. 'He can work as steady as any man,' my father explained. 'And he can shoot as straight as any who has been signed today. I am the boy's father.' It must have been the way he said the words . . . [because] the officer handed me the pen and ordered, 'sign here.' "

Telegraph operators for the Union army relax during the siege of Petersburg, Virginia

Such support was rare, however, and most boys had to get in by less honest means. A fifteen-year-old Wisconsin boy, Elisha Stockwell, Jr., was one of them. "We heard there was going to be a war meeting at our little log school house," Stockwell recalled. "I went to the meeting and when they called for volunteers, Harrison Maxon (21), Edgar Houghton (16), and myself, put our names down. . . . My father was there and objected to my going, so they scratched my name out, which humiliated me somewhat. My sister gave me a severe calling down . . . for exposing my ignorance before the public, and called me a little snotty boy, which raised my anger. I told her, 'Never mind, I'll go and show you that I am not the little boy you think I am.' "

Elisha's hurt and anger calmed after his sister and mother apologized for what had been said. He even promised not to enlist again if he could attend school that winter. They agreed, and Elisha put aside his zeal to fight the Confederacy.

Unfortunately, Elisha's father had other plans for Elisha's winter. He'd signed up himself and his son to burn charcoal, a tedious, dirty, and backbreaking job. When Elisha learned this, he devised a new plan to enlist. First he told his parents he was going to a dance in town. Then he persuaded a friend's father, a captain in the Union army, to accompany him to a nearby recruitment center.

"The Captain got me in by my lying a little, as I told the recruiting officer I didn't know just how old I was but thought I was eighteen. He didn't measure my height, but called me five feet, five inches high. I wasn't that tall two years later when I re-enlisted, but they let it go, so the records show that as my height."

Elisha went home to gather up some clothes and found his sister in the kitchen preparing dinner. He did not mention anything about fighting for the Union, and after a brief conversation, "I told her I had to go down town. She said, 'Hurry back, for dinner will soon be ready.' But I didn't get back [home] for two years."

So I Became a Soldier

Meet the Author

Jim Murphy, who grew up in Kearny, New Jersey, spent most of his time playing sports. He played football and baseball. He ran track on a national championship team. In high school he was the prep school state champion in the 60-, 100-, and 220-yard dashes and placed in the top ten of high school sprinters.

He wasn't much of a reader until a teacher told him he was not allowed to read Ernest Hemingway's *A Farewell to Arms*. He read it immediately. From then on, he began reading anything that might shock his teacher and discovered he really enjoyed reading. He also began writing his own poetry, stories, and plays. His first book was *Weird and Wacky Inventions*.

Since then, he has written both fiction and nonfiction. He especially enjoys writing nonfiction history based on first-hand accounts. "So I Became A Soldier" was taken from his book *The Boys' War*. Some of his other award-winning titles include *The Long Road to Gettysburg*, *Across America on an Emigrant Train*, *The Call of the Wolves*, and *The Last Dinosaur*.

Theme Connections

Think About It

With a small group of classmates, consider why boys were eager to fight in the Civil War.

- How did the cultural differences between the North and the South affect people's attitudes toward a civil war?
- What were some reasons that many boys thought the Civil War should be fought?

Check the Concept/Question Board to see if there are any questions there that you can answer now. If the selection or your discussions about the selection have raised any new questions about the Civil War, put the questions on the Concept/Question Board. Maybe the next selection will help answer the questions.

Record Ideas

How was life different for boys who lived at the time of the Civil War than it is for boys today? Record your notes and ideas in your Writing Journal.

Research Ideas

- Explore the personal accounts of other soldiers who fought in the Civil War.
- Find out more about the events and consequences of the battle for Fort Sumter.

Charley Skedaddle

from the book by Patricia Beatty
illustrated by Charles Shaw

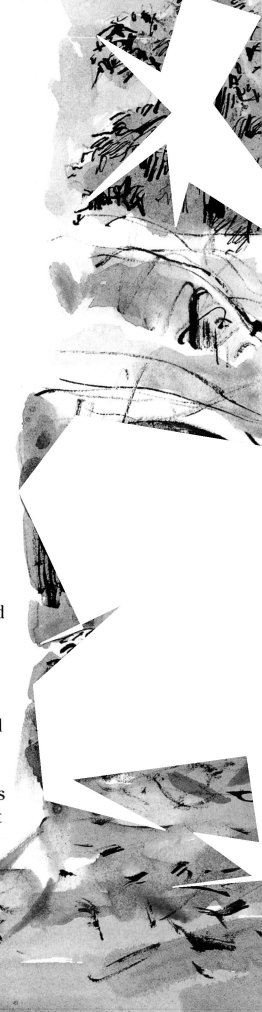

*Twelve-year-old Charley Quinn has run away
from his sister in New York City, lied about his age,
and joined the 140th New York Volunteers
as a drummer boy. Charley is proud of his abilities
as a fighter and longs to get even with the
Confederates for the death of his brother Johnny,
who died at Gettysburg while serving in the 140th.
On May 5, 1864, Charley experiences his first battle.*

Charley awoke trembling at sunrise to find
a hand on his shoulder, shaking him. Over
the crackle of musket fire in the distance, a
man's voice said into his ear, "Boy, get up and go
to the colonel."

Charley got up, fastened on his drum, and hurried
to where he'd seen his colonel lie down on a blanket
like any other soldier. Something important was
happening, for sure. Fallon was there with his bugle
when he arrived.

Colonel Ayres, a medium-sized, handsome, bearded
man, turned from his officers to the two boys. "The
Confederates know we're here. That's skirmish fire
you're hearing. They must have been just a few miles
from us during the night. We're waiting to hear what
orders General Griffin will give us."

Charley dared ask, "Will we be fighting here in the Wilderness, sir?"

"It appears so. Go out with your instruments and get the men up and ready. It doesn't matter how much noise you make now."

"Yes, sir," said Charley softly.

Together he and the bugler left the officers. Fallon blew reveille, and Charley beat out the signal Silas had shown him to assemble the men.

Things happened quickly after that.

A rider came at a gallop down the Orange Turnpike to the 140th and the other units of the 1st Division. Griffin had ordered them to advance at seven-thirty with their entire force—to attack along the road.

By that hour, the whole division, thousands of men, was in full battle array. A moment after Charley heard the buglers of the various units sound the "advance," the 140th and all the others started forward down the turnpike and through the forest lining its sides, as they'd been ordered.

Then came what men feared most about this part of Virginia—getting lost. As soldiers moved forward, picking their way through the forest where twisting vines and thickets tore at their bodies and small trees grew so close to each other that it was impossible to squeeze through, their progress was slowed. Each part of the trackless Wilderness, though not far out of sight of the road, looked like every other part. Grimly, men walked onward, ever alert for the unseen enemy; but as they moved, they did lose sight of one another and their regiments.

Charley Quinn got lost with them, but by shouting and then by drumming his special signal, he finally was able to reassemble his scattered regiment in one spot. Pulling out Johnny's pocket watch, Charley saw that it was now late morning. They'd been lost for hours. He cursed the Wilderness.

When all of the lost regiments of the 1st Division eventually re-formed in the shelter of trees on the north side of the Orange Turnpike, two lines of attack were drawn up there. The 140th New York was on the left of the first long blue line, and behind

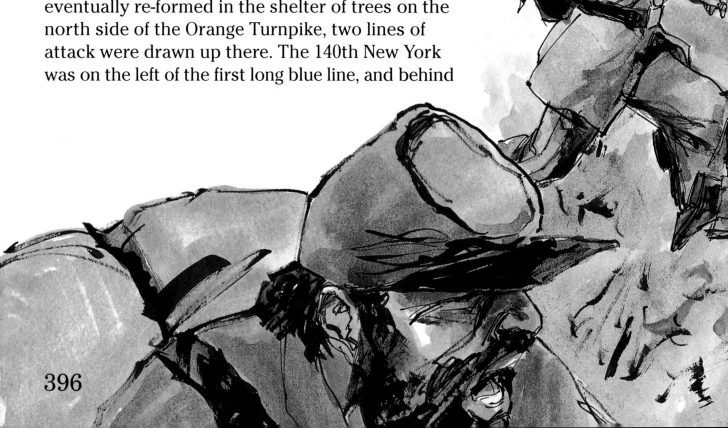

them stood their old Gettysburg comrades, the 146th New York, nicknamed Garrard's Tigers.

At ten minutes to noon, Colonel Ayres gave Fallon and Charley the order to sound and beat the "charge." Charley drummed the long roll, a difficult signal that he had just mastered, and Fallon blew "forward." The hoarse cheer that roared up from the men thrilled Charley to the soles of his shoes. He cheered with them as they ran south out of their forest cover in a line of bright bayonets in the midday sunshine and into the trees across the turnpike. Sprinting beside the color-bearer, his heart beating as fast as his drum, Charley Quinn went forward with his regiment. As he ran and drummed, he whooped like an Indian or yelled "Hi-hee" along with the others around him.

Yankee cannon that had been brought down the Orange Turnpike from Culpeper sent shells screeching over their heads to smash into tree trunks, shattering them and sending limbs crashing down among the running men. Hundreds of sparrows fled shrieking from the mutilated trees. A red doe broke in alarm from her thicket and darted across the march of the 140th into a tall brake in one graceful, bounding motion.

Now unseen Rebel skirmishers, sharpshooters sent out ahead of their regiments, commenced to fire on the advancing bluecoats. The crackle of rifles was suddenly all around Charley as he beat his drum with fingers slick with sweat. He saw men throw up their arms and fall on either side of him as he ran to keep pace with the color-bearer. He stared down at the fallen soldiers in horror, but his drumbeat drove him on as it did the others. Not realizing what he did, he moved along like the others, head downward, leaning forward as against a strong wind.

At Sanders Field, a clearing with a gully in it, the advancing boy caught sight of his first Johnny Rebs, men not in gray as he had expected but in butternut brown. They were running away, looking over their shoulders as they fled down the gully and up over the slope onto the other side. The 140th came after them without a pause. Charley heard Colonel Ayres shouting, "Steady. Steady, men, steady," and Charley came along steadily, his blood drumming in his ears and his thoughts disconnected and fleeting— of his sister Noreen and her sewing machine, of Broadway's traffic which he dodged so nimbly, of the boy from the Dead Rabbit gang he had fought.

The 140th soon learned why the Rebels had given up the fight and fled so easily before them. It had been a trap! Hundreds of Confederates lay at the top of the gully behind felled trees made into breastworks. Down in the gully, Charley Quinn's regiment drew a hideous cross fire from Rebel-filled stands of timber in front of them and to the right.

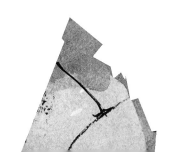

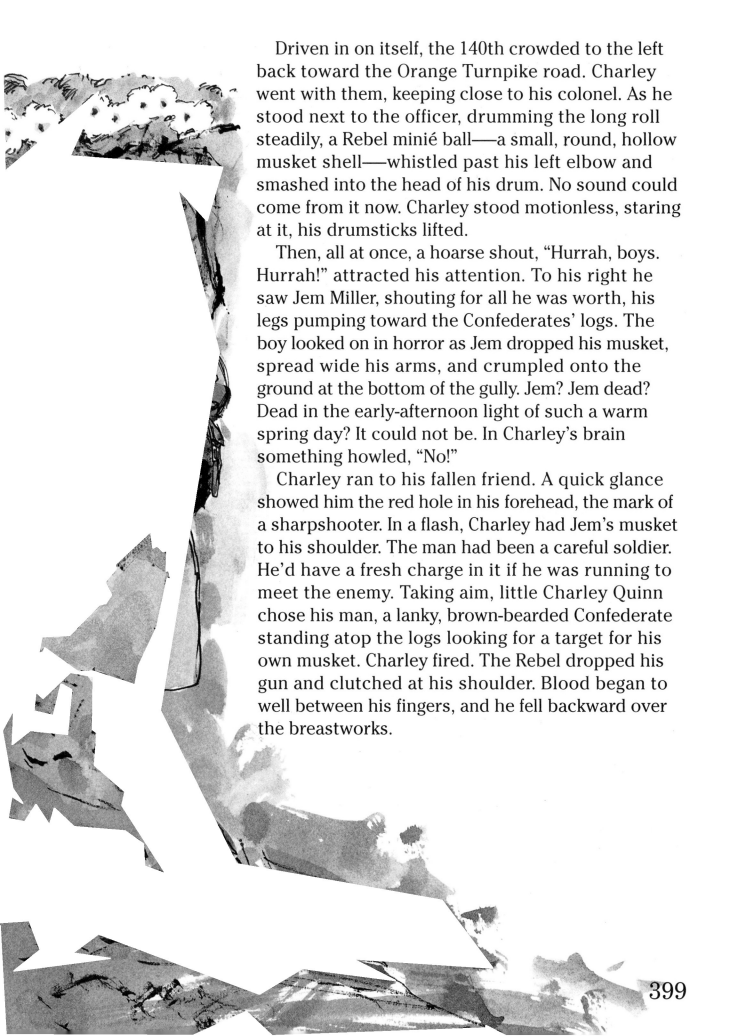

Driven in on itself, the 140th crowded to the left back toward the Orange Turnpike road. Charley went with them, keeping close to his colonel. As he stood next to the officer, drumming the long roll steadily, a Rebel minié ball——a small, round, hollow musket shell——whistled past his left elbow and smashed into the head of his drum. No sound could come from it now. Charley stood motionless, staring at it, his drumsticks lifted.

Then, all at once, a hoarse shout, "Hurrah, boys. Hurrah!" attracted his attention. To his right he saw Jem Miller, shouting for all he was worth, his legs pumping toward the Confederates' logs. The boy looked on in horror as Jem dropped his musket, spread wide his arms, and crumpled onto the ground at the bottom of the gully. Jem? Jem dead? Dead in the early-afternoon light of such a warm spring day? It could not be. In Charley's brain something howled, "No!"

Charley ran to his fallen friend. A quick glance showed him the red hole in his forehead, the mark of a sharpshooter. In a flash, Charley had Jem's musket to his shoulder. The man had been a careful soldier. He'd have a fresh charge in it if he was running to meet the enemy. Taking aim, little Charley Quinn chose his man, a lanky, brown-bearded Confederate standing atop the logs looking for a target for his own musket. Charley fired. The Rebel dropped his gun and clutched at his shoulder. Blood began to well between his fingers, and he fell backward over the breastworks.

Now the truth flooded Charley's consciousness. Gone were thoughts of heroism and revenge. He had shot a man! He was only twelve years old, and he'd shot and killed a human being. What should he do now? He didn't know.

He cried out wordlessly, threw down Jem's musket, and with the useless drum banging at his hip, sprinted for the wooded clearing to the left. Musket balls speeding toward him hummed beelike and tore away fragments of cloth from his sleeve and trousers.

As he ran, he spied Silas Gorman lying sprawled not thirty feet away. He could see him clearly through drifting curls of smoke. Silas had torn away the seams of one leg of his trousers and was staring down at a bloody wound on his shin. He saw Charley and beckoned to him, his mouth open in a call for help that could not be heard over the shouting, screaming, crackling, and booming that filled the gully. Silas wanted him! Silas needed him!

But Charley Quinn did not break his stride to go to his friend. He ran on among the dead and wounded, racing faster, stumbling forward.

Something strange had happened to his vision. Everything he saw was crystal-clear—fluffy white smoke drifting over the clearing from all the firing going on, falling leaves clipped by musket balls, the open red mouths of the yelling, charging men of the 140th—and the startled eyes of Con Sullivan as he saw Charley fleeing.

As the boy ran by him, he heard Con's voice bellowing, "Charley, skedaddle! Go on. Run away. Run, ye coward Bowery bummer!"

An officer picked up Sullivan's cry. "Run, run, ye whelp. Run home to your mama!" he shouted, and lifted his pistol to shoot at Charley but did not pull the trigger.

Running toward the end of the bluecoat troops, Charley spotted Dan Whaley, the Dead Rabbit who had recognized him that first day in Culpeper. He didn't shout at him but watched as Charley streaked past. Other men who knew him as the regimental drummer boy saw and marked him with their eyes. An officer at the rear swatted at him with the flat of his sword to drive him back and missed.

Charley Quinn kept on running to the left even when he'd passed by all of the men of the 140th New York. He ran like a fear-crazed animal up over the rim of the gully until a clump of roots lying in his path brought him down to a crashing halt flat on his face.

There he lay for a little while panting for breath. The sound of firing and yelling behind him came clearly to his ears. He got up, detached the useless drum from its sash, and dropped both it and the sash onto the earth. The drumsticks were behind him where he'd dropped them at the clearing. He lurched over to the little creek coming out of a swamp, the creek he'd passed, drumming proudly, just a few minutes before. He bent down to cup water to soothe his burning face. Then he got up, waded across the water, and followed the swamp quite a distance to a particularly dense thicket of undergrowth.

Crawling inside it, Charley sat, with his head on his drawn-up knees, listening to the battle, trying to pray, sobbing in the shame and misery of his desertion. In his mind, he saw Johnny's and Jem's and Silas's accusing faces. He could hear Con's well-remembered voice taunting him. As the boy sat there, a terrorized rabbit came leaping into the thicket to snuggle wild-eyed up against his arm. Charley looked at its quivering sides and trembling whiskers. The battle had made a runaway, a skedaddler, out of it, too, but it was only a rabbit, not a soldier. A rabbit could be expected to run—but not Charley Quinn. That skedaddler had killed a man and then had turned and run—and everybody knew it.

Deep sobs racked Charley's body. He threw himself full-length onto the earth, pounding it, startling the rabbit that had sought refuge by him, making it pin back its ears and lope away. He'd failed this poor frightened creature, too. Charley sat up again, folded his arms on his knees, and lay his head on the blue cloth he was not fit to wear.

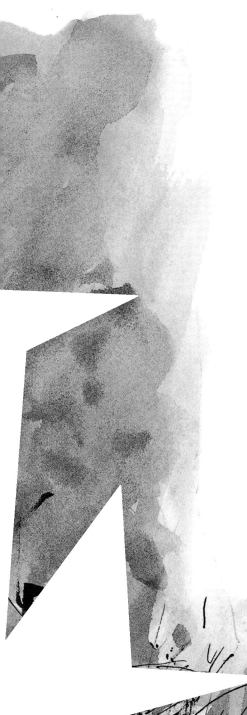

The night was quiet, but not the dawn of the sixth of May. The crackling of musket fire came to Charley's ears on all sides. More fighting. Not knowing what else to do, he stayed where he was until a new fear propelled him into action. Fire! Fires from the sparks of thousands of cannon shells had sprung up among the dry leaves of the Wilderness and roared over acres of timberland. Now the gray smoke billowing from them, mixing with gunpowder fumes, drove Charley Quinn out of his protective thicket.

Coughing, frightened by the smoke, he bent to wet his pocket handkerchief in swamp water and tie it around his nose and mouth. As he stooped at the edge of the stinking dark water, he heard a sharp clicking sound he recognized. The cocking of a pistol. Straightening and whirling around, Charley looked up into the face of a lantern-jawed, sallow, yellow-haired man in a brown-yellow short jacket, blue Union army trousers, and a gray forage cap. A Rebel, for sure! In his hand was a huge, long-barreled cavalry pistol. It was aimed at Charley's head. The boy froze.

First the man shot a wad of tobacco juice at Charley's feet, then he asked softly, "What've we got here? I'd say it was a redhead Yankee boy. Kinda small, ain'tcha? If you were a turtle now, I'd throw you back in the swamp to grow up some. Who'd you be?"

Charley faltered. "I was a drummer boy. My name's Charley." After that he fell silent.

"Charley what?"

"Make it Skedaddle," Charley told him bitterly.

The Confederate laughed. "That's some queer old name you got. Come along with me, boy. My officer'll want to talk to you. Give me your knapsack and jest move out ahead of me."

"Who are you?" Charley asked.

"Who I am don't matter."

Was he a prisoner? Charley sank his teeth into his lower lip to keep from crying. What would happen to him now? What did the Johnny Rebs do with Yankee drummer boy prisoners?

Charley tied the wet cloth over his face and, hands in the air, began to walk ahead of his Rebel captor. It was hard going through the tangle of vines and hickory bushes that tore at his uniform. Twice he fell and was prodded to his feet by the toe of his captor's boot and the words, "Git on up, Yankee boy. I ain't got all day to fetch you back to where we got to go."

Deep among the thickets and trees, Charley could not see fifteen feet ahead of him, but on either side he saw clearly the dead bodies of men dressed in blue and butternut-brown and gray uniforms lying stiff and staring. Sometimes tongues of flame shot up so near that their clothing was singed. The brush

hissed and popped in the heat as bright red sparks flew over their heads. Surely this was like the hell the sisters in school and the priest in church had warned him about.

After much turning and twisting, they arrived at a clearing filled with men dressed in the butternut-brown color of the Confederate Army. A half dozen bluecoat soldiers sat on the ground with their hands folded on top of their heads.

Charley's captor told him, "Git on over there and sit down with them other bluebellies."

The boy did as he was told. Looking from face to face, he was relieved to see no one he knew. He took the handful of skillet-parched corn a Reb gave him and tried to chew it. He couldn't and had to spit it out. Rebel soldiers watching him laughed. One said, "It's what we got to eat. Ain't it good enough for you, Yankee brat?"

A Rebel officer in a very tattered, soiled gray coat came over to the prisoners to warn, "Don't you Union men do any talking to one another. I'll personally shoot the man who does. Someone'll be coming to get you soon."

His words proved true. Very shortly three Confederate soldiers with muskets and shining bayonets came to roust the Yankees up and send them walking ahead of them.

An hour's marching of nearly three miles brought Charley and the others through the Wilderness to a large open space where they once again were told to sit. There was a farmhouse, a barn, and some other outbuildings here, as well as hundreds of shabbily dressed Confederate soldiers. Most were gaunt and grimy. Not a few were shoeless. Some wore gray forage caps; others wore brown slouch hats over a mixture of gray and butternut-brown jackets and coats. Some had on Union-blue trousers stripped from the enemy dead.

White smoke from the muskets firing among the trees mingled with the darker smoke from the Wilderness fires. Coming across the open space in acrid-smelling wreaths, it made men cough and sneeze. Charley put the handkerchief up over his nose and mouth again.

The boy was just settling himself onto the ground when he was forced to leap to his feet to keep from being run over by a host of men racing toward him. Rebels! Rebels retreating as fast as they could.

Then a great animal-like roar rose up from a thousand throats, and Charley saw other tattered Rebels racing forward through the ranks of their retreating comrades. A charge! As they ran, they screeched the famous Rebel yell, *"Ee ee-ee-ee-ee!"*

Behind them came a tall, gray-bearded officer in a gray uniform under a black cloak, riding a dapple-gray horse with a black mane and tail. As the officer reached the charging men, a few of them, hearing the hoofbeats, slackened their speed. At once, a wild shouting rose up from these men: "Go back, General Lee. Go back!"

Lee? Robert E. Lee? Charley Quinn gaped in amazement, as did the other prisoners. Generals were seldom seen anywhere, and certainly not in infantry charges.

Charley watched, fascinated, as a sergeant of the charging Texas Brigade sprang forward to grab hold of the bridle of Lee's horse, stopping the famous Traveller from going into battle with his master.

Now many Texans halted their attack to turn and shout, "We won't go unless you go back!"

A Confederate officer rode up to Lee's side and began to argue with him. When Lee slowly shook his head, the sergeant let go of the rein to release it to his commander-in-chief. An enormous cheer crashed into the smoky air as Robert E. Lee turned his horse around and began to ride toward some horsemen in a knoll to his right.

"Lee! Lee!" echoed soldiers' deep voices. While their comrades cheered, those men of the Texas Brigade who had forced Lee back to safety resumed their charge against the Yankees among the trees.

As for Charley Quinn, he sat down again at a bayonet's prod until a corporal came over, pointed to him, and then jerked him to his feet. Hustled along, he was taken to a tent where a sad-faced, balding Confederate officer sat at a little folding table. It was hot inside, and the front and rear tent flaps were open for ventilation.

Once the corporal had gone, the officer asked, "Who are you, lad?"

"Charley. Charley Skedaddle."

"I know that word. And I doubt that is your real last name."

Charley swallowed and said, "It's Quinn, sir."

"You are not a soldier, are you?"

"No, sir. I never signed any papers to enlist. I was only a drummer."

At this, the officer put down the pen he had in his hand. "A drummer boy. I thought as much. What is your age?"

"Twelve, sir."

"What is your regiment?"

Charley didn't answer. All soldiers had been warned that if they were ever captured, they were to tell only their name and rank. He had done that already, and now he said, "I can't tell you that, sir."

The officer smiled slightly. "Have you ever gone to school?"

"Oh, yes, sir. I can read and write just dandy."

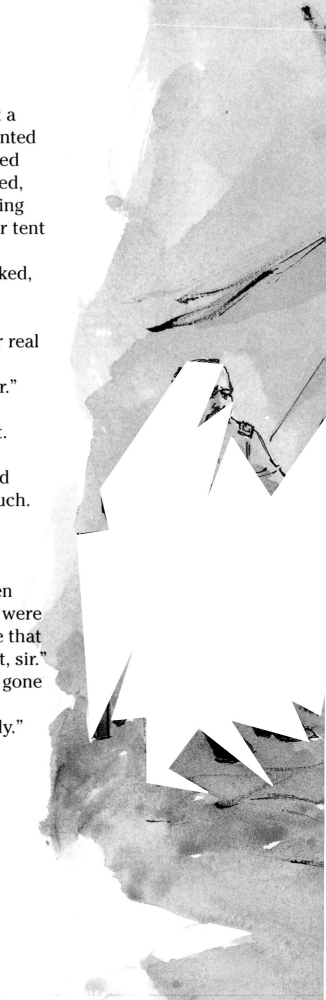

"I'm glad to hear it. I was a schoolmaster at one time." He sighed. "How did you get separated from your regiment? I think you can tell me *that,* you know."

Blushing, Charley lowered his gaze. He stuttered, "I—I got scared when I saw my drum hit by a minié ball and saw my friend Jem get killed, so I ran away." No, he wouldn't dare say he'd picked up a musket and killed a Reb. That'd bring him more trouble, for sure.

"So you ran away? I thought you had. Well, you are only a child, after all. Have you ever heard of Andersonville Prison?"

"No, sir, I haven't."

The Confederate officer sighed again. "It's a prison camp for Yankee soldiers down in Georgia. It would be a very bad place to send a boy your age. You should be in a classroom. If any of the men from your regiment in Andersonville found out you were a deserter, it would be even worse for you. Well, then, I think I shall have to do something else with you. You will note that I have not written down one word about you. I'll have no record of you."

"What will you do with me, sir?"

"Have you any money with you?"

"A little bit."

"Good. Yankee money is worth quite a bit more here than our money. Do you see the open tent flap behind me?"

"Yes, sir, I do."

"Then be so good, Charley Skedaddle, as to skedaddle through it right now. As I see it, you are of no use to us. And I don't want it on my conscience that I sent a twelve-year-old boy to Andersonville."

"You're letting me go?"

"Yes, I am. There is a thicket of some size behind this tent. Get into it and stay there until this battle is over and we move on."

"But where'll I go after that, sir?"

"That is up to you." The officer frowned. "If you go north, you'll run into your own troops. If you go south, you'll be captured again and may fare differently with some other man. If you go east, you could run into battle after battle. That's where the fighting is going to be next, unless I miss my guess. What's left to you, then?"

"The west!" said Charley, unable to believe his good fortune.

"Then west it has to be. That's mountain country here in Virginia. You will find it very different from New York City, but I see it as your only refuge right now."

Charley gasped out, "How did you know I was from New York City?"

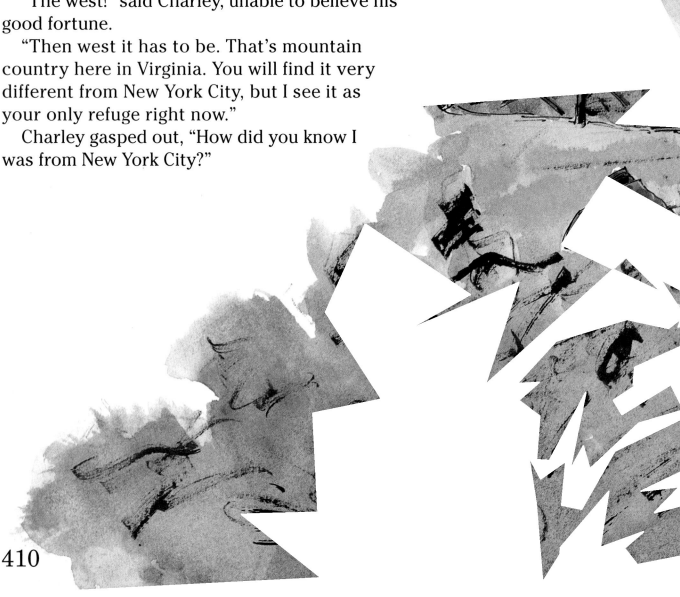

"Your manner of speaking and how you pronounce words. I've been there. I've made a study of accents. That's why I was given this particular chore with prisoners who will not talk. Get rid of your uniform if you know what is good for you. Now, my boy, do as I tell you. Skedaddle before I change my mind. I don't fancy deserters—no matter how young they may be."

"Thank you, thank you, sir." After lifting his hat, Charley Quinn shot like a bolt past the man's table and out the rear flap of the tent. He sprinted for the nearby hickory thicket and dived inside, all the while thanking the guardian angel the sisters said he always had with him for his deliverance. Once inside the thicket, he took off his blue uniform blouse, discarded his cap, and began to pick at the stripe sewn along the sides of his trousers as part of his splendid drummer boy's uniform.

411

Lying on his belly in the thicket on that long, hot day, Charley had a lot of time to think and wonder, and the heat of shame crept up to his cheeks as he thought of Silas and Jem. They had not run! They'd fought it out. Had Silas died, too? What had happened to the 140th? Where were they now? Still fighting here in the Wilderness? Were most of them dead, as his friends were?

Would Noreen get a letter from someone in the 140th telling her that he had run away, or would whoever wrote her be kind enough to say he was "missing in action," perhaps even mention that he had picked up a musket and used it?

Used a musket? Yes. Each time he closed his eyes, Charley could again see the man he'd shot and killed.

He'd committed a mortal sin. He wasn't a real soldier who had orders to do that to an enemy. Where could he confess his sin? Where could he find a priest? He should have gone back to the rear of his regiment and halted there, ready to be captured; or else he should have tried to get a new drum from the supply wagon. If he'd done that, he wouldn't be caught in this nightmare now.

But he hadn't. He'd killed a man, and then he'd run and kept on running. Now look at him—he was no longer in any uniform at all. And he was alone and nameless in a thicket somewhere in the dreaded Wilderness.

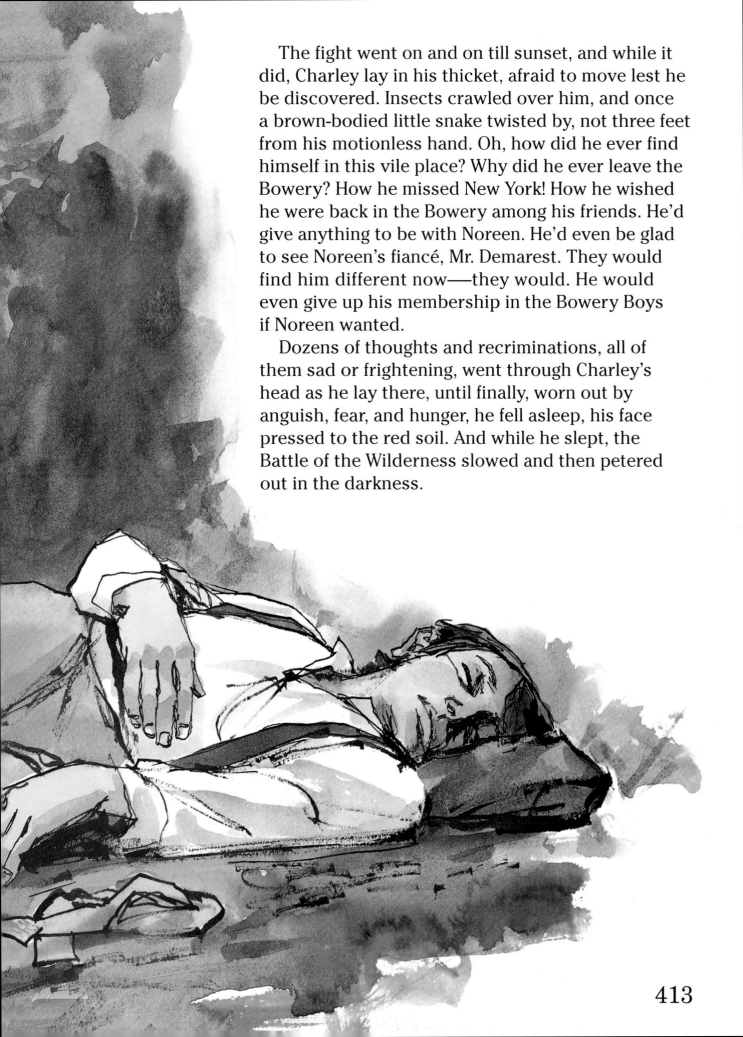

The fight went on and on till sunset, and while it did, Charley lay in his thicket, afraid to move lest he be discovered. Insects crawled over him, and once a brown-bodied little snake twisted by, not three feet from his motionless hand. Oh, how did he ever find himself in this vile place? Why did he ever leave the Bowery? How he missed New York! How he wished he were back in the Bowery among his friends. He'd give anything to be with Noreen. He'd even be glad to see Noreen's fiancé, Mr. Demarest. They would find him different now—they would. He would even give up his membership in the Bowery Boys if Noreen wanted.

Dozens of thoughts and recriminations, all of them sad or frightening, went through Charley's head as he lay there, until finally, worn out by anguish, fear, and hunger, he fell asleep, his face pressed to the red soil. And while he slept, the Battle of the Wilderness slowed and then petered out in the darkness.

Charley Skedaddle

Meet the Author

Patricia Beatty, when she was ten, became very ill and had to be in the hospital for five months. Reading helped her to pass the time. Said Ms. Beatty, "This childhood illness had a great deal to do with my later becoming a writer."

Ms. Beatty went on to teach high school English and history. She later became a librarian, which inspired her to write historical fiction for children.

Later, the heritage and culture of California became one of Ms. Beatty's favorite book topics. To encourage others to write children's books on this subject, she established the John and Patricia Beatty Award through the California Library Association.

Meet the Illustrator

Charles Shaw loves to illustrate the Texas frontier, children, and jazz musicians. He is so well-known for his illustrations of Texas frontier life that the University of Texas asked him to create 248 illustrations for a book called *Texas*, written by James Michener. Mr. Shaw has also contributed his illustrations to numerous other books and magazine articles.

Theme Connections

Think About It

With a small group of classmates, consider how a soldier's wartime experiences might affect his attitudes about war.

- Why didn't Charley return to his unit after running away?
- Can the deaths of so many people be justified, even for such a noble cause as ending slavery?

Check the Concept/Question Board to see if there are any questions there that you can answer now. If the selection or your discussions about the selection have raised any new questions about the Civil War, put the questions on the Concept/Question Board. Maybe the next selection will help answer the questions.

Record Ideas

How do you think you would have acted in Charley's circumstances? Use your Writing Journal to record your notes and ideas.

Research Ideas

- Compare the Civil War with other wars, such as World Wars I and II, the Vietnam War, and the Persian Gulf War.
- Find out more about Andersonville Prison, the prison camp in Georgia where Union soldiers were held.

FINE Art

A Ride for Liberty—the Fugitive Slave. c. 1862. **Eastman Johnson.** Oil on board. 22 x 26¼ in. The Brooklyn Museum of Art; Gift of Miss Gwendolyn O. L. Conking (40.59.A)

Ruins of Richmond, Virginia, April 1865. **Photographer unknown.** Photo: Library of Congress.

Tidings from the Front. **Gilbert Gaul.** Oil on canvas. $33\frac{1}{4} \times 38\frac{1}{4}$ in.
Collection of the Birmingham Museum of Art, Birmingham, Alabama; Gift
of John Meyer.

A Rainy Day in Camp. 1871. **Winslow Homer.** Oil on canvas. 20×36 in.
The Metropolitan Museum of Art, Gift of Mrs. William F. Milton, 1923
(23.77.1) Photograph ©1995 The Metropolitan Museum of Art.

The *Siege* of Vicksburg

from ***The Tamarack Tree***
by Patricia Clapp
illustrated by Lydia Halverson

Seventeen-year-old Rosemary Leigh was born in England, but has lived since her mother's death with her older brother Derek in Vicksburg, Mississippi. Living with Rosemary and Derek are their cook Amanda and Amanda's daughter Betsy. Amanda's husband, Hector, is a free black man who was once active in the Underground Railroad.

It was midafternoon yesterday when Mary Byrd Blair and I stumbled up the hill on our way home from the hospital. We were untidy and stained from the work we had been doing, and so weary we could scarcely put one foot before the other. The firing was slight and I commented on it.

"I wonder why they have stopped so suddenly. I don't like it."

"I expect it's time for tea," Mary Byrd said airily. "Isn't it true that in England everything stops for tea?"

"If only we were in England now!" Then I giggled. "I wonder if the soldiers crook their little fingers when they hold their cups. And do you suppose they're having cucumber sandwiches with their tea?"

"Stop talking about food! If a chicken squawked by right now I'd eat it! Feathers and all!"

I laughed. "Once I would have considered that a disgusting thought."

"Well, maybe I'd pull some of the feathers off," she admitted. "I never knew before what it was to be truly hungry, did you, Rosemary?"

"Never. There may be *something* to eat at our house." Casually I added, "I don't know whether Derek is home or not," and glanced sideways at Mary Byrd. I saw her blush and smiled to myself.

"Well, I'll stop," she said, "but I can't stay long. Mamma goes into a real swivet when the shelling starts and she doesn't know where I am."

We walked across the broad lawn, untended now and full of weeds, and my dog Woof came slowly to meet us. How thin he was! I leaned and stroked him, and together we went into the house. Amanda and Betsy were in the kitchen, Betsy on her mother's lap. Amanda looked up, her face worried.

"What is it?" I asked. "Is Betsy not feeling well?"

"She's so cold, Miss Rosemary. Seems like she can't stop shivering."

"Do you know what's the matter with her?"

"No. I sure wish I did."

I knelt beside the rocking chair and took Betsy's hand in mine. "Where does it hurt, Betsy? What is the trouble, baby, can you tell us?"

Betsy raised dark teary eyes. "I'm so hungry," she murmured, "and I'm so ascared of all the shootin', and my head aches." Burrowing that black curly head in Amanda's shoulder she sobbed quietly.

"I was just about to go get us the milk," her mother said, "and maybe I could get an egg or two. Those neighbors still have a few chickens nobody found yet." She smiled wryly. "They're keeping them in their back parlor so nobody knows. With a dab of milk and an egg I could fix something for the child here. But I can't take her, and I don't like to leave her alone."

"We'll watch her," Mary Byrd said. "You go along, Amanda. We'll take good care of Betsy." She gazed at Amanda in quiet wonder. "I didn't know there was a chicken or a cow left within a hundred miles," she added. "Amanda, you're amazing!"

"Seems I just know some real handy folks," she said rising, and gesturing for me to sit down, she placed Betsy in my lap. "I'll be back soon's I can," she said, gathering up her old cloth bag and going out the kitchen door.

I sat rocking, Betsy huddled in my arms. Mary Byrd sat on the floor beside us, and started to sing very softly. It was some sort of lullaby, and her sweet voice made it a tender, soothing melody. Betsy's eyes began to droop, and after a moment or two I felt her relax in sleep.

"I never heard you sing before," I said quietly. "You have a lovely voice."

"There hasn't been much to sing about lately, sugar. When is it ever going to be over, Rosemary?"

"There was talk about the fourth of July, remember? And that's the day after tomorrow. At least it's quiet now."

Just as I spoke those ill-timed words the guns started again, louder and closer than I had ever heard them. It seemed as if the earth shook with their thunder. Betsy jerked upright in my arms and screamed, and I could not stop her. I cupped my hands over her ears, but it was no help.

"Let's take her down to the basement," I shouted at Mary Byrd. "It may shut out some of the noise."

Mary Byrd nodded, and together we managed to get a hysterical Betsy down the kitchen steps, Woof slinking along beside us. We laid the child on one of the mattresses and I sat beside her and tried to comfort her, but she was beyond hearing me. As the shelling continued, almost paralyzing in its intensity, shriek after shriek came from her, her eyes shifted like those of a frightened horse, her hands clutched at me. Mary Byrd moved close to us, and I don't think either of us knew whether we were huddling together for mutual solace or for protection.

And then a shell crashed through the cellar wall, rolled a few feet toward us, and lay there, round and ugly, hissing. If Betsy had not fainted I am sure I would have. Suddenly I was scanning the walls of the basement frantically, looking for the entrance to the secret tunnel I knew was there.

"The wine racks," I shouted at Mary Byrd. "Behind the wine racks."

She looked at me as if I had gone mad, but when I stood up, leaving Betsy unconscious on the mattress, she rose with me, her eyes on mine. I ran to the wall lined with racks and racks of dusty bottles, pushing against them, pulling at them, muttering to myself, unheard in that continuing racket, glancing over my shoulder at the sinister shell that lay across the basement from us, and I prayed. Oh, how I prayed! And then I felt one tier of shelves give a little under my hand, and as I struggled with it, it slowly came away from the wall, moving on hinges as a door does. Behind it another door opened slowly outward. Woof kept getting under my feet, Mary Byrd was at my shoulder, her blue eyes huge as she stared into the damp, musty-smelling darkness behind that door. When I ran back to the mattress on which Betsy lay, she was beside me, helping drag child and mattress through the door, into that stygian blackness, helping me shut the door behind us, closing us in. Just as I sank down on the edge of the mattress there came an ear-splitting crash from the other side of the door, followed by the roar of falling wood and plaster, and the sharp sound of shattered glass. I threw myself across Betsy and my head knocked hard against another head, Mary Byrd's, as she did precisely the same thing.

For what seemed an eternity we lay that way, Woof shaking as he huddled close into me, until the noise stopped. I sat up, and when I spoke my voice seemed very loud in the sudden quiet.

"Betsy. Are you all right?"

Her voice was small but clear. "I think so, Miss Romy. But I'm a mite squashed. Why you two ladies pounce on me like that?"

Mary Byrd started to laugh, and after a second I laughed with her. "Squashed!" she said, and went off into another gale. We couldn't stop, until finally, with gasps for breath, she managed to speak. "Where in the name of heaven are we?"

"In a tunnel under the house," I told her.

"Oh." A pause. "Rosemary, *why* is there a tunnel under the house?"

"It's an escape tunnel for slaves."

"Oh." Another pause. "I see. I've heard of them."

There was not a glimmer of light anywhere. The blackness was as thick and heavy as a rug. I could feel Woof trembling against me, but I could not see him. I felt for Betsy's hand and held it tightly in mine, but I could not see her. I groped for Mary Byrd's hand, found it and clasped it. The darkness was absolute.

"I don't think I like this very much," Mary Byrd said. "I wonder what the basement is like. Perhaps we should open the door and look."

"I'll try."

"I'll help."

I stood up and stepped inch by inch toward where I thought the door must be, Mary Byrd clutching my skirt. I felt for the rough wooden surface of the door, and in a step or two, found it.

"It's here," I said, and pushed against the door. It didn't move. "It seems to be stuck."

"Let's push together. One, two, three——*push!*" It was useless. "Maybe if we put our backs against it," Mary Byrd suggested.

Together we leaned our backs against the stubborn door, pushing with all our strength. It did not give an inch. I felt a sudden movement from Mary Byrd and heard her gasp a quick "Oh!"

"What is it?"

"My foot slipped and I twisted my ankle. It's nothing."

"Are you all right?"

"Of course. Let's sit down for a moment and decide what to do next."

But when she tried to take the few steps to the mattress I could hear her inhale sharply, and I knew the ankle must be painful.

"Put your arm across my shoulders and hop," I told her. "I'll hold you up."

With my arm about her waist she hopped, and I helped her settle on a corner of the mattress.

"Is it very bad?" I asked.

"As you would say, Rosemary, don't worry. What do you think we should do now?"

"Be very brave," I answered aloud, and said silently to myself, Be *very* brave, Rosemary! I could feel the cold damp

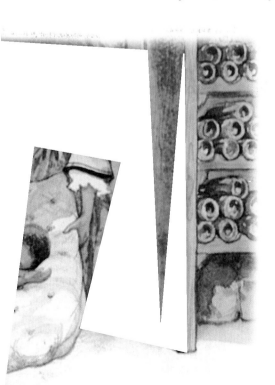
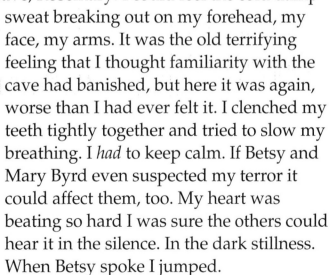

sweat breaking out on my forehead, my face, my arms. It was the old terrifying feeling that I thought familiarity with the cave had banished, but here it was again, worse than I had ever felt it. I clenched my teeth tightly together and tried to slow my breathing. I *had* to keep calm. If Betsy and Mary Byrd even suspected my terror it could affect them, too. My heart was beating so hard I was sure the others could hear it in the silence. In the dark stillness. When Betsy spoke I jumped.

"I've been in here before. Dada showed me this place."

"Your daddy showed you, Betsy?" Mary Byrd asked. "How did he know about it?"

The child's voice held pride. "Dada helped to dig it."

"Your *father*? Hector helped dig this tunnel?"

"Yes, Miss Mary Byrd. It's a great long tunnel, too."

"Does Derek know about it, Rosemary?"

"Yes," I managed, though my voice seemed to squeak.

"I see," Mary Byrd said after a pause. "He never told me."

"I wish there was a light in here," I said. It was almost a whisper.

Betsy moved and was sitting beside me, her hand on my shoulder. I wondered if she could feel me shaking.

"There might be," she said.

"There might be what?"

"A light. A candle maybe. I 'member. When I was here with Dada he showed me little . . . shelf things. In the walls. There was a box with candles and matches."

I looked around straining my eyes, but the darkness was impenetrable. "Where, Betsy? Where were the shelves? Can you remember?" As I spoke I found myself getting to my feet. Anything was better than sitting there shivering.

"They're just sort of stuck on the walls. I don't know where."

"Maybe I can find them."

Mary Byrd's hand grasped my skirt. "Rosemary, sit down! You'll get lost!"

I swallowed hard and tried to sound calm. "If this is a tunnel I can't get very far lost. If I don't find any shelves I'll . . . I'll just turn around and come back. Hold Woof's collar. I don't want to trip over him."

Mary Byrd's voice came in a mutter. "I wish somebody would hold *your* collar!"

My knees felt like water, but I forced myself to take

a few steps in that solid blackness, stretching out my arms, my fingers brushing along the clay walls. From behind me Betsy spoke.

"The shelves are 'bout at the top of my head," she offered.

"Thank you," I said politely.

This is what it's like to be blind, I thought. Blind and buried alive. Step by trembling step I moved, fingers trailing along the walls. How far had I come? Not far——I could turn now and in a few steps be back with Betsy and Mary Byrd and Woof. In the dark. No, it was better to go on if there was any chance of light. What an atavistic fear it is, the fear of darkness! I wanted to claw through the walls to light and air. The fingers of my right hand stubbed against rough wood. "Ow!"

"What is it?" Mary Byrd's voice seemed a long way off.

"I think I found a——yes! A shelf! Wait . . . there's something . . . a box, I think. . . ." My hand, shaking uncontrollably, felt a square outline. I tried to lift it, but it seemed fastened to a wooden shelf projecting from the wall. "I can't see how it opens . . . wait, yes . . . I can." My blind fingers raised a lid, scrabbled in the box, felt the blessed smooth waxen shape of candles! Matches? Oh, please God, let there be matches! A smaller box, I could feel roughness on the outside. Gently, oh, so gently——I pushed at one end of it. If they should spill I'd never find them! The little drawer of the matchbox opened, inside . . . yes . . . oh, thank you God! Inside were matches.

"I found them. Candles——and matches! If I can just light one . . . "

"I knew they were there," came Betsy's smug voice.

"You are wonderful!" I said and meant each syllable. With icy cold fingers I took a match from the little box and struck it against the roughness. It sparked and went out. Another. This one broke in my shaking hand. A third.

A tiny flame that wavered in my heavy breathing. I closed my mouth tight, held the match carefully until the flame strengthened, took the candle from the box—and lit it! It was like life after death! I had never, in all my life, been so proud of myself. I turned back to where the others must be.

"Look!"

"Just like Mamma tells from the Bible," Betsy remarked. "Let there be light."

"And there was light," Mary Byrd finished, her voice solemn.

Holding the lighted candle, shielding it with my other hand, I moved back. Six shining eyes watched as I approached. I felt exhausted and exhilarated—and almost in control of my fear.

"I 'membered, I 'membered," Betsy crowed, bright-eyed with excitement.

"Where does the tunnel go, Betsy? Can you remember that?"

"I don't know, Miss Romy. Dada and me, we never went all the way. He just showed it to me once, and said he helped dig it. He said it was very long."

I pushed my brain to recall what Hector had said. I could hear his deep voice: "About a mile . . ." Could I possibly walk a mile in this clammy place? "I could go along to the end and bring someone back to help us," I said.

"And you'd probably step out right spang in the middle of Yankeedom!" Mary Byrd said flatly. "Don't you move! We're going to sit right here on this mattress until someone gets us out." She stopped suddenly, and when she went on her voice was very small. "Someone *will* get us out, won't they?"

"Of course," I said, trying to sound confident.

How long would it take Amanda to get back? When would Derry come home? It might not be for hours. Would anyone think to look for us here? And if they found us, could they get the door open? There must be piles of rubbish against it. . . . I tipped the candle until a little wax dripped onto the floor, and then set the candle in it. My hand felt too weak to hold it any longer. In the small circle of flickering light we all looked at each other.

Mary Byrd reached out one hand and took Betsy's, with her other hand she took mine. Softly she started to sing.

"Row, row, row your boat . . . "

If she could do it, I could. I gritted my teeth against panic, and at the appropriate moment I joined in. A few bars later, Betsy's shrill little voice picked up the old round.

"Merrily, merrily, merrily, merrily, life is but a dream." No, like a nightmare, I thought, but we kept singing, over and over, our voices getting louder, until we were shouting the repetitive words at the tops of our lungs.

As I paused for breath I heard what seemed an echo—but the voices were deeper. Male voices. "Row, row, row your boat," they sang determinedly, and from beyond the door came the noise of heavy objects being moved, the crash of broken glass, the scrape of things being pulled across other things. I jumped to my feet and rushed at the door, pounding on it.

"Hello out there! Let us out! We're stuck in here! Let us out!"

"Just what we're aimin' to do, ma'am," came a deep, cheery voice. "It's a right poor mess out here. You all right?"

"Oh yes! Yes! Who are you?"

"Just three friendly old Southern boys—just you sit tight now."

And then another voice, filled with distress. "Miss Rosemary——is Betsy in there? You got my baby with you?"

"Yes, Amanda," I shouted, "she's here——she's all right!"

Betsy was beside me, beating on the door with her small fist. "Mamma! Mamma! I told Miss Romy 'bout the candles. I 'membered Dada showing me! I did, Mamma, I did!"

"Bless you, Betsy," Amanda said in a voice that wasn't quite steady.

And then the strong masculine voice again. "Stand back from the door, ladies. Stand back."

I took Betsy's hand and moved back to stand beside Mary Byrd, Woof quivering at my knee. With a tremendous wrenching sound the door was pulled open, leaving a space filled with faces. Amanda's, smiling through tears, and three others——men I had seen before——where? Then I recalled. They were men who had begged for the scrapings from Amanda's kitchen bowl. Dirt-streaked, sweating,

haggard, and thin, with torn uniforms and bleeding hands——they were all grinning as they faced us in that almost impassable basement.

I thought my heart would burst open with joy.

I guided Betsy to the opening, noting with relief that whatever ailment she had been suffering earlier had disappeared in (I assumed) the pleasant importance of knowing where light might be found. I kissed her soft cheek as she was lifted straight into her mother's arms.

Then, leaning over Mary Byrd, I placed my arms under hers. "See if you can make it up on your good foot. I'll hold you."

With a tiny wince of pain she pushed herself up until she was standing. The men watched carefully.

"You hurt, ma'am?" one asked. "Why, it's Miss Blair, isn't it? You hurt, Miss Blair?"

"It's nothing. I just twisted my ankle a bit. . . ."

The soldier set one foot into the tunnel, leaned forward and scooped Mary Byrd up as if she had been an armload of feathers. I blew out the candle and stepped out, Woof following closely. Out! I took a deep breath and was almost overcome by the suffocating smell of wine from dozens of broken bottles. The poor Bartletts who owned this house! I hoped they wouldn't think we had drunk all of it.

I turned toward the kitchen stairs. The broken steps were covered with debris.

"How did you get in?" I asked the men.

"The same way the shell did. Through that hole," one said, and pointed to a wide gap in the wall. "We heard the explosion, and this here lady——" he indicated Amanda, "she was afeared someone might be down here. So we came in, and we heard you-all singin' in there. It sounded real pretty!"

Betsy was boosted through the open space, with Amanda after her, and then one of the men pulled himself through and turned to lift Mary Byrd out, seating her gently on the grass. Then it was my turn, and there was an assist for Woof. Poor Woof! There had been a time when he could

have jumped the distance, but not now. I made sure the men climbed out safely and watching them, wondered where they had found the strength to rescue us. Their bodies were close to skeletal from hunger, their faces drawn. And yet they still smiled. When Mary Byrd, in her stained hospital apron, with dirt streaks on her face and cobwebs in her hair, pulled from somewhere a ravishing smile of her own, the men grinned delightedly.

"You're just the sweetest little ol' boys I've had the pleasure of meetin'," she said. "You must give me your names so I can invite you the next time we have a party."

The *Siege* of Vicksburg

Meet the Author

Patricia Clapp says she started composing poems and stories as soon as she learned how to write. She went on to study journalism in college, but left school for an emergency appendectomy, and never returned.

It wasn't until she was asked to produce a play for her daughter's Girl Scout troop that she began writing again. She couldn't find a play she liked, so she wrote one. She's been writing plays and novels ever since.

Even as the winner of several book awards, Ms. Clapp says she does not consider herself a professional writer. Today she divides her time between writing, community theater, and her family.

Meet the Illustrator

Lydia Halverson has used her education in art and history to become a book illustrator and designer. Says Ms. Halverson, "When I was little, my mother told me countless folktales and fairy tales that she loved as a girl in Italy. I've gravitated toward the folktale genre ever since. I've illustrated American Indian, Italian, Japanese, Chinese, Aztec, Slovakian, French, and Danish folktales. Any wonderful story with a feeling for history and characters in costume excites me. I try to imagine what it was like living in the era of the story I am illustrating. Sometimes I am so wrapped up in the story I forget [what year it really is]."

Theme Connections

Think About It

With a small group of classmates, discuss the difficulties faced by civilians living under siege conditions.

- What happened to those people who didn't have access to a safe hiding place?
- What new roles and responsibilities did many women take on during the Civil War?

Check the Concept/Question Board to see if there are any questions there that you can answer now. If the selection or your discussions about the selection have raised any new questions about the Civil War, put the questions on the Concept/Question Board. Maybe the next selection will help answer the questions.

Record Ideas

Should civilians be allowed to leave an area under siege? Record your notes and ideas in your Writing Journal.

Research Ideas

- Find out more about how siege tactics were used in the Civil War and other wars.
- Investigate the damage caused to various areas during the Civil War and how the cities were rebuilt.

Under Siege

from **Voices from the Civil War**
by Milton Meltzer

The most wearing time in war for soldiers——and
civilians——is the siege. A siege may last for weeks,
months, or even years. It is the time when an army
is positioned in front of a fortified place in order to force
its surrender. The besiegers simply wait for the army
penned up inside to give up because supplies and morale
are low, or they may hasten surrender by bombardment
and a series of assaults.

The siege of Vicksburg, a city high on a bluff above
the Mississippi River, was a prime target of the Union
campaign for the river. General Grant hoped to cut off the
West from the other Rebel states, and to open up passage
from the Gulf of Mexico to the North. By the spring of
1862 much of this had been achieved, except for taking
Vicksburg and Port Hudson.

Grant made two attacks upon Vicksburg, but was
repulsed. Then he decided to lay siege to the city, with an
army of seventy thousand and over two hundred guns.
After a six-week bombardment, on July 4, 1863, General
Pemberton surrendered the city and over thirty thousand
troops, the largest haul of manpower up to that time.

A Union woman (we don't know her name), caught
somehow inside Vicksburg amid the Southerners,
describes the tension and danger in a diary she kept:

MARCH 20, 1863——The slow shelling of Vicksburg goes on all the time, and we have grown indifferent. It does not at present interrupt or interfere with daily avocations [chores], but I suspect they are only getting the range of different points; and when they have them all complete, showers of shot will rain on us all at once. Noncombatants have been ordered to leave or prepare accordingly. Those who are to stay are having caves built. Cave-digging has become a regular business; prices range from twenty to fifty dollars, according to size of cave. Two diggers worked at ours a week and charged thirty dollars. It is well made in the hill that slopes just in the rear of the house, and well propped with thick posts, as they all are. It has a shelf also, for holding a light or water. When we went in this evening and sat down, the earthy, suffocating feeling, as of a living tomb, was dreadful to me. I fear I shall risk death outside rather than melt in that dark furnace. The hills are so honeycombed with caves that the streets look like avenues in a cemetery. . . .

This watercolor by an unknown artist shows General Grant's attack on Vicksburg on May 19, 1863.
Pencil and watercolor. M. & M. Karolik Collection,
Museum of Fine Arts, Boston

APRIL 28——I never understood before the full force of those questions——what shall we eat? what shall we drink? and wherewithal shall we be clothed? We have no prophet of the Lord at whose prayer the meal and oil will not waste. Such minute attention must be given the wardrobe to preserve it that I have learned to darn like an artist. Making shoes is now another accomplishment. Mine were in tatters. H. came across a moth-eaten pair that he bought me, giving ten dollars, I think, and they fell into rags when I tried to wear them; but the soles were good, and that has helped me to shoes. A pair of old coat sleeves saved—— nothing is thrown away now——was in my trunk. I cut an exact pattern from my old shoes, laid it on the sleeves, and cut out thus good uppers and sewed them carefully; then soaked the soles and sewed the cloth to them. I am so proud of these homemade shoes, think I'll put them in a glass case when the war is over, as an heirloom. . . .

I have but a dozen pins remaining, so many I gave away. Every time these are used they are straightened and kept from rust. All these curious labors are performed while the shells are leisurely screaming through the air; but as long as we are out of range we don't worry. For many nights we have had but little sleep, because the Federal gunboats have been running past the batteries. The uproar when this is happening is phenomenal. The first night the thundering artillery burst the bars of sleep, we thought it an attack by the river. To get into garments and rush upstairs was the work of a moment. From the upper gallery we have a fine view of the river, and soon a red glare lit up the scene and showed a small boat, towing two large barges, gliding by. The Confederates had set fire to a house near the bank. Another night, eight boats ran by, throwing a shower of shot, and two burning houses made the river clear as day. One of the batteries has a remarkable gun they call "Whistling Dick," because of the screeching, whistling sound it gives, and certainly it does sound like a tortured thing. Added to all this is the indescribable Confederate yell, which is a soul-harrowing sound to hear. . . . Yesterday the *Cincinnati* attempted to go by in daylight, but was disabled and sunk. It was a pitiful sight; we could not see the finale, though we saw her rendered helpless. . . .

MAY 28——The regular siege has continued. We are utterly cut off from the world, surrounded by a circle of fire. Would it be wise like the scorpion to sting ourselves to death? The fiery shower of shells goes on day and night. H.'s occupation, of course, is gone; his office closed. Every man has to carry a pass in his pocket. People do nothing but eat what they can get, sleep when they can, and dodge the shells. There are three intervals when the shelling stops, either for the guns to cool or for the gunners' meals, I suppose——about eight in the morning, the same in the evening, and at noon. In that time we have both to prepare and eat ours. Clothing cannot be washed or anything else done. On the 19th and 22d, when the assaults were made on the lines, I watched the soldiers cooking on the green opposite. The half-spent balls coming all the way from those lines were flying so thick that they were obliged to dodge at every turn. At all the caves I could see from my high perch, people were sitting, eating their poor suppers at the cave doors, ready to plunge in again. As the first shell again flew they dived, and not a human being was visible. The sharp crackle of

This painting by Howard Pyle shows a Confederate soldier and two women shrinking back from a Federal shell with a sputtering fuse. Behind them is the entrance to a cave.
The Shell. 1908. Howard Pyle. Oil on canvas. Private collection, Photography courtesy of Brandywine River Museum.

the musketry firing was a strong contrast to the scream of the bombs. I think all the dogs and cats must be killed or starved; we don't see any more pitiful animals prowling around. . . .

JUNE 25——A horrible day. The most horrible yet to me, because I've lost my nerve. We were all in the cellar, when a shell came tearing through the roof, burst upstairs, tore up that room, and the pieces coming through both floors down into the cellar, one of them tore open the leg of H.'s pantaloons. This was tangible proof the cellar was no place of protection from them. On the heels of this came Mr. J. to tell us that young Mrs. P. had had her thighbone crushed. When Martha went for the milk she came back horror-stricken to tell us the black girl there had her arm taken off by a shell. For the first time I quailed [lost heart]. I do not think people who are physically brave deserve much credit for it; it is a matter of nerves. In this way I am constitutionally brave, and seldom think of danger till it is over; and death has not the terrors for me it has for some others. Every night I had lain down expecting death, and every morning rose to the same prospect, without being unnerved. It was for H. I trembled. But now I first seemed to realize that something worse than death might come: I might be crippled, and not killed. Life, without all one's powers and limbs, was a thought that broke down my courage. I said to H., "You must get me out of this horrible place; I cannot stay; I know I shall be crippled." Now the regret comes that I lost control, because H. is worried, and has lost his composure, because my coolness has broken down. . . .

Under Siege

Meet the Author

Milton Meltzer was born in 1915 in Worcester, Massachusetts. He grew up in a neighborhood of immigrant families. As a young man he got his first writing job on a state funded theater project. From there, he went on to have many jobs that involved writing. He was an editor, a journalist, a speechwriter, and the author of scripts for radio documentaries. However, he did not write his first book until he was forty years old.

His books were inspired by the many important historical events he had lived through. He was an infant during World War I, a young man during the Great Depression, and an air traffic controller during World War II. Because of this, he has used writing to search for connections between the past and the present. It was also his goal to help young people learn about the struggles of the many different cultural groups that make up America.

Theme Connections

Think About It

With a small group of classmates, discuss whether this selection has changed your original perceptions of the Civil War.

- Would the Civil War have lasted longer without the use of advanced military technology and tactics?
- Should the Confederate army have surrendered sooner in order to spare the citizens of Vicksburg additional hardship and suffering?

Check the Concept/Question Board to see if there are any questions there that you can answer now. If the selection or your discussions about the selection have raised any new questions about the Civil War, put the questions on the Concept/Question Board. Maybe the next selection will help answer the questions.

Record Ideas

How do you think you would cope with weeks of siege and bombardment? Use your Writing Journal to record your notes and ideas.

Research Ideas

Investigate other personal accounts of the Civil War and compare the perspectives of people living in the North and the South.

Emancipation

from *To Be a Slave*
by Julius Lester
illustrated by Charles Shaw

Julius Lester's book To Be a Slave *consists of selections from collections of interviews done shortly after the Civil War. In the chapter "Emancipation," former slaves talk about their reactions to the news that they are free.*

Granma used to tell this story to everybody that would listen, and I expect I heard it a hundred times. Granma say she was hired out to the Randolphs during the war. One day while she was weeding corn another slave, Mamie Tolliver, come up to her and whispered, "Sarah, they tell me that Massa Lincoln done set all us slaves free." Granma say, "Is that so?" and she dropped her hoe and run all the way to the Thacker's place—seven miles it was—and run to ol' missus and looked at her real hard. Then she yelled, "I'm free! Yes, I'm free! Ain't got to work for you no more. You can't put me in your pocket now!" Granma say Missus Thacker started boo-hooing and threw her apron over her face and run in the house. Granma knew it was true then.

BETTY JONES
The Negro in Virginia, p. 209

Some slave owners moved to Texas with their slaves when it appeared that the South might lose the war. By moving to Texas they hoped that they might hold on to their slaves a while longer.

We wasn't there in Texas long when the soldiers marched in to tell us that we were free. Seems to me like it was on a Monday morning when they come in. Yes, it was a Monday. They went out to the field and told them they was free. Marched them out of the fields. They come a-shouting. I remembers one woman. She jumped on a barrel and she shouted. She jumped off and she shouted. She jumped back on again and shouted some more. She kept that up for a long time, just jumping on a barrel and back off again.

ANNA WOODS
Library of Congress

445

The news that they were free was the fulfillment of the dream they had taken to bed each night and risen with each morning. How many times they had tried to imagine what that moment would be like, and now it had come. Some found it hard to believe.

One day I was out milking the cows. Mr. Dave come down into the field and he had a paper in his hand. "Listen to me, Tom," he said. "Listen to what I read you." And he read from a paper all about how I was free. You can't tell how I felt. "You're joking me," I says. "No, I ain't," says he. "You're free." "No," says I, "it's a joke." "No," says he, "it's a law that I got to read this paper to you. Now listen while I read it again."

But still I wouldn't believe him. "Just go up to the house," says he, "and ask Mrs. Robinson. She'll tell you." So I went. "It's a joke," I says to her. "Did you ever know your master to tell you a lie?" she says. "No," says I, "I ain't." "Well," she says, "The war's over and you're free." By that time I thought maybe she was telling me what was right. "Miss Robinson," says I, "can I go over to see the Smiths?" They was a colored family that lived nearby. "Don't you understand," says she, "you're free. You don't have to ask me what you can do. Run along, child." And so I went. And do you know why I was a-going? I wanted to find out if they was free, too. I just couldn't take it all in. I couldn't believe we was all free alike.

Was I happy? You can take anything. No matter how good you treat it——it wants to be free. You can treat it good and feed it good and give it everything it seems to want——but if you open the cage——it's happy.

Tom Robinson
Library of Congress

Most slaves, though, had no difficulty at all believing the news when they heard it.

The news come on a Thursday and all the slaves been shoutin' and carryin' on till everybody was tired out. I remember the first Sunday of freedom. We was all sittin' around restin' and tryin' to think what freedom meant and everybody was quiet and peaceful. All at once ol' Sister Carrie who was near 'bout a hundred started into talking:

Tain't no mo' sellin' today.
Tain't no mo' hirin' today.
Tain't no mo' pullin' off shirts today.
It's stomp down freedom today.
Stomp it down!

And when she says, "Stomp it down," all the slaves
commence to shoutin' with her:

Stomp down freedom today.
Stomp it down!
Stomp down freedom today.

Wasn't no more peace that Sunday. Everybody
started in to sing and shout once more. First thing you
know they done made up music to Sister Carrie's stomp
song and sang and shouted that song all the rest of the
day. Child, that was one glorious time!

CHARLOTTE BROWN
The Negro in Virginia, p. 212

Daddy was down to the creek. He jumped right in the water up to his neck. He was so happy he just kept on scoopin' up handfulls of water and dumpin' it on his head and yellin', "I'se free! I'se free! I'se free!"

LOUISA BOWES ROSE
The Negro in Virginia, p. 208

The war was over and when the South surrendered to the North at Appomattox, it was appropriate that there were blacks present to watch the official end of the war and slavery.

General Lee tipped his hat first and then General Grant tipped hissen. General Lee got off his horse, and General Grant got off hissen. General Lee got on a new uniform with gold braid and lots of buttons, but General Grant got on an old blue coat that's so dirty it look black. They stood there talking about half an hour and then they shake hands and us what was watching know that Lee done give up. Then General Lee tipped his hat and General Grant tipped hissen, and General Lee rode over to the rebel side. General Grant rode over to our side and the war was over.

TOM HESTER
The Negro in Virginia, p. 204

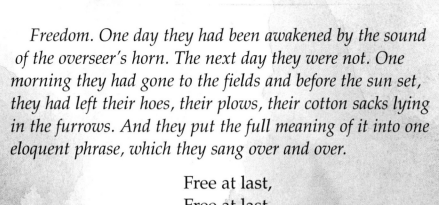

Freedom. One day they had been awakened by the sound of the overseer's horn. The next day they were not. One morning they had gone to the fields and before the sun set, they had left their hoes, their plows, their cotton sacks lying in the furrows. And they put the full meaning of it into one eloquent phrase, which they sang over and over.

Free at last,
Free at last,
Thank God A-Mighty,
I'm free at last.

Emancipation

Meet the Author

Julius Lester was born in Missouri, but grew up in Kansas and Tennessee. Thanks to his father and grandmother, he was greatly influenced by music and stories from the Southern rural Black tradition. He began playing the piano at age five and loved to read comic books, mysteries, and Westerns.

Most of Lester's own stories for children are based in the South and influenced by history. *To Be a Slave* was his first children's book, which he wrote in only three months.

In his spare time, Lester enjoys hiking, stamp collecting, and doing the New York Times crossword puzzle. His favorite foods are soups and fish. He lives with his wife Alida in Amherst, where he teaches literature, history, and Judaic studies at the University of Massachusetts.

Meet the Illustrator

Charles Shaw was a soldier in the Army National Guard during the time that John F. Kennedy was president of the United States. He is now an artist who loves to illustrate the Texas frontier, children, and jazz musicians. His work can be found in a number of Texas museums and historical societies. He is so well-known for his illustrations of Texas frontier life that the University of Texas asked him to create 248 illustrations for a book called *Texas*, written by James Michener. Mr. Shaw has also contributed his illustrations to numerous other books and magazine articles.

Theme Connections

Think About It

With a small group of classmates, discuss the importance of freedom.

- What details from the interviews you read help to convey the significance of the moment the slaves learned they were free?
- Why did some slaves have a hard time believing that they had been freed?

Check the Concept/Question Board to see if there are any questions there that you can answer now. If the selection or your discussions about the selection have raised any new questions about the Civil War, put the questions on the Concept/Question Board. Maybe the next selection will help answer the questions.

Record Ideas

How do you think you would have reacted to the news of your freedom if you had been a slave in 1863? Use your Writing Journal to record your notes and ideas.

Research Ideas

- Explore the lives of former slaves in the South after the Civil War.
- Investigate the effect of the Emancipation Proclamation on business in the South.

The Gettysburg Address

DELIVERED AT GETTYSBURG, PENNSYLVANIA, NOVEMBER 19, 1863

by Abraham Lincoln
illustrated by Michael McCurdy

Fourscore and seven years ago our fathers brought forth upon this continent a new nation, conceived in liberty, and dedicated to the proposition that all men are created equal.

Now we are engaged in a great civil war, testing whether that nation, or any nation so conceived and so dedicated, can long endure. We are met on a great battlefield of that war. We have come to dedicate a portion of that field as a final resting place for those who here gave their lives that that nation might live. It is altogether fitting and proper that we should do this.

But in a larger sense we cannot dedicate, we cannot consecrate, we cannot hallow this ground. The brave men, living and dead, who struggled here, have consecrated it far above our poor power to add or detract. The world will little note, nor long remember, what we say here; but it can never forget what they did here.

It is for us, the living, rather to be dedicated here to the unfinished work which they who fought here have thus far so nobly advanced. It is rather for us to be here dedicated to the great task remaining before us, that from these honored dead we take increased devotion to that cause for which they gave the last full measure of devotion; that we here highly resolve that these dead shall not have died in vain; that this nation, under God, shall have a new birth of freedom, and that government of the people, by the people, and for the people, shall not perish from the earth.

The Gettysburg Address

Meet the Author

Abraham Lincoln was born in a log cabin near Hodgenville, Kentucky, in 1809. He belonged to a pioneer family, so he did not have a lot of continuous schooling. However, he learned much through his avid reading. He grew up to become a store clerk, a soldier, a lawyer, a politician, and finally the president of the United States.

During his presidency Lincoln sought to abolish slavery and mend the split between the Confederate and Union states. This goal was accomplished when the Civil War ended. However, Lincoln was assassinated by John Wilkes Booth five days later. Lincoln was the first United States president ever to be assassinated.

Meet the Illustrator

Michael McCurdy states that the drawings for the book *Gettsyburg Address* were exciting to create, due to his fascination with the Civil War and Abraham Lincoln. One of McCurdy's great-grandfathers took part in the battles of Gettysburg and Antietam. When McCurdy made the drawings for this book, he had his great-grandfather in mind. Says Mr. McCurdy "In creating these illustrations for Lincoln's greatest speech, I felt I was closer to the men of the Civil War than I had ever been."

Theme Connections

Think About It

With a small group of classmates, talk about why the Gettysburg Address is regarded as a classic speech.

- The speech given immediately before President Lincoln's address lasted two hours. Do you think the contrast in length between the two speeches contributed to the impact of Lincoln's words?
- How does Lincoln express his respect for the soldiers who died at Gettysburg?

Check the Concept/Question Board to see if there are any questions there that you can answer now. If the selection or your discussions about the selection have raised any new questions about the Civil War, put the questions on the Concept/Question Board.

Record Ideas

How do you think Abraham Lincoln's speech was received by the families of Confederate soldiers who died in the battle? Record your notes and ideas in your Writing Journal.

Research Ideas

- Examine the events and outcome of the Battle of Gettysburg.

The Civil War

Bibliography

Across the Lines

by Carolyn Reeder.   Edward and Simon couldn't have been more different: one the son of a privileged Virginia plantation owner and the other his slave and companion. When Edward's family flees the advancing Yankee army, Simon joins the Union troops. Can their friendship survive?

A Ballad of the Civil War

by Mary Stolz.   If you have ever wondered what it was like for families who were divided over which side to fight on in the Civil War, this book will show you what happens when brothers had different views.

Bull Run

by Paul Fleischman.   Meet a variety of characters from the North and South who tell about their relationship to the Civil War and the important Battle of Bull Run.

Harriet Tubman: Conductor on the Underground Railroad

by Ann Petry.   Take a ride on the freedom train with conductor Harriet Tubman!

An Island Far From Home

by John Donahue. A young Massachusetts boy becomes the pen pal of an imprisoned Confederate soldier and learns that life is not as simple as he thought.

The Perfect Tribute

by Mary Andrews. When he received no applause at Gettysburg, President Lincoln thought his speech had been a flop. It wasn't until he returned to Washington that he learned its impact and met a special soldier.

Pink and Say

by Patricia Polacco. This is the moving story of two fifteen-year-old Union soldiers, one black, one white, whose friendship transcended everything.

A Separate Battle:
Women and the Civil War

by Ina Chang. Who were the women who served as soldiers, nurses, or spies during the Civil War? This book tells their stories.

New Frontiers

Some familiar images connected with the American West are of wagon trains crossing its wide prairies, seemingly endless deserts, and rugged mountains. Who were the people who made these grueling trips to find new land and new lives? Who were the people who already lived in this "new frontier," and what was their history? How has the West changed over the years?

Buffalo Hunter. c.1844. **Artist Unknown.**
Oil on canvas. Gift of Harriet Cowles Hammet Graham,
in memory of Buell Hammet, Santa Barbara Museum of Art.

Buffalo Hunt

from the book by Russell Freedman

A Gift from the Great Spirit

Over blazing campfires on winter nights, Indian storytellers spoke of the buffalo. They told tales of buffalo giants and buffalo ghosts, of buffalo that changed magically into men, of children who were raised by buffalo and understood their language.

In olden times, it was said, buffalo used to eat Indians. They ate so many Indians that a legendary figure called Old Man had to put a stop to it. He organized a race between the buffalo and the Indians to decide who should eat whom. The Indians won.

On the Great Plains of North America, every Indian tribe had a rich and ready store of buffalo tales and legends. According to the Comanche, buffalo came from gigantic caves somewhere on the windswept ranges of the Texas Panhandle. Each spring, the Great Spirit sent throngs of buffalo from those hidden caves onto the open plains, as a gift to the Indian people.

Up North, the Blackfoot said that a lake in Canada was the place where the buffalo began. They were born beneath the water, in the darkest depths of the lake. If you could visit that sacred spot on the right night, at exactly the right time, you would hear an eerie rumbling coming from the middle of the lake. Then you would see the buffalo rise out of the water and crowd onto the shore, their shaggy fur wet and dripping, their curved horns gleaming in the moonlight.

To the Plains Indians, the buffalo, or American bison, was the most important animal on Earth. This snorting, lumbering beast provided almost everything the Indians needed to stay alive. The buffalo kept their bellies full and their bodies warm. It supplied raw materials for their weapons, tools, ornaments, and toys. The rhythm of their daily lives was ruled by the comings and goings of the great buffalo herds.

It is little wonder that the Indians worshipped the buffalo as a sacred animal. Before and after every hunt, they praised the spirit of the buffalo and thanked him for giving his meat. Men, women, and children carried buffalo-shaped rocks and fossils for good luck. They believed in the powerful magic of buffalo dreams. When they died, they hoped to go to a happy hunting ground in the sky where buffalo flourished. Looking into the night sky, the Pawnee believed that the Milky Way was formed by dust left behind by the spirit-buffalo.

As recently as 150 years ago, countless millions of buffalo still roamed the prairies and plains. They ranged from the Mississippi River westward to the Rockies, and from Canada down to the Rio Grande. Native American hunters had been stalking the animals for many thousands of years. During most of that time, the Indians had neither horses nor guns. They hunted on foot, and they killed their prey with stone-tipped arrows and spears. They knew how to creep up on a grazing herd, how to surround the buffalo, and how to drive them into corrals or stampede them over cliffs.

Without horses, the Indians had to travel on foot whenever they moved their encampments. Back then, they used big shaggy dogs as pack animals to help carry their tipis and other belongings. Sometimes on a long journey the dogs would grow tired and begin to droop and lag and hang their tongues. Then someone would cry, "Buffalo ahead! Fresh meat in plenty!" And the dogs would bound forward as though they had just set out. Later, the Indians would remember that era as their Dog Days.

The first horses were brought to North America by Spanish explorers in the 1500s. Within a century or so, runaway horses had drifted northward from Spanish settlements in Mexico and were roaming the plains in wild herds. The Indians learned to capture and tame those wild horses, and the horses changed their lives.

Now they could travel long distances to find the buffalo. They could chase the herds and kill the choicest animals. And with pack horses, they could

Catching the Wild Horse. **George Catlin.** The Thomas Gilcrease Institute of American History and Art, Tulsa, Oklahoma.

carry bigger tipis and more possessions with them as they traveled across the plains. In time, the Indians became some of the world's finest horsemen, experts at hunting and fighting on horseback.

When white trappers and traders began to visit the Great Plains in the early 1800s, about 250,000 Indians were living in the region. They belonged to some two dozen distinct tribes, each with its own language and customs. Many of these tribes had migrated from the woodlands of the East, but only a few, like the Pawnee of Kansas and Nebraska, still practiced the old arts of farming and fishing.

Most of the Plains Indians had given up the settled life of farmers and fishermen to follow the buffalo herds. They spent the winter in sheltered camps. But in spring they folded their tipis and roamed the plains. They hunted other animals besides the buffalo, of course— deer, antelope, elk, and an occasional bear. But buffalo

Painted elkskin robe. Late 19th Century. Crow. The National Museum of the American Indian, Smithsonian Institution. 3249.

meat was their staple food, buffalo hunting their main occupation.

A Plains tribe was made up of many small, independent bands. Once or twice a year, all the bands belonging to a tribe would assemble for a great religious ceremony, a tribal council, or a communal hunt. But mostly, the bands moved about on their own. Each band had its own encampments, or villages. And each band hunted in a different part of the tribal territory.

Hunting was a man's responsibility. Every able-bodied boy was taught that he should become a fearless hunter and warrior. Small boys ran about yip-yapping in play hunts, dreaming of the day when they would be big enough to ride after a herd of stampeding buffalo. A successful hunter could provide for many people. He became a man of influence, entitled to honors and privileges.

Women were responsible for putting the buffalo and other game to good use. It was a woman's job to skin and butcher the buffalo, to preserve the meat and tan the hides. As Indian girls grew up, they learned from their mothers and grandmothers the art of transforming a dead buffalo into a thousand practical and useful objects.

The buffalo was the biggest animal on the plains. A full-grown bull stood six feet tall at the humped shoulders and weighed a ton or more. An angry bull could stab a bear to death. He could toss a wolf so high into the air that the wolf would be killed by the fall.

While buffalo were somewhat dim-sighted, they could hear the faintest sounds and smell enemies from three miles away. And when they sensed danger, they moved fast. A bull or cow could wheel about on its slim hind legs and run as fast as a horse. When a whole herd stampeded, the earth trembled.

White explorers were astonished at the size of the herds they saw as they crossed the Great Plains. There were times when buffalo stretched endlessly across the countryside as far as the eye could see. Artist George Catlin described these herds when he traveled west during the 1830s to study and paint the Indians. "Buffalo graze in immense herds and almost incredible numbers," he wrote. "And they roam over vast tracts of country."

No one really knows how many buffalo roamed the prairies and plains before the white man came. The Indians thought there were enough buffalo to last forever. It seemed impossible that they could ever disappear.

The Hunt

On the day set for starting a hunt, everyone was up at sunrise. The women went right to work, packing their household belongings and getting everything ready for the move. Youngsters rounded up the horses and dogs. The men gathered in small groups to discuss the day's plans.

After a quick morning meal, the leaders of the hunt, the marshals, assembled. They took their feathered banners in their hands, mounted their horses, and gave the signal to break camp.

With that, the Indian village disappeared almost like a puff of smoke. Tipis dropped to the ground as the women removed the buffalo-skin walls and took down the long poles that held the tipis erect.

The poles were now put to a different use. Lashed to the sides of a horse so they trailed behind on the ground, the poles supported a sturdy rawhide platform

Band of Sioux Moving Camp with Dogs and Horses. 1837–39.
George Catlin. Oil on canvas. National Museum of American Art,
Smithsonian Institution. Photo: Art Resource.

called a travois (tra-VOY). This platform held the folded
tipi walls and the family's household goods. Sometimes
small children or sick people sat on top of the pile to be
hauled along by a strong packhorse. Dogs also worked
as pack animals, pulling travois designed to fit their size
and strength.

When the horses and dogs were harnessed and
loaded and ready to go, the people and their animals
moved out across the plains. The warriors, mounted on
the best hunting horses, rode along in front. They were
followed by boys and girls driving the herd of extra
horses. Behind them came the women leading the
packhorses, along with the small children and the old
folks, some riding, some walking, and some being
carried on the travois. Every woman had a heavy pack
on her back. The men never carried packs. They kept
their arms free to use their weapons in case of a
surprise attack.

Scouts rode far ahead of the marching people, and far
to either side, watching for signs of buffalo or lurking
enemies. Other warriors acted as a rear guard. They

followed the group at a distance, seeing that no one lagged behind.

Strung out across the prairie, the Indians formed a grand procession. People sang as they marched along, dogs barked, horses whinnied, bells jingled. They moved forward each day by easy stages, so their horses would be in good condition when they found the buffalo.

At the end of a day's march, the marshals picked the spot where they would pitch camp. The women quickly put up the tipis and prepared the evening meal as the men gathered to chat and smoke. On the open plains, the Indians usually camped in a circle, with the doorway of each tipi facing east to catch the morning sun.

When they reached the territory where they expected to hunt, the scouts fanned out across the countryside, looking for buffalo. Everyone else waited in the hushed camp. Marshals moved quietly from one tipi to the next. They reminded people in low tones not to sing or shout or make any loud noise that might scare off the buffalo, which could hear weak and distant sounds.

The scouts, meanwhile, searched for buffalo signs. Sometimes they relied on animal helpers. The Comanche watched for ravens. They thought that if a raven circled four times overhead and cawed, it would then fly off toward the buffalo. A Cheyenne hunter would find a cricket, hold it in his hand, and wait to see which way its antennae pointed. The buffalo, he believed, would be found in that direction.

When a herd was sighted, the successful scout rushed back to camp. As he arrived, people crowded around, greeting him with congratulations and thanks. First he smoked a ceremonial pipe with one of the band's elders. Then he reported what he had seen.

The chase usually started the next morning. As soon as it was light enough to see, the hunters mounted their horses. Riding close together, they stayed downwind from the herd, so the buffalo would not catch their scent.

When they were as close as they could get without disturbing the buffalo, they paused and waited. The marshals looked over the area and selected the best spot to launch the attack. Silently, they led the hunters forward and spaced them evenly, so that each would have a fair start. Then one of the marshals rode out in view of both hunters and buffalo. He waved his hand above his head, and the chase began.

Bending low over their horses, the Indians galloped toward the grazing herd. At first the buffalo paid little attention. Often the hunters would almost reach the herd before the buffalo became alarmed and started to run.

Each man acted on his own now. Holding his bow in his left hand, urging his horse on with the whip strapped to his right wrist, a hunter picked his target and went after it at full speed. His horse was trained to approach the buffalo from the right, so the rider could shoot his arrow to the left, toward the animal. As he closed in, he aimed for a spot just behind the buffalo's last rib, where the arrow would pierce the animal's lungs. A single well-aimed arrow could kill the biggest buffalo.

Buffalo Chase with Bows and Lances. 1832–33. **George Catlin.** Oil on canvas. National Museum of American Art, Smithsonian Institution. Photo: Art Resource.

Sometimes an arrow would strike with such force that it would be completely buried. It might pass all the way through the animal, come out the other side, and drop to the ground. If an arrow failed to go deep enough, the hunter might reach over, pull it out of the buffalo, and use it again.

Once an arrow hit its mark, the hunter instantly took off after another buffalo. His horse understood exactly what to do. Running free, guided only by words or knee pressure, a trained hunting pony would leap away from a buffalo's horns as soon as it heard the twang of the bowstring.

Some men found the bow and arrow too tame. They preferred to use spears, for it took more strength and courage to spear a buffalo. To carry only a spear on the hunt was a mark of daring and pride.

With any weapon, the chase was risky. Horses stumbled in prairie-dog holes. Wounded buffalo lashed out with their horns. Sometimes an enraged bull crashed headlong into a horse and rider. The buffalo claimed many victims as hunters were trampled in the dust or died of broken bones.

While the chase was thrilling, it wasn't always the best way to hunt. During a typical chase on horseback, each hunter might bring down two or three buffalo. Under the right conditions, the Indians could get better results with less danger by hunting in the old way——on foot.

In that case, they would stake their horses and creep up on the buffalo, crawling on hands and knees through tall grass. As long as the Indians were hidden, the buffalo would go right on grazing, even as arrows flew silently around them. Each man might shoot several buffalo in quick succession before the others became frightened and ran off.

In winter, when the grass offered little cover, a hunter might sneak up on a herd disguised in a buffalo robe. Or he could drape himself in the skin of a white wolf. Healthy buffalo in herds did not fear wolves and didn't run when they saw one.

If a herd was small enough, the Indians sometimes surrounded the buffalo on foot. Approaching downwind, they fanned out, moved in from all sides, and formed a tight ring. Then they ran in circles around the herd, whooping and yelling and waving their arms as the terrified animals milled about in confusion. Slowly the Indians closed the circle until they were close enough to let go with their arrows and spears.

The first buffalo to be hit would fall near the outside of the circle, blocking the path of those inside the ring. As more buffalo fell, their bodies trapped the others. Sometimes not a single animal escaped alive.

On horseback, the Indians could surround bigger herds, galloping around them in a circle. One afternoon in 1832, the artist George Catlin, armed with his pencil and sketchbook, watched from a distance as 500 Sioux horseman surrounded a herd near the present site of Pierre, South Dakota. By sundown, the hunters had killed 1,400 buffalo.

The Buffalo Hunt No. 39. 1919. **Charles M. Russell.** Oil on canvas. Amon Carter Museum, Fort Worth, Texas. 1961.146.

The Silk Robe. c. 1890. **Charles M. Russell.** Oil on canvas. Amon Carter Museum, Fort Worth, Texas. 1961.135.

From the Brains to the Tail

A successful hunt called for a feast. Beside the campfire that evening, a medicine man offered prayers of thanksgiving. He thanked the spirits for their aid during the chase, and he thanked the buffalo for giving his meat to the people. Choice bits of meat were sliced off, held up for the spirits to see, then buried as an offering.

There was plenty for everyone to eat. A single fat buffalo cow supplied enough meat to feed a hundred hungry people. They gorged themselves on fresh tongue roasted over the open fire, on tasty morsels cut from the buffalo's hump. They ate hot, dripping ribs and steaks. And they feasted on yards of roasted gut, turned inside out, stuffed with chunks of meat, and seared over glowing coals. The sweet, nutritious bone marrow was saved for the old folks. It was the only meat their toothless gums could chew.

Most of the meat taken during a big hunt was preserved for the future. The women cut the meat into strips and hung it over high poles to dry. After several days, this sun-dried meat, called jerky, was so well preserved that it would last for months. It could be carried anywhere and would not spoil, even during the hottest months.

Some of the dried meat was pounded to a pulp, mixed with buffalo fat, and flavored with crushed nuts, berries, and fruit. This was called pemmican. Packed in buffalo-skin bags, pemmican would last for years without spoiling. Sliced and dipped in wild honey, it was nourishing and delicious, a favorite food among the Indians, and later the white fur traders as well.

Every part of the buffalo that could be chewed, swallowed, and digested was used for food. And every other part was put to some use.

Indian women spent a great deal of time and effort tanning buffalo hides. After a hunt, the fresh hides were spread out on the ground, hairy side down, and pegged in place. Using scrapers made of buffalo bone, the women scraped all the flesh, fat, and blood from the hides. They cured and bleached the hides in the sun, and soaked them in a tanning fluid of buffalo brains, liver, and fat mixed with water. Then they worked the hides for several days—rubbing, kneading, squeezing, stretching—to make them soft and supple. A good hunter might have several wives working on hides taken from the animals he had killed.

If the hides were to be used as winter robes, the hair was left in place. Thick-furred buffalo robes made warm and comfortable cloaks and bedding. They could be cut and stitched into caps, earmuffs, leggings, and mittens. The finest robes came from buffalo killed during the winter, when nature gave the animal a full coat to protect it from snow and cold.

With the hair scraped off, the hides were smoked over fires to make them waterproof. They could then be fashioned into dozens of useful articles. They were used for the walls of tipis, for clothing and moccasins, for pouches, purses, and saddlebags. Babies were carried in cradleboards lined with the softest buffalo calfskin. The

Comanche Village in Texas, Women Dressing Robes and Drying Meat. 1834–35. **George Catlin.** Oil on canvas. National Museum of Art, Smithsonian Institution. Photo: Art Resource.

dead were laid to rest wrapped in buffalo-hide winding sheets.

Thick rawhide from the necks of old bulls was stretched to make tough war shields and the soles of winter moccasins. Strong sinews from the neck and back of the buffalo provided bowstrings and thread. The buffalo's hair was twisted into ropes and bridles, woven into ornaments, stuffed into leather balls. Its stomach became a water jug, its tail a flyswatter.

Buffalo horns were used for cups, ladles, and spoons, and to carry hot coals to the next campground. The hooves produced glue; the fat, soap. The bones were shaped into knives, spears, and tools of many kinds. On the northern plains, the backbone with ribs attached made a toboggan for children in winter.

Even the buffalo's droppings were valuable. On the treeless plains, firewood was scarce. But there was an endless supply of sundried buffalo dung left behind by the grazing herds. These prized "buffalo chips" burned slowly, produced a hot fire, and were ideal for cooking. They were used for that purpose by the Indians, and later by white settlers too.

A fall buffalo hunt would continue until the band had all the hides and meat it needed for the winter. Then the Indians would settle down in their winter camps. Every band had its favorite winter camping sites near woods, in a sheltered canyon, or along a river bottom. Instead of camping in a circle, as they did on the open plains, the Indians pitched their winter tipis in a line that sometimes stretched for miles along the canyon floor or the river's banks.

A tipi provided a warm and cozy winter home. Because it was shaped like a cone, it could withstand the most violent winds and blizzards. Its walls were waterproof. An open fire in the center of the tipi furnished heat, light, and a stove for indoor cooking. The smoke spiraled up through an adjustable smoke hole at the top of the tipi. At night, firelight would shine through the translucent buffalo-skin walls, and from the outside, the tipi glowed like a lantern.

Tipis were usually owned by the women who made them. A typical tipi measured perhaps fifteen feet across at the base, allowing sufficient living space for the family and its possessions. It could be put up in fifteen minutes by the women of the household. It could be taken down in five minutes. And it could be packed on a horse travois and carried anywhere.

When the hunting was good, the Indians went into winter camp with tons of sun-dried buffalo meat. They didn't have to hunt day after day, all winter long, for fear of starving. Between hunts, they were free to do as they wished. "It was a great life," said Tom Le Forge, a white man who lived several years with the Crows. "At all times I had ample leisure for lazy loafing and dreaming and visiting."

With the Buffalo Gone

Year after year without fail, the buffalo drifted back and forth across the plains in tune with the seasons. Usually they traveled in small bands. But during the late summer rutting season, they gathered in enormous herds that numbered hundreds of thousands of animals. A truly great herd might be fifty miles long and take days to pass by.

Buffalo Chase, A Single Death. 1832-33. **George Catlin.** National Museum of American Art, Smithsonian Institution, Washington, DC. Photo: Art Resource, NY.

Indians had hunted the buffalo for thousands of years without making much of a dent in the herds. Sometimes they killed more animals than they could use. When they drove a herd over a cliff, they could not always carry away all the meat. But for the most part, the Indians were not wasteful. They hunted when they needed meat and hides.

As white people came to the plains, the buffalo herds began to dwindle. By the early 1800s, trading posts were springing up all over the West. White traders wanted buffalo robes and tongues for profitable markets in the East. In exchange, they offered guns, tools, tobacco, whiskey, and trinkets. The Indians had always hunted for their own needs. Now, by killing a few more buffalo, they could obtain the white man's goods.

Soon the Indians were killing buffalo for their hides and tongues alone. Tongues packed in salt were shipped in barges down the Missouri River, to be sent to the cities of the East, where they were sold as an expensive delicacy. Buffalo robes became fashionable as lap robes and blankets. White people had them made into fur coats. During the 1830s and 1840s, hundreds of thousands of robes were shipped east.

By then, white hunters were beginning to kill more buffalo than the Indians. Pioneers traveling westward in covered wagons shot the animals for food along the way, scaring off entire herds. Before long, few buffalo could be found along the great trails leading west. Then the United States Army hired professional hunters to supply buffalo meat to western military posts. And as railroads were built across the prairies and plains, white hunters furnished buffalo meat for the railroad construction crews.

The Herd on the Move. 1862. **William J. Hays.** Toned lithograph. Amon Carter Museum, Fort Worth Texas. 1967.40

   Buffalo hunting became a popular sport. Many travelers felt that a trip west wasn't complete unless they had shot themselves a buffalo. American millionaires and European noblemen toured the West in style, with servants to hand them their guns and champagne to drink after the hunt. Railroads began to feature special excursion trains through buffalo country. As the trains chugged along, passengers could poke their guns through the open windows and fire away at the grazing herds.

   By the 1860s, Indian tribes found that the buffalo were disappearing from their traditional hunting grounds. When they went elsewhere to hunt, they were followed almost immediately by white hunters, soldiers, and settlers. "Wherever the whites are established, the buffalo is gone," complained the Sioux Chief White Cloud, "and the red hunters must die of hunger."

   Indians who once had been friendly to white people vowed to go on the warpath. Alarmed by the large-scale slaughter of their herds, angry warriors from many tribes banded together. They began to attack wagon trains, ranch houses, and railroad construction crews.

   There were still about eight million buffalo left on the plains in 1870, when a newly invented tanning process sealed the fate of the remaining herds. For the first time, commercial tanneries in the East could turn buffalo hides into expensive leather. A single hide now brought as much as $3——more than a factory worker earned in a week in those days. A professional hide hunter could bag as many as two hundred buffalo in one day.

Organized bands of hide hunters shot their way south from Kansas to Texas. Armed with powerful long-range rifles with telescopic sights, they began to slaughter buffalo at the rate of a million a year. As the animals fell, gangs of skinners stripped them of their valuable hides and left the carcasses to rot on the prairie.

Indian war parties attacked the hide hunters wherever they found them, but the hunters could not be stopped. Within a few years, the Indians saw their main source of food, clothing, and shelter vanish.

At one time, perhaps sixty or seventy million buffalo had roamed the plains. By the early 1880s, the endless herds had been wiped out. Only a few hundred wild buffalo were still hiding out in remote mountain valleys.

With the buffalo gone, the proud and independent Plains Indians became a conquered people. Their way of life was destroyed, their hunting grounds taken over by white ranchers and settlers. Swept by starvation and disease, the great hunting tribes were confined to reservations, where they depended on government food rations. Their children were sent to boarding schools to learn the language and customs of the white man.

The days of the buffalo hunters had faded like a dream. But Indian storytellers still gather on winter nights to keep the old tales alive. They speak of a time when buffalo ruled the plains, and Indian warriors rode out to meet them.

I go to kill the buffalo.
The Great Spirit sent the buffalo.
On hills, in plains and woods.
So give me my bow; give me my bow;
I go to kill the buffalo.
——SIOUX SONG

Buffalo Hunt

Meet the Author

Russell Freedman seemed destined to
be a writer. He grew up in a home frequently
visited by authors. He later became a reporter
and stumbled across a story about a sixteen-
year-old boy who invented the braille
typewriter. The story inspired his first book,
Teenagers Who Made History.

Mr. Freedman travels widely to do the
research for his books. When he is not writing, he
enjoys attending films, concerts, and plays.

Meet the Illustrators

George Catlin made a series of journeys into
unmapped Native American territory, visiting most of
the major tribes from the Upper Missouri River to the
Mexican Territory in the far Southwest. He wandered
alone from tribe to tribe, fearlessly entering their
villages, where he was greeted with courtesy and
friendship. From these visits, he created hundreds of
paintings and drawings, giving most of the outside
world its first glimpse at Native American life.

Charles M. Russell visited the Montana Territory
when he was sixteen and soon made that part of the
country his home. He worked as a hunter and as a
cowboy, while painting and sculpting in his spare time.
He later became a full-time artist, famous for his
paintings and sculptures of cowboy life.

Theme Connections

Think About It

With a small group of classmates, consider the reasons for the clashes between Native Americans and the new settlers.

- How would life on the Great Plains today be different if the large buffalo population hadn't been destroyed?
- Who "really" had a right to the buffalo herds and the land on which they roamed?

Check the Concept/Question Board to see if there are any questions there that you can answer now. If the selection or your discussions about the selection have raised any new questions about the American West, put the questions on the Concept/Question Board. Maybe the next selection will help answer the questions.

Record Ideas

Do you think some compromise could have been reached between the Native Americans and the new settlers? Record your notes and ideas in your Writing Journal.

Research Ideas

- Study the many changes that occurred as the American West was being settled. Examine the reasons for the changes and the effects each had on the lives of the inhabitants of the region.
- Compare the materials and resources used by the Native Americans with those used today in your community.

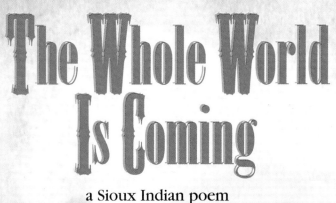

The Whole World Is Coming

a Sioux Indian poem
illustrated by Stella Ormai

The whole world is coming,
A nation is coming, a nation is coming,
the eagle has brought the message to the tribe.
Over the whole earth they are coming;
the buffalo are coming, the buffalo are coming,
the crow has brought the message to the tribe.

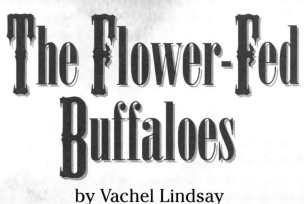

The Flower-Fed Buffaloes

by Vachel Lindsay
illustrated by Stella Ormai

The flower-fed buffaloes of the spring
In the days of long ago,
Ranged where the locomotives sing
And the prairie flowers lie low:
The tossing, blooming, perfumed grass
Is swept away by the wheat,
Wheels and wheels and wheels spin by
In the spring that still is sweet.
But the flower-fed buffaloes of the spring
Left us, long ago.
They gore no more, they bellow no more,
They trundle around the hills no more:
With the Blackfeet, lying low,
With the Pawnees, lying low,
Lying low.

485

Old Yeller & the Bear

from **Old Yeller**
by Fred Gipson
illustrated by Jennifer Heyd Wharton

Fourteen-year-old Travis lives with his family in Texas during the 1860s. Travis feels responsible for his mother and brother while his father is away on a long cattle drive. Travis thinks the big yellow dog that adopts his family is a useless nuisance until a bear shows him how wrong he is.

That Little Arliss! If he wasn't a mess! From the time he'd grown up big enough to get out of the cabin, he'd made a practice of trying to catch and keep every living thing that ran, flew, jumped, or crawled.

Every night before Mama let him go to bed, she'd make Arliss empty his pockets of whatever he'd captured during the day. Generally, it would be a tangled-up mess of grasshoppers and worms and praying bugs and little rusty tree lizards. One time he brought in a horned toad that got so mad he swelled out round and flat as a Mexican tortilla and bled at the eyes. Sometimes it was stuff like a young bird that had fallen out of its nest before it could fly, or a green-speckled spring frog or a striped water snake. And once he turned out of his pocket a wadded-up baby copperhead that nearly threw Mama into spasms. We never did figure out why the snake hadn't bitten him, but Mama took no more chances on snakes. She switched Arliss hard for catching that snake. Then she made me spend better than a week, taking him out and teaching him to throw rocks and kill snakes.

That was all right with Little Arliss. If Mama wanted him to kill his snakes first, he'd kill them. But that still didn't keep him from sticking them in his pockets along with everything else he'd captured that day. The snakes might be stinking by the time Mama called on him to empty his pockets, but they'd be dead.

Then, after the yeller dog came, Little Arliss started catching even bigger game. Like cottontail rabbits and chaparral birds and a baby possum that sulled and lay like dead for the first several hours until he finally decided that Arliss wasn't going to hurt him.

Of course, it was Old Yeller that was doing the catching. He'd run the game down and turn it over to Little Arliss. Then Little Arliss could come in and tell Mama a big fib about how he caught it himself.

I watched them one day when they caught a blue catfish out of Birdsong Creek. The fish had fed out into water so shallow that his top fin was sticking out. About the time I saw it, Old Yeller and Little Arliss did, too. They made a run at it. The fish went scooting away toward deeper water, only Yeller was too fast for him. He pounced on the fish and shut his big mouth down over it and went romping to the bank, where he dropped it down on the grass and let it flop. And here came Little Arliss to fall on it like I guess he'd been doing everything else. The minute he got his hands on it, the fish finned him and he went to crying.

But he wouldn't turn the fish loose. He just grabbed it up and went running and squawling toward the house, where he gave the fish to Mama. His hands were all bloody by then, where the fish had finned him. They swelled up and got mighty sore; not even a mesquite thorn hurts as bad as a sharp fish fin when it's run deep into your hand.

But as soon as Mama had wrapped his hands in a poultice of mashed-up prickly-pear root to draw out the poison, Little Arliss forgot all about his hurt. And that night when we ate the fish for supper, he told the biggest windy I ever heard about how he'd dived 'way down into a deep hole under the rocks and dragged that fish out and nearly got drowned before he could swim to the bank with it.

But when I tried to tell Mama what really happened, she wouldn't let me. "Now, this is Arliss's story," she said. "You let him tell it the way he wants to."

I told Mama then, I said: "Mama, that old yeller dog is going to make the biggest liar in Texas out of Little Arliss."

But Mama just laughed at me, like she always laughed at Little Arliss's big windies after she'd gotten off where he couldn't hear her. She said for me to let Little Arliss alone. She said that if he ever told a bigger whopper than the ones I used to tell, she had yet to hear it.

Well, I hushed then. If Mama wanted Little Arliss to grow up to be the biggest liar in Texas, I guessed it wasn't any of my business.

All of which, I figure, is what led up to Little Arliss's catching the bear.

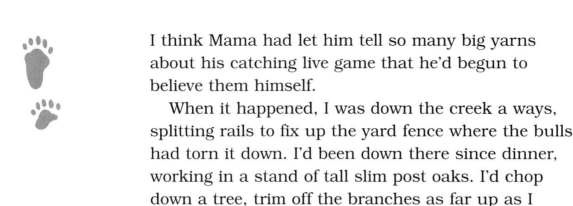

I think Mama had let him tell so many big yarns about his catching live game that he'd begun to believe them himself.

When it happened, I was down the creek a ways, splitting rails to fix up the yard fence where the bulls had torn it down. I'd been down there since dinner, working in a stand of tall slim post oaks. I'd chop down a tree, trim off the branches as far up as I wanted, then cut away the rest of the top. After that I'd start splitting the log.

I'd split the log by driving steel wedges into the wood. I'd start at the big end and hammer in a wedge with the back side of my axe. This would start a little split running lengthways of the log. Then I'd take a second wedge and drive it into this split. This would split the log further along and, at the same time, loosen the first wedge. I'd then knock the first wedge loose and move it up in front of the second one.

Driving one wedge ahead of the other like that, I could finally split a log in two halves. Then I'd go to work on the halves, splitting them apart. That way, from each log, I'd come out with four rails.

Swinging that chopping axe was sure hard work. The sweat poured off me. My back muscles ached. The axe got so heavy I could hardly swing it. My breath got harder and harder to breathe.

An hour before sundown, I was worn down to a nub. It seemed like I couldn't hit another lick. Papa could have lasted till past sundown, but I didn't see how I could. I shouldered my axe and started toward the cabin, trying to think up some excuse to tell Mama to keep her from knowing I was played clear out.

That's when I heard Little Arliss scream.

Well, Little Arliss was a screamer by nature. He'd scream when he was happy and scream when he was mad and a lot of times he'd scream just to hear himself make a noise. Generally, we paid no more mind to his screaming than we did to the gobble of a wild turkey.

But this time was different. The second I heard his screaming, I felt my heart flop clear over. This time I knew Little Arliss was in real trouble.

I tore out up the trail leading toward the cabin. A minute before, I'd been so tired out with my rail splitting that I couldn't have struck a trot. But now I raced through the tall trees in that creek bottom, covering ground like a scared wolf.

Little Arliss's second scream, when it came, was louder and shriller and more frantic-sounding than the first. Mixed with it was a whimpering crying sound that I knew didn't come from him. It was a sound I'd heard before and seemed like I ought to know what it was, but right then I couldn't place it.

491

Then, from way off to one side came a sound that I would have recognized anywhere. It was the coughing roar of a charging bear. I'd just heard it once in my life. That was the time Mama had shot and wounded a hog-killing bear and Papa had had to finish it off with a knife to keep it from getting her.

My heart went to pushing up into my throat, nearly choking off my wind. I strained for every lick of speed I could get out of my running legs. I didn't know what sort of fix Little Arliss had got himself into, but I knew that it had to do with a mad bear, which was enough.

The way the late sun slanted through the trees had the trail all cross-banded with streaks of bright light and dark shade. I ran through these bright and dark patches so fast that the changing light nearly blinded me. Then suddenly, I raced out into the open where I could see ahead. And what I saw sent a chill clear through to the marrow of my bones.

There was Little Arliss, down in that spring hole again. He was lying half in and half out of the water, holding onto the hind leg of a little black bear cub no bigger than a small coon. The bear cub was out on the bank, whimpering and crying and clawing the rocks with all three of his other feet, trying to pull away. But Little Arliss was holding on for all he was worth, scared now and screaming his head off. Too scared to let go.

How the bear cub ever came to prowl close enough for Little Arliss to grab him, I don't know. And why he didn't turn on him and bite loose, I couldn't figure out, either. Unless he was like Little Arliss, too scared to think.

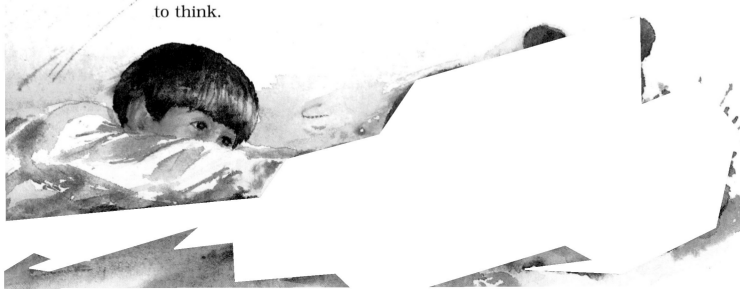

But all of that didn't matter now. What mattered was the bear cub's mama. She'd heard the cries of her baby and was coming to save him. She was coming so fast that she had the brush popping and breaking as she crashed through and over it. I could see her black heavy figure piling off down the slant on the far side of Birdsong Creek. She was roaring mad and ready to kill.

And worst of all, I could see that I'd never get there in time!

Mama couldn't either. She'd heard Arliss, too, and here she came from the cabin, running down the slant toward the spring, screaming at Arliss, telling him to turn the bear cub loose. But Little Arliss wouldn't do it. All he'd do was hang with that hind leg and let out one shrill shriek after another as fast as he could suck in a breath.

Now the she bear was charging across the shallows in the creek. She was knocking sheets of water high in the bright sun, charging with her fur up and her long teeth bared, filling the canyon with that awful coughing roar. And no matter how fast Mama ran or how fast I ran, the she bear was going to get there first!

I think I nearly went blind then, picturing what was going to happen to Little Arliss. I know that I opened my mouth to scream and not any sound came out.

Then, just as the bear went lunging up the creek bank toward Little Arliss and her cub, a flash of yellow came streaking out of the brush.

493

It was that big yeller dog. He was roaring like a mad bull. He wasn't one-third as big and heavy as the she bear, but when he piled into her from one side, he rolled her clear off her feet. They went down in a wild, roaring tangle of twisting bodies and scrambling feet and slashing fangs.

As I raced past them, I saw the bear lunge up to stand on her hind feet like a man while she clawed at the body of the yeller dog hanging to her throat. I didn't wait to see more. Without ever checking my stride, I ran in and jerked Little Arliss loose from the cub. I grabbed him by the wrist and yanked him up out of that water and slung him toward Mama like he was a half-empty sack of corn. I screamed at Mama. "Grab him, Mama! Grab him and run!" Then I swung my chopping axe high and wheeled, aiming to cave in the she bear's head with the first lick.

But I never did strike. I didn't need to. Old Yeller hadn't let the bear get close enough. He couldn't handle her; she was too big and strong for that. She'd stand there on her hind feet, hunched over, and take a roaring swing at him with one of those big front claws. She'd slap him head over heels. She'd knock

him so far that it didn't look like he could possibly get back there before she charged again, but he always did. He'd hit the ground rolling, yelling his head off with the pain of the blow; but somehow he'd always roll to his feet. And here he'd come again, ready to tie into her for another round.

I stood there with my axe raised, watching them for a long moment. Then from up toward the house, I heard Mama calling: "Come away from there, Travis. Hurry, son! Run!"

That spooked me. Up till then, I'd been ready to tie into that bear myself. Now, suddenly, I was scared out of my wits again. I ran toward the cabin.

But like it was, Old Yeller nearly beat me there. I didn't see it, of course; but Mama said that the minute Old Yeller saw we were all in the clear and out of danger, he threw the fight to that she bear and lit out for the house. The bear chased him for a little piece, but at the rate Old Yeller was leaving her behind, Mama said it looked like the bear was backing up.

But if the big yeller dog was scared or hurt in any way when he came dashing into the house, he didn't show it. He sure didn't show it like we all did. Little Arliss had hushed his screaming, but he was trembling all over and clinging to Mama like he'd never let her go. And Mama was sitting in the middle of the floor, holding him up close and crying like she'd never stop. And me, I was close to crying, myself.

Old Yeller, though, all he did was come bounding in to jump on us and lick us in the face and bark so loud that there, inside the cabin, the noise nearly made us deaf.

The way he acted, you might have thought that bear fight hadn't been anything more than a rowdy romp that we'd all taken part in for the fun of it.

Old Yeller & the Bear

Meet the Author

Fred Gipson was born in Texas. He wrote adventure novels for children and adults. These stories usually featured animals. His first big success was *Hound-Dog Man*, which was later made into a film. He is best known, however, for *Old Yeller* and its sequel, *Savage Sam*, both of which were produced as movies.

A lover of animals, Mr. Gipson raised cattle and hogs on his own farm. He enjoyed fly fishing and hunting deer, wild turkey, quail, and doves. Of his work he said, "I've always liked true adventure tales and have always felt I learned more history of my country from these tales than I ever did from history books."

Meet the Illustrator

Jennifer Heyd Wharton's illustrations are often seen in children's books, newspapers, and magazines. She uses her skillful blending of hue and light to capture and share the joyful moments that weave the fabric of our lives. Ms. Wharton says, "I use my art to sing what my voice cannot. And the song I strive to share is that of praise for the wonder and joy of life always present in the harmony of shapes and colors that surround us." She currently operates her own studio in Annapolis, Maryland.

Theme Connections

Think About It

With a small group of classmates, discuss the dangers and challenges that frontier families faced.

- Why did the Texas settlers choose to stay in a land where they faced attacks by ferocious animals?
- How did families cope with the difficulty of being separated while the men were away on cattle drives?

Check the Concept/Question Board to see if there are any questions there that you can answer now. If the selection or your discussions about the selection have raised any new questions about the American West, put the questions on the Concept/Question Board. Maybe the next selection will help answer the questions.

Record Ideas

Would you have liked to live on the rugged and dangerous

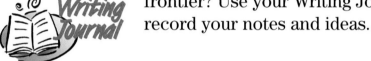 frontier? Use your Writing Journal to record your notes and ideas.

Research Idea

- Compare and contrast the difficulties faced by settlers of the American West and the dangers people in that region face today. Examine how these problems were dealt with or solved.

Death of the Iron Horse

by Paul Goble

Long ago, long before the white people ever came to this land, the Cheyenne Prophet, called Sweet Medicine, had a terrible dream: In his dream he saw strange hairy people coming from the East. There were more of them than buffaloes—as many, even, as the grasshoppers. They killed his people, and those few who were left alive were made to live in little square houses. And Sweet Medicine saw them kill all the buffaloes, so there was nothing left to eat, and the people starved. He saw the hairy people tear open our Mother, the earth, exposing her bones, and they bound her with iron bands. Even the birds and animals were afraid, and no longer spoke with people. It was a terrible dream, and they say that Sweet Medicine died of awful sadness not long afterward.

And then, one day, white people did come from the East. First a few came, and then more and more: they wanted all the land for themselves. Soldiers attacked and burned the tipi villages. They killed women and children, and drove off the horses. The people fought back bravely to protect themselves and to keep the land they loved. But they lived in fear. People said that those things which Sweet Medicine had foretold were surely coming true.

One day scouts galloped into camp, and told of something they called the Iron Horse:

"It is huge! It breathes out smoke and has the voice of Thunder. It is coming this way. The white men are making an iron road for it to go on. *Nothing* can stop the Iron Horse!" They tried to describe it. People had terrifying images in their minds.

Was it an enormous snake, or even an underwater monster which had crawled out of the river? Was this what Sweet Medicine had spoken about? Then there was even greater fear. In the minds of the children fear grew that the Iron Horse would suddenly come over the hill, right into camp.

Spotted Wolf, Porcupine, Red Wolf, Yellow Bull, Big Foot, Sleeping Rabbit, Wolf Tooth, and many others whose names are not now remembered, wanted to protect the people from the Iron Horse. They were not much older than boys, and knew they would have to be brave, even ready to die, like the warriors who had died defending the helpless ones.

"The soldiers have defeated us and taken everything that we had, and made us poor. We have no more time to play games around camp. Let us go and try to turn back this Iron Horse." They left camp without telling anyone.

They rode all night and most of the next day, and came to a ridge overlooking the wide valley of the river. Thick black smoke was rising in the far distance.

"It is a grass fire," said one.

"No, the smoke has a strange shape. *Look!* The smoke is coming this way, *against the wind!*"

"Impossible," said another, "fire cannot go against the wind. . . ."

But the smoke kept on coming, and underneath it something was growing larger.

"It is the Iron Horse; nothing else can make smoke go against the wind. See, it puffs and puffs like a white man's pipe."

When the Iron Horse had disappeared in the distance, the young men went on again.

"Let us see the trail it leaves," they said to each other. But nobody had ever seen anything like its tracks.

"These must surely be the iron bands binding our Mother, earth, which Sweet Medicine dreamed about. We must cut them apart and set her free."

With only tomahawks and knives it seemed an impossible task. But they dug down and chopped the ties in the middle, and hacked out spikes until the rails no longer joined together. The moon had long passed overhead when they finished.

Dawn was just showing when they saw a small light over the level plain.

"Morning Star is rising," someone said.

"No," said another, "it is the eye of the Iron Horse shining."

Those with the fastest horses galloped up the track to find out.

When they saw it was indeed the Iron Horse, they turned around, but their horses were not fast enough. The Iron Horse came up behind, huffing and panting, and belching out clouds of black smoke. It thundered alongside, sending forth screams and hissing and shooting sparks high into the air:

puff-a-puff-a-puff-a-puff-a-puff-a-puff-a-puff-a-puff-a-puff-a-puff-a-puff-a-puff-a-

The young men shot their arrows; one tried to throw a rope over the engine, but the horses were terrified and ran from the monster. Suddenly the locomotive jumped right into the air, and all the boxcars slammed and zig-zagged together with a dreadful crash.

Everything was twisted up in clouds of dust and smoke and steam.

The dust blew away. The hissing steam faded. There was silence. One white man was on the ground; another was in the cab. They were both dead.

"The Iron Horse does not breathe any longer," someone said. The sun rose as they stood looking in bewilderment at what they had done. Suddenly a door in the caboose opened;

a man jumped down and started running back up the track. He died full of arrows.

"Come on; let us see what white people carry in these wagons."

They broke open the first car; inside was a jumble of broken boxes and barrels. The first box was filled with axes. Then everyone was hacking open cases, excited to see what was inside. They had never seen so many different things; they did not know what most of them were. But there were pans and kettles; china plates and glass vases; cups, files, and knives, like those which cost many buffalo robes in trade with the white men. Everyone found something useful. There were mountains of boxes: shoes, shirts, pants, jackets, tall black hats, and hats with ribbons and feathers. They scattered them everywhere. Best of all, there were soldiers' uniforms and blankets, and glasses which the soldier chiefs used for looking into the distance. They even found flags, and someone uncovered a beautiful shiny bugle.

In the caboose there were things to eat, and bottles of sweet juice. There was also a heavy tin box which would not open. They knocked off the lock; it was filled with bags of silver coins and bundles of little bits of green paper. The coins they took because the women knew to make holes in them and hang them on their dresses. But they threw the bits of green paper into the air and watched them blowing like leaves.

There were bolts of cloth in another boxcar; cloth of every color and pattern.

"Ha! Look at all this! Here is more than the stingy traders have! This is all ours! Look how much!"

"Well, this one is mine," someone said, and he ran off, holding onto an end while the cloth unrolled behind him.

"I am taking this one," said another, and he jumped on his horse and galloped away with the cloth unfurling and floating after him like a long ribbon. And then everybody did it. When one tied an end to his pony's tail, others tried to step on the cloth, hoping to jerk him out of the saddle. They had great fun. The horses joined in the excitement, galloping this way and that over the prairie with the lengths of cloth sailing behind them. When they became old men they loved to laugh about that day . . .

It was only a smudge on the horizon, but first one, then another one stopped galloping to look.

"Another Iron Horse is coming. This time there will be soldiers with horses in the wagons."

They quickly gathered up all the precious things they could carry. And then someone said: "We will burn this and leave nothing for the soldiers."

Taking red-hot coals out of the locomotive, they set the boxcars alight. They reached the high ridge and looked back. The valley was filled with smoke.

"Now our people need not fear the Iron Horse. We will make them glad when we give them all these things. Let's go.

Death of the Iron Horse

Meet the Author and Illustrator

Paul Goble was born in England. As a boy he spent hours studying native American culture. Says Mr. Goble, "I have been interested in everything Indian since I can remember . . . . [Their world] was so different from the crowded island where I lived. And yet perhaps growing up so far from this country sharpened my need to know more. Over many years I acquired a considerable library of the better books concerning Native Americans and I really studied those books."

Paul Goble went to art school and became an industrial designer. However, his hobby continued to be the study of Native American culture. He later moved to the Black Hills of South Dakota and became a permanant resident of the United States. He met with Native American tribes on their reservations, attended their ceremonies, and visited historical museums around the country. With his research, he has written more than eighteen books about Native Americans. He is now a full-time writer and illustrator.

Theme Connections

Think About It

With a small group of classmates, consider what this selection has taught you about Cheyenne beliefs and values.

- What does Sweet Medicine's dream reveal about the way they viewed their land and the animals with which they shared it?
- What did you learn about their material values based on what the warriors did with the contents of the train cars?

Check the Concept/Question Board to see if there are any questions there that you can answer now. If the selection or your discussions about the selection have raised any new questions about the American West, put the questions on the Concept/Question Board. Maybe the next selection will help answer the questions.

Record Ideas

Do you think there was any way the Native Americans could have prevented new settlers from coming to their region? Record your notes and ideas in your Writing Journal.

Research Ideas

- Find out more about other famous battles between Native American groups and new settlers in the American West.
- Investigate the effects of new inventions during the development of the American West.

FINE Art

Buckskin Ghost Dance Arapaho Dress.
Buckskin. Courtesy of the National
Museum of the American Indian.
Smithsonian Institution #3249.

***Among the Sierra
Nevada in California.***
1868. **Albert Bierstadt.**
Oil on canvas.
183 × 305 cm. National
Museum of American
Art, Smithsonian
Institution, Washington,
DC. Photo: Art
Resource, NY.

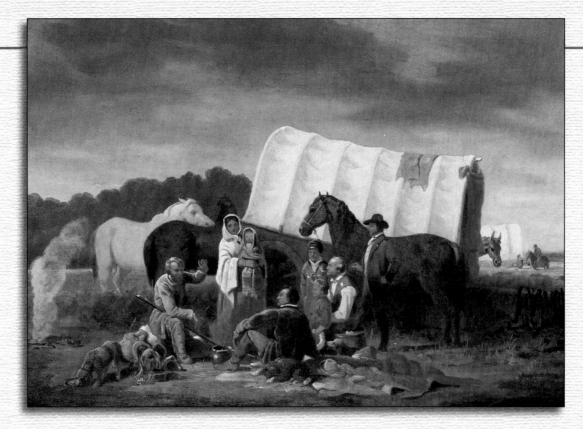

Advice on the Prairie. **William T. Ranney.** Oil on canvas.
14 × 20 in. From the Collection of Gilcrease Museum, Tulsa.

Vaqueros in a Horse Corral. 1877. **James Walker.** Oil on canvas.
24 × 40 in. From the Collection of Gilcrease Museum, Tulsa.

The Coming of the Long Knives

from *Sing Down the Moon*
by Scott O'Dell
illustrated by Den Schofield

*The year is 1864. Bright Morning, a fourteen-year-old
Navaho girl, lives with her family in what is now Arizona. Bright
Morning, her family, and her friend Tall Boy, who was crippled
saving Bright Morning from Spanish slave traders, have no idea that
an encounter with the United States soldiers they call the Long
Knives will change their lives forever.*

The pinto beans pushed up through the earth and the
peaches began to swell. Wool from the shearing was stored
away for the winter weaving. My father and brother went
into the mountains and brought back deer meat which we cut
into strips and dried. It was a good summer and a good autumn.

Then early one winter morning three Long Knives came.
They were from the white man's fort and they brought a
message from their chief. When all of our people were gathered
in the meadow one of the soldiers read the message, using
Navaho words. He read fast and did not speak clearly, but this
is what I remember.

> People of the Navaho Tribe are commanded
> to take their goods and leave Canyon de Chelly.

The Long Knife read more from the paper which I do not
remember. Then he fastened the paper to a tree where all in the
village could see it and the three soldiers rode away.

There was silence after the soldiers left. Everyone was too
stunned to speak or move. We had been threatened before by the
Long Knives, but we lived at peace in our canyon, so why should
they wish to harm us?

Everyone stared at the yellow paper fastened to the cottonwood tree, as if it were alive and had some evil power. Then, after a long time, Tall Boy walked to the tree. Grasping the paper, he tore it into many pieces and threw them into the river. We watched the pieces float away, thinking as they disappeared that so had the threat of the white men. But we were wrong. At night, in the dark of the moon, the Long Knives came.

The morning of that day we knew they were coming. Little Beaver, who was tending his mother's sheep, saw them from the high mesa. He left his flock and ran across the mesa and down the trail, never stopping.

He fell in front of his mother's hogan and lay there like a stone until someone threw a gourd of water in his face. By that time all the people in the village stood waiting for him to speak. He jumped to his feet and pointed into the south.

"The white men come," he cried. "The sun glints on their knives. They are near."

"How many?" Tall Boy said.

"Many," cried Little Beaver, "too many."

My father said, "We will take our goods and go into the high country. We will return when they are gone."

"We will go," said the other men.

But Tall Boy held up his hand and shouted, facing the elder Indians, "If we flee they will follow. If we flee, our goods will remain to be captured. It is better to stay and fight the Long Knives."

"It is not wise to fight," my father said.

"No, it is not," my uncle said, and all the older men repeated what he said.

It was decided then that we should go. But Tall Boy still would not yield. He called to five of the young men to join him in the fight. They went and stood by him.

"We will need you," my father said to the six young men. "We will have to go into high country. Your strength will help us there."

Tall Boy was unbending. My father looked at him, at his arm held helplessly at his side.

"How is it, Tall Boy, that you will fight?" he said. "You cannot string a bow or send a lance. Tell me, I am listening."

I watched Tall Boy's face darken.

"If you stay and cannot fight, what will happen?" my father asked him. "You will be killed. Others will be killed."

Tall Boy said nothing. It hurt me to watch his face as he listened to words that he knew were true. I left them talking and went down to the river. When I came back Tall Boy had gathered his band of warriors and gone.

We began to pack at once. Each family took what it could carry. There were five horses in the village and they were driven up the mesa trail and left there. The sheep and goats were driven a league away into a secret canyon where they could graze. My flock, my thirty sheep, went too, with the rest. I would have gone with them if I had not thought that in a few days the Long Knives would leave and we could come back to our village. I would never have abandoned them.

When the sun was high we filed out of the village and followed the river north, walking through the shallow water. At dusk we reached the trail that led upward to the south mesa. Before we went up the trail the jars were filled with water. We took enough to last us for a week and five sheep to slaughter. The cornmeal we carried would last that long. By that time the soldiers would be gone.

The soldiers could not follow our path from the village because the flowing water covered our footsteps as fast as they were made. But when we moved out of the river our steps showed clear in the sand. After we were all on the trail some of the men broke branches from a tree and went back and swept away the marks we had left. There was no sign for the soldiers to see. They could not tell whether we had gone up the river or down.

The trail was narrow and steep. It was mostly slabs of stone which we scrambled over, lifting ourselves from one to the other. We crawled as much as we walked. In places the sheep had to be carried and two of them slipped and fell into a ravine. The trail upward was less than half a mile long, but night was falling before we reached the end.

We made camp on the rim of the mesa, among rocks and stunted piñon trees. We did not think that the soldiers would come until morning, but we lighted no fires and ate a cold supper of corncakes. The moon rose and in a short time shone down into the canyon. It showed the river winding toward the south, past our peach orchards and corrals and hogans. Where the tall cliffs ended, where the river wound out of the canyon into the flatlands, the moon shone on white tents and tethered horses.

513

"The soldiers have come," my uncle said. "They will not look for us until morning. Lie down and sleep."

We made our beds among the rocks but few of us slept. At dawn we did not light fires, for fear the soldiers would see the rising smoke, and ate a cold breakfast. My father ordered everyone to gather stones and pile them where the trail entered the mesa. He posted a guard of young men at the trail head to use the stones if the soldiers came to attack us. He then sent three of the fastest runners to keep watch on the army below.

I was one of the three sent. We crawled south along the rim of the mesa and hid among the rocks, within sight of each other. From where I crouched behind a piñon tree, I had a clear view of the soldiers' camp.

As the sun rose and shone down into the narrow canyon I could see the Long Knives watering their horses. They were so far below me that the horses seemed no larger than dogs. Soon afterward six of the soldiers rode northward. They were riding along the banks of the river in search of our tracks. Once they got off their horses and two of them climbed up to Rainbow Cave where cliff dwellers had lived long ago. But they found the houses deserted.

The soldiers went up the river, past the trail that led to the place where we were hidden. They did not return until the sun was low. As they rode slowly along, they scanned the cliff that soared above them, their eyes sweeping the rocks and trees, but they did not halt. They rode down the river to their tents and unsaddled the horses. We watched until they lighted their supper fires, then we went back to our camp.

Tall Boy was sitting on a rock near the top of the trail, at work on a lance. He held the shaft between his knees, using his teeth and a hand to wrap it with a split reed.

I was surprised to see him sitting there, for he and the other young warriors had ridden out of the canyon on the morning the Long Knives came. No one had heard from them since that day. Even his mother and father and sisters, who were hiding with us on the mesa, did not know where he was. At first I thought that he had changed his mind and come back to help protect them. But this was not the reason for his return.

Mumbling something that I could not understand, he went on with his work. I stood above him and as I looked down I noticed a deep scratch across his forehead and that a loop of his braided hair had pulled loose.

"Did you hurt yourself climbing the trail?" I said.

He knotted the reed around the shaft and bit the ends off with his teeth. His right arm hung useless at his side.

"The climb is not difficult," he said.

It was a very difficult climb, but I did not say so, since he wanted me to think otherwise. "Where are the warriors?" I asked him. "Are they coming to help us?"

"They have left the canyon," he said.

"But you did not go," I said, noticing now that he had lost one of his moccasins.

For an instant he glanced up at me. In his eyes I saw a look of shame, or was it anger? I saw that the young warriors had left him behind with the women and old men and children. He was no longer of any use to them.

He held up the lance and sighted along the shaft. "It has an iron point," he said. "I found it in the west country."

"It will be a mighty weapon against the Long Knives," I said.

"It is a weapon that does not require two hands."

"One hand or the other," I said, "it does not matter."

That night we ate another cold supper, yet everyone was in good spirits. The white soldiers had searched the canyon and found no trace of us. We felt secure. We felt that in the morning they would ride away, leaving us in peace.

In the morning guards were set again at the head of the trail. Running Bird and I crawled to our places near the piñon tree and crouched there as the sun rose and shone down on the camp of the Long Knives. Other lookouts hid themselves along the rim of the mesa, among the rocks and brush.

Nothing had changed in the night. There were the same number of tents among the trees and the same number of horses tethered on the riverbank. Our hogans were deserted. No smoke rose from the ovens or the fire pits. There was no sound of sheep bells.

The camp of the Long Knives was quiet until the sun was halfway up the morning sky. Men strolled about as if they had nothing to do. Two were even fishing in the river with long willow poles. Then——while Running Bird and I watched a squirrel in the piñon tree, trying to coax him down with a nut——I saw from the corner of an eye a puff of smoke rise slowly from our village. It seemed no larger than my hand. A second puff rose in the windless air and a third.

516

"Our homes are burning!"

The word came from the lookout who was far out on the mesa rim, closest to the village. It was passed from one lookout to the other, at last to me, and I ran with it back to our camp and told the news to my father.

"We will build new homes," he said. "When the Long Knives leave we will go into the forest and cut timber. We will build hogans that are better than those the soldiers burned."

"Yes," people said when they heard the news, "we will build a new village."

Tall Boy said nothing. He sat working on his lance, using his teeth and one hand, and did not look up.

I went back to the piñon and my father went with me. All our homes had burned to the ground. Only gray ashes and a mound of earth marked the place where each had stood. The Long Knives were sitting under a tree eating, and their horses cropped the meadow grass.

My father said, "They will ride away now that they have destroyed our village."

But they did not ride away. While we watched, ten soldiers with hatchets went into our peach orchard, which still held its summer leaves. Their blades glinted in the sunlight. Their voices drifted up to us where we were huddled among the rocks.

Swinging the hatchets as they sang, the soldiers began to cut the limbs from the peach trees. The blows echoed through the canyon. They did not stop until every branch lay on the ground and only bare stumps, which looked like a line of scarecrows, were left.

517

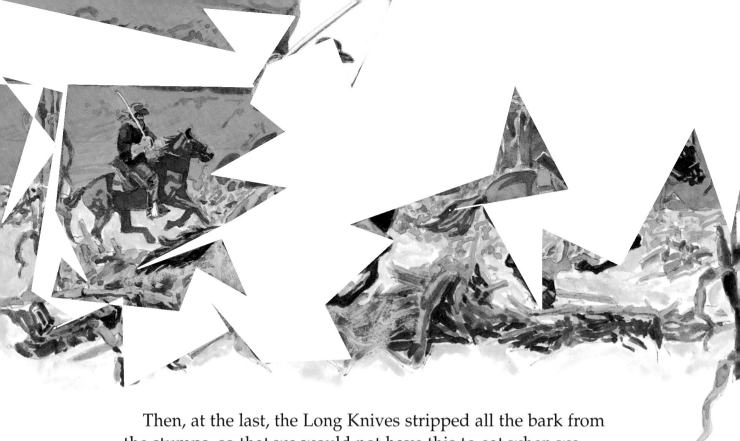

Then, at the last, the Long Knives stripped all the bark from
the stumps, so that we would not have this to eat when we
were starving.

"Now they will go," my father said, "and leave us in peace."

But the soldiers laid their axes aside. They spurred their
horses into a gallop and rode through the cornfield, trampling
the green corn. Then they rode through the field of ripening
beans and the melon patch, until the fields were no longer
green but the color of the red earth.

"We will plant more melons and corn and beans," my
father said.

"There are no seeds left," I said. "And if we had seeds and
planted them they would not bear before next summer."

We watched while the soldiers rode back to their camp. We
waited for them to fold their tents and leave. All that day and
the next we watched from the rim of the mesa. On the third
day the soldiers cut alder poles and made a large lean-to, which
they roofed over with the branches. They also dug a fire pit and
started to build an oven of mud and stones.

It was then we knew that the Long Knives did not plan to
leave the canyon.

"They have learned that we are camped here," my father
said. "They do not want to climb the cliff and attack us. It is
easier to wait there by the river until we starve."

Clouds blew up next morning and it began to rain. We cut brush and limbs from the piñon pines and made shelters. That night, after the rain stopped, we went to the far side of the mesa where our fires could not be seen by the soldiers and cooked supper. Though there was little danger that the soldiers would attack us, my father set guards to watch the trail.

We were very careful with our jars of water, but on the sixth day the jars were empty. That night my father sent three of us down the trail to fill the jars at the river. We left soon after dark. There was no moon to see by so we were a long time getting to the river. When we started back up the trail we covered our tracks as carefully as we could. But the next day the soldiers found that we had been there. After that there were always two soldiers at the bottom of the trail, at night and during the day.

The water we carried back lasted longer than the first. When the jars were nearly empty it rained hard for two days and we caught water in our blankets and stored it. We also discovered a deep stone crevice filled with rainwater, enough for the rest of the summer. But the food we had brought with us, though we ate only half as much as we did when we were home in the village, ran low. We ate all of the corn and slaughtered the sheep we had brought. Then we ground up the sheep bones and made a broth, which was hard to swallow. We lived on this for two days and when it was gone we had nothing to eat.

Old Bear, who had been sick since we came to the mesa, died on the third day. And that night the baby of Shining Tree died. The next night was the first night of the full moon. It was then that my father said that we must leave.

Dawn was breaking high over the mesa when we reached the bottom of the trail. There was no sign of the soldiers.

My father led us northward through the trees, away from our old village and the soldiers' camp. It would have been wiser if we had traveled in the riverbed, but there were many who were so weak they could not walk against the current.

519

As soon as it grew light we found patches of wild berries among the trees and ate them while we walked. The berries were ripe and sweet and gave us strength. We walked until the sun was overhead. Then, because four of the women could go no farther, we stopped and rested in a cave.

We gathered more berries and some roots and stayed there until the moon came up. Then we started off again, following the river northward, traveling by the moon's white glow. When it swung westward and left the canyon in darkness we lay down among the trees. We had gone no more than two leagues in a day and part of a night, but we were hopeful that the soldiers would not follow us.

In the morning we built a small fire and roasted a basket of roots. Afterward the men held council to decide whether to go on or to stay where we were camped.

"They have burned our homes," my father said. "They have cut down the trees of our orchard. They have trampled our gardens into the earth. What else can the soldiers do to us that they have not already done?"

"The Long Knives can drive us out of the canyon," my uncle said, "and leave us to walk the wilderness."

At last it was decided that we stay.

We set about the cutting of brush and poles to make shelters. About mid-morning, while we were still working on the lean-tos, the sound of hoofs striking stone came from the direction of the river.

Taking up his lance, Tall Boy stepped behind a tree. The rest of us stood in silence. Even the children were silent. We were like animals who hear the hunter approach but from terror cannot flee.

The Long Knives came out of the trees in single file. They were joking among themselves and at first did not see us. The leader was a young man with a red cloth knotted around his neck. He was looking back, talking to someone, as he came near the place where Tall Boy stood hidden.

Tall Boy stepped from behind the tree, squarely in his path. Still the leader did not see him.

Raising the lance, Tall Boy quickly took aim and drew back, ready to send it toward the leader of the Long Knives. He had

practiced with the lance before we came down the mesa, time after time during all of one day, trying to get used to throwing it with his left hand. With his right hand he had been the best of all the warriors. It was with a lance that he had killed the brown bear beyond Rainbow Mountain, a feat of great skill.

But now, as the iron-tipped weapon sped from his grasp, it did not fly straight. It wobbled and then curved upward, struck the branch of a tree, and fell broken at the feet of the soldier's horse.

The horse suddenly stopped, tossing its head. Only then did the soldier turn to see the broken lance lying in front of him. He looked around, searching for the enemy who had thrown it. He looked at my father, at my uncle, at me. His eyes swept the small open space where we stood, the women, the children, the old people, all of us still too frightened to move or speak.

Tall Boy, as soon as he had thrown the lance, dodged behind the tree where he had hidden before, backed away into the brush and quietly disappeared. I saw his face as he went past me. He no longer looked like a warrior. He looked like a boy, crushed and beaten, who flees for his life.

The rest of the Long Knives rode up and surrounded us. They searched us one by one, making certain that no one carried a weapon, then they headed us down the canyon.

We passed the ruined fields of beans and corn and melons,
the peach trees stripped of their bark and branches, our
burned-out homes. We turned our eyes away from them and
set our faces. Our tears were unshed.

Soon we were to learn that others bore the same fate, that
the whole nation of the Navahos was on the march. With the
Long Knives at their backs, the clans were moving—the Bitter-
Water, Under-His-Cover, Red-House, Trail-to-the-Garden,
Standing-House, Red-Forehead, Poles-Strung-Out—all the
Navahos were marching into captivity.

The Coming of the Long Knives

Meet the Author

Scott O'Dell was born in Los Angeles. At that time, California was still frontier country. "That is why," he told one interviewer, "I suppose, the feel of the frontier and the sound of the sea are in my books."

O'Dell was a cameraman on the original motion picture of *Ben Hur*, carrying the first Technicolor camera. It wasn't until after serving in the Air Force during WWII that he became involved with books. He was an editor and an author of books for adult readers before finding his true calling, writing for children. He once said, "Writing for children is more fun than writing for adults and more rewarding." He believed in children's special ability to live through the people they read about in stories.

Meet the Illustrator

Den Schofield was always reading as a child and the artwork in the stories captured his attention. His parents encouraged his interest in drawing and history. He pursued a degree in illustration but immediately joined the military after college. Mr. Schofield finally started working for the publishing industry after being released from active duty. He now makes an effort to obtain work relating to his favorite subjects: history, the outdoors, and western or adventure themes.

Theme Connections

Think About It

With a small group of classmates, discuss the role of the United States soldiers in the American West.

- One of the soldiers' duties was to resolve conflicts between Native Americans and settlers. Do you think the soldiers were objective in resolving these disputes?
- How do you think the soldiers felt about having to force the Native Americans from their homes?

Check the Concept/Question Board to see if there are any questions there that you can answer now. If the selection or your discussions about the selection have raised any new questions about the American West, put the questions on the Concept/Question Board. Maybe the next selection will help answer the questions.

Record Ideas

Has this selection changed your view about who had a right to the land in the American West? Use your Writing Journal to record your notes and ideas.

Research Ideas

- Find out more about the Navaho nation as it exists today and how the Navahos have attempted to retain their culture on the reservations.

Bill Pickett

Rodeo-Ridin' Cowboy

by Andrea D. Pinkney

illustrated by Brian Pinkney

*Folks been tellin' the tale
since way back when.*

*They been talkin' 'bout
that Pickett boy.*

Growed up to be a rodeo-ridin' man.

*His story keeps spreadin' on
like swollen waters in the wide Red River.*

*Yeah, folks been tellin' the tale
since way back when.*

*And they'll keep on tellin' it
till time's time ends.*

—A.D.P.

Long before Bill Pickett was born, a wagon train traveled west, all the way from South Carolina. It was 1854. Eager Americans were packing up their belongings and wheeling on to the Great Plains. Some of these pioneers were white folks, looking for a new life in a new land. The rest were black——enslaved people forced to follow their masters.

The men, women, and children loaded everything they owned into those covered wagons: croaker-sacks, homespun duds, and bedclothes bundled tight. To pass the time on the slow, steady trek, the southerners sang traveling songs:

> *Westward ho, where the gettin's good.*
> *On to the land of opportunity.*
> *Westward ho, gonna stake my claim.*
> *On to Texas, the Lone Star State.*

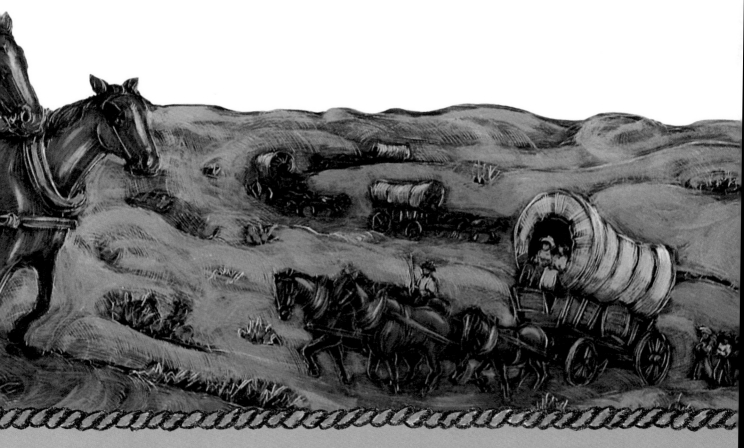

During this long journey a baby boy was born. His name was Thomas Jefferson Pickett. He was a free-spirited young'un. But he wasn't free. Born into slavery, he had to wake when his master said *wake*, work when his master said *work*, sleep when his master said *sleep*.

On the Texas plains Thomas grew up learning to brand cattle and swing a lariat. He and his family worked for the white folks, helping them tame the parched soil into prospering feed crops.

Then the Civil War ravaged the United States. And when the war ended, all enslaved people were declared free——as free as the bluebonnet blossoms that covered the Texas prairie.

Thomas married a woman named Mary Virginia Elizabeth Gilbert. They settled with other freed slaves at Jenks-Branch, a small community just north of Austin, Texas. Heaven blessed Thomas and Mary with thirteen children.

Their second-born child was Willie M. Pickett, but folks called him Bill. A young'un who took after his father, Bill was the feistiest boy south of Abilene. He was quick as a jackrabbit, more wide-eyed than a hooty owl——and curious.

Bill's parents now owned a small plot of land, where they raised chickens and pigs and grew sweet corn, tomatoes, and collards. They sold the vegetables and fruits in town to earn their living.

Bill's brothers and sisters helped tend the crops. But Bill was always wandering off. Most days he straddled the rickety corral gate to watch cattle drives tramp along the Chisholm Trail, a gritty stretch of road that snaked from the Rio Grande to the heart of Kansas.

Bill watched as the cowboys drove thousands of ornery longhorn steers past his parents' farm to stockyards in Kansas. Each trail crew had a trail boss, a cook, and a slew of cowboys. Bill always offered them a friendly "How do?" Some cowboys tipped their hats to signal hello. But they hardly ever stopped. And behind them they left hoof-beaten dirt and the smell of adventure.

In the evenings, after the last batch of corn pone had been eaten, Bill and his family would gather round the stove fire for a night of story swapping.

Bill had two cousins, Anderson Pickett and Jerry Barton, who were trail-driving horsemen. When they came to visit, they bragged about roping steer, breaking ponies, and protecting their trail crews against buffalo stampedes. Bill and his family loved to learn their campfire songs about nights on the trail, when Anderson and Jerry slept under the black western sky with nobody watching them but the stars.

All these songs and stories sparked Bill's imagination. They made him more up-jumpy than ever. He would lie in his bed and dream of the day when he'd be old enough to rope mossback cattle and help stray dogies keep up with the herd.

One afternoon Bill was straddling the gate as usual when he spotted an eye-popping sight. A bulldog was holding a restless cow's lower lip with its fangs. Bill moved closer to get a good look at how the dog's bite kept the squirming cow down. Soon Bill got to wondering: *If a small bulldog can bite-hold a big-lipped cow, why can't I do the same?*

Days later, on his way to school, Bill passed a band of cowboys from the Littlefield Cattle Company. The men were having a hard time branding their calves.

"Want some help?" Bill called to them. The cowboys looked at this brazen boy and went back to their work.

"I can hold one of them calves by the lip with my teeth, just like a bulldog," Bill went on. "I can do it sure as my name's Bill Pickett."

The cowboys turned out a rip-roarin' laugh.

But one of them put forth a challenge: "Let the boy go 'head and try it, if he dares."

The men roped the calf and threw it to the ground. Bill put his face down and sunk his teeth into the animal's lip. Then Bill held the calf firm while the cowboys pressed a hot branding iron into its side.

"Bulldoggin'——done by a young'un!" The cowboys cheered. Invented there and then by feisty Bill Pickett, that was bulldogging, bite-'em style.

When he was no more than fifteen and still itching for adventure, Bill set out to find his own way. Like many young'uns who came from large families, Bill had to go out and earn a living to help make ends meet.

Bill found work as a cowhand on ranches all over Texas. He spent long days saddling horses and mucking out their stalls. During the winter it was Bill's job to watch for wolves that crept up to the henhouses.

Bill learned to lasso and ride like the cowboys he'd seen pass by on the Chisholm Trail. He practiced bulldogging by catching steers that charged off into the mesquite brush. Soon Bill could tame broncs better than almost any other ranch hand. And every now and then, when work was slow, Bill went home to his mama and daddy's farm. Each time he had a new story of his own to tell his family.

Word of Bill's fearless riding spread from ranch to ranch. On Sundays folks gathered at local barnyards to watch Bill snatch a fire-eyed steer by the horns. Men, women, and young'uns rode on horseback and in their buggies to admire Bill's skill. They dropped coins in his hat to show how much they liked his horsemanship.

One morning, while he was working at a ranch in Taylor, Texas, Bill heard that the Williamson County Livestock Association had brought a fair to town. The fair included a full-scale rodeo. Men from the association had parked their wagons on a hill a few miles south of Taylor. Their rodeo was going to be a big event. Bill was determined to compete.

For the first time Bill performed his bulldogging stunt before a large rodeo crowd. As the steer thundered into the arena, Bill jumped from the back of his horse and grabbed it by the horns. Then, before the beast knew what was coming, Bill dug his teeth into the animal's tender upper lip. He raised his hands in victory as the grizzly critter went down without a fight.

Somebody let out a holler. "*Hooeee! Hooeee-hi-ooooh!*" All the folks watching the rodeo clapped and stomped.

"He throwed that beast but good!"

"That cowboy's brave clear down to his gizzards!"

"*Hot-diggity-dewlap!*"

After that Bill bulldogged at rodeos throughout the West. When he wasn't bulldogging for show, he still worked on ranches to make ends meet. But stories about Bill's rodeo ridin' kept on keeping on——from Texas to Arkansas to Oklahoma to Kansas to Colorado and on up through the hills of Wyoming. Now everybody wanted to see Bill perform his special bulldogging feat.

Two years later, in 1890, Bill married Maggie Turner. Bill and Maggie made Taylor, Texas, their home, and together they birthed two boys and seven girls. Sometimes Maggie and the young'uns came to watch Bill perform when he bulldogged at rodeos near their small farm. They cheered the loudest of all.

Finally Bill decided to trade ranch work for rodeo. At first it wasn't easy. He had to leave Maggie and his children for weeks at a time. And some rodeos turned Bill away. Many rodeo owners believed black cowboys should ride with their own kind.

But the newspapers didn't seem to care if Bill was black or white——Bill's *bulldogging* was news! The *Wyoming Tribune* and the *Denver Post* printed stories about the wild-riding South Texas brushpopper who could tackle a steer with his bare hands, and his bite. Slowly Bill began to earn his living as a bulldogger.

Whenever Bill came home after time on the road, he would sit his family down and let loose his tales of the rodeo. He told Maggie and their children how, everywhere he went, folks called him the Dusky Demon on account of the dusty dirt cloud that billowed behind him whenever he performed his fearless riding. All his young'uns listened close, the same way their daddy had done to his cousins' stories when he was a boy.

In 1905, when Bill was performing in the Texas Fort Worth Fat Stock Show, he was taken by surprise. After the rodeo a fine-talkin' man named Zack Miller approached Bill and shook his hand.

Zack Miller and his brothers, Joe and George, owned one of the biggest ranches in the West. Their 101 Ranch spread over three towns——White Eagle, Red Rock, and Bliss——in Oklahoma. The Miller brothers also owned a traveling Wild West show, a spectacle greater than the small-time rodeos where Bill usually performed. The 101 Ranch Wild West Show had ninety cowboys and cowgirls, three hundred animals, and sixteen acts.

The Millers' show was famous. But to make it the best, they had to have a cowboy who could draw crowds and keep folks yip-yapping for more. The Millers had heard about Bill Pickett. After seeing Bill perform that day, Zack knew Bill was just the cowboy they needed. He asked Bill to join the 101 Ranch Wild West Show. He even told Bill that Maggie and their children would be welcome to live at the 101 Ranch while Bill traveled.

Bill didn't have to think twice. Zack's offer was the best he'd ever got. It wasn't long before Bill and his show horse, Spradley, became the 101's star attraction.

Soon Bill began to take his bulldogging to the far corners of the world. Crowds stood up and cheered when Bill bulldogged at Madison Square Garden in New York City.

In Mexico City townspeople filled the stands at El Toro, the national building, to watch the Dusky Demon face a fighting bull that was meaner than ten bulls in one.

Bill bulldogged in Canada and in South America, too. And in 1914 he performed in England for King George V and Queen Mary!

Bill's bulldog act helped turn the 101 Ranch Wild West Show into a high-falutin' wonder. Even more important, Bill helped make rodeo one of the best-loved sports of his time.

After years of bulldogging with the 101 show, Bill decided to give traveling a rest. He wanted to spend more time with Maggie and their children. So he returned to the 101 Ranch, where he lived and worked as a cowhand. To keep his skills strong, he bulldogged in rodeos closer to home.

Bulldogging lived on long after Bill died in 1932. But nobody could snatch a steer the way Bill did. When Bill's children were grown, they gathered up their own young'uns and told them about their grandfather, Bill Pickett——the feisty cowboy-child from south of Abilene who grew up to be the Dusky Demon.

More About Black Cowboys

America's history is rich with heroes. Cowboys——the men who tamed the Wild West during the late 1800s——are perhaps the most celebrated of all American legends. Nearly thirty-five thousand cowboys drove cattle when the Old West was in its prime. About one in four of these pioneers was African American.

While many enslaved black people migrated west with their masters before the Civil War, others came after the war ended in 1865 to take advantage of the work opportunities they hoped would come with their newly gained freedom. With their families these courageous people sometimes built self-sufficient, all-black towns. They became cavalrymen, trail bosses, barbers, trappers, nurses, state legislators——and cowboys.

When black men and women arrived on the western plains, they brought with them their own tradition of working with livestock and tending the land. Under the lash of slavery they had cultivated the skills of branding cattle and rounding up and taming horses. They'd worked long hours in plantation fields and had made an art of growing crops from seed to stalk under the harshest conditions.

Their knowledge——along with the care and dignity with which they performed their work——was well suited to the needs of the growing cattle business in the western states from 1865 to the turn of the century.

When the Civil War ransacked the nation, many Texans went off to fight, leaving their ranches to ruin. After the war, longhorn steers wandered wild throughout Texas, while in the northern and eastern states a demand for beef grew. During the Reconstruction period, some Texans saw a business opportunity to turn the Southwest into what came to be called the Cattle Kingdom. To make this empire grow, these businessmen needed strong, capable cowboys to work on their ranches. Black cowboys were willing and eager to take on the challenge.

In the Cattle Kingdom, skill, not skin color, was the primary concern. Along with white cowboys African Americans drove longhorn cattle for hundreds of miles to railroad cars stationed in Abilene, Kansas. Once the steers reached the Kansas railroad, they were shipped to stockyards in Chicago, Illinois, and Kansas City, Missouri.

Cowboys paid tribute to their workaday world by competing in rodeos. Rodeos began as small contests among cowboys to see who could rope and ride the best. By 1870 rodeo competitions were common and popular throughout the Southwest. They eventually became large spectator events that charged admission and paid cash prizes to participants.

Today seven standard contest events make up a rodeo: saddle bronc riding, bareback riding, bull riding, calf roping, team roping, barrel racing, and steer wrestling, which is also called bulldogging.

Bill Pickett's one-of-a-kind bulldogging established steer wrestling as a rodeo event. Today's "doggers" don't sink their teeth into a steer's lip like Bill did in his heyday. But they do try——with all the might and muscle they can muster——to wrestle the snorting beast to the dirt.

In 1971 Bill Pickett became the first African American inducted into the National Cowboy Hall of Fame and Western Heritage Center in Oklahoma City, Oklahoma. A bronze statue that depicts Bill bulldogging was unveiled in 1987 at the Fort Worth Cowtown Coliseum in Fort Worth, Texas. Today folks still praise Bill as Zack Miller, owner of the 101 Ranch, once did: "Bill Pickett was the greatest sweat-and-dirt cowhand that ever lived——bar none."

——*Andrea Davis Pinkney*

Bill Pickett
Rodeo-Ridin' Cowboy

Meet the Author and Illustrator

Andrea and Brian Pinkney are the husband-and-wife team that worked together to publish "Bill Pickett: Rodeo-Ridin' Cowboy." Andrea did the writing and Brian did the illustrating. Andrea has a degree in journalism. She has been a novelist, a picture-book writer, and the author of articles for *The New York Times* and *Highlights for Children*.

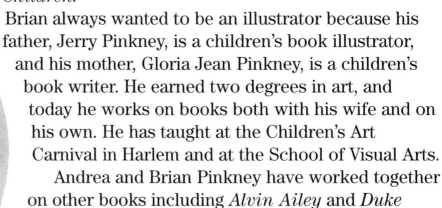

Brian always wanted to be an illustrator because his father, Jerry Pinkney, is a children's book illustrator, and his mother, Gloria Jean Pinkney, is a children's book writer. He earned two degrees in art, and today he works on books both with his wife and on his own. He has taught at the Children's Art Carnival in Harlem and at the School of Visual Arts.

Andrea and Brian Pinkney have worked together on other books including *Alvin Ailey* and *Duke Ellington: The Piano Prince and His Orchestra*.

Theme Connections

Think About It

With a small group of classmates, discuss what you have learned about the role of the cowboy in the American West.

- The height of the cowboy period lasted only 20 years. Why do you think so many books and movies have been created about such a brief period of time?
- What were some of the reasons African-Americans moved west?

Check the Concept/Question Board to see if there are any questions there that you can answer now. If the selection or your discussions about the selection have raised any new questions about the American West, put the questions on the Concept/Question Board. Maybe the next selection will help answer the questions.

Record Ideas

Why do you think westerns are such a popular genre? Do they accurately depict the historic American West? Record your notes and ideas in your Writing Journal.

Research Ideas

- Study the history of the cowboy and the developments that eliminated the need for cowboys.
- Find out more about other famous African-American cowboys.

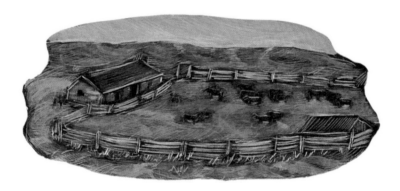

McBroom the Rainmaker

by Sid Fleischman

illustrated by Bill Ogden

I dislike to tell you this, but some folks have no regard for the truth. A stranger claims he was riding a mule past our wonderful one-acre farm and was attacked by woodpeckers.

Well, there's no truth to that. No, indeed! Those weren't woodpeckers. They were common prairie mosquitoes.

Small ones.

Why, skeeters grow so large out here that everybody uses chicken wire for mosquito netting. But I'm not going to say an unkind word about those zing-zanging, hot-tempered, needle-nosed creatures. They rescued our farm from ruin. That was during the Big Drought we had last year.

Dry? Merciful powers! Our young'uns found some tadpoles and had to teach them to swim. It hadn't rained in so long those tadpoles had never seen water.

That's the sworn truth——certain as my name's Josh McBroom. Why, I'd as soon grab a skunk by the tail as tell a falsehood.

Now, I'd best creep up on the Big Drought the way it crept up on us. I remember we did our spring plowing, as usual, and the skeeters hatched out, as usual. The bloodsucking rapscallions could be mighty pesky, but we'd learned to distract them.

"Will*jill*hester*chester*peter*polly*tim*tom*mary*larry*and-little*clarinda!*" I called out. "I hear the whine of gallinippers. We'd better put in a patch of beets."

Once the beets were up, the thirsty skeeters stuck in their long beaks like straws. Didn't they feast though! They drained out the red juice, the beets turned white, and we harvested them as turnips.

548

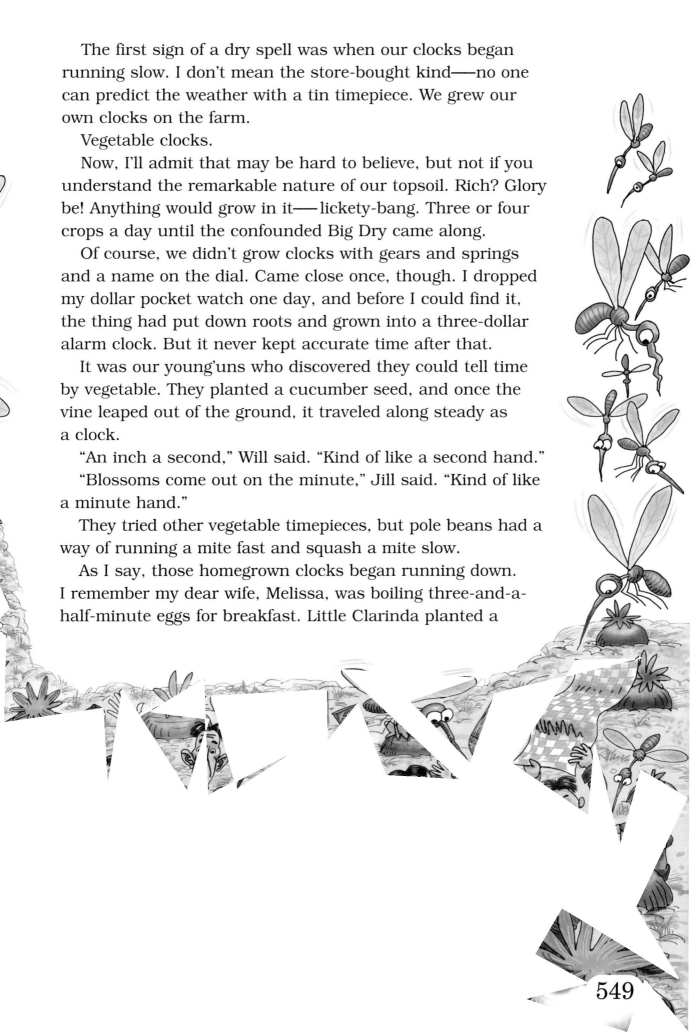

The first sign of a dry spell was when our clocks began running slow. I don't mean the store-bought kind—no one can predict the weather with a tin timepiece. We grew our own clocks on the farm.

Vegetable clocks.

Now, I'll admit that may be hard to believe, but not if you understand the remarkable nature of our topsoil. Rich? Glory be! Anything would grow in it——lickety-bang. Three or four crops a day until the confounded Big Dry came along.

Of course, we didn't grow clocks with gears and springs and a name on the dial. Came close once, though. I dropped my dollar pocket watch one day, and before I could find it, the thing had put down roots and grown into a three-dollar alarm clock. But it never kept accurate time after that.

It was our young'uns who discovered they could tell time by vegetable. They planted a cucumber seed, and once the vine leaped out of the ground, it traveled along steady as a clock.

"An inch a second," Will said. "Kind of like a second hand."

"Blossoms come out on the minute," Jill said. "Kind of like a minute hand."

They tried other vegetable timepieces, but pole beans had a way of running a mite fast and squash a mite slow.

As I say, those homegrown clocks began running down. I remember my dear wife, Melissa, was boiling three-and-a-half-minute eggs for breakfast. Little Clarinda planted a cucumber seed, and before it grew three blossoms and thirty inches, those eggs were hard-boiled.

"Mercy!" I declared. "Topsoil must be drying out."

Well, the days turned drier and drier. No doubt about it—our wonderful topsoil was losing some of its get-up-and-go. Why, it took almost a whole day to raise a crop of corn. The young'uns had planted a plum tree, but all it would grow was prunes. Dogs would fight over a dry bone—for the moisture in it.

"Will*jill*hester*chester*peter*polly*tim*tom*mary*larry*and-little*clarinda!*" I called. "Keep your eyes peeled for rain."

They took turns in the tree house scanning the skies, and one night Chester said, "Pa, what if it doesn't rain by Fourth of July? How'll we shoot off firecrackers?"

"Be patient, my lambs," I said. We used to grow our own firecrackers, too. Don't let me forget to tell you about it. "Why, it's a long spell to Fourth of July."

My, wasn't the next morning a scorcher! The sun came out so hot that our hens laid fried eggs. But no, that wasn't the Big Dry. The young'uns planted watermelons to cool off and beets to keep the mosquitoes away.

"Look!" Polly exclaimed, pointing to the watermelons. "Pa, they're rising off the ground!"

Rising? They began to float in the air like balloons! We could hardly believe our eyes. And gracious me! When we cut those melons open, it turned out they were full of hot air.

Well, I was getting a mite worried myself. Our beets were growing smaller and smaller, and the skeeters were growing larger and larger. Many a time, before dawn, a rapping at the windows would wake us out of a sound sleep. It was those confounded, needle-nosed gallinippers pecking away, demanding breakfast.

Then it came——the Big Dry.

Mercy! Our cow began giving powdered milk. We pumped away on our water pump, but all it brought up was dry steam. The oldest boys went fishing and caught six dried catfish.

"Not a rain cloud in sight, Pa," Mary called from the tree house.

"Watch out for gallinippers!" Larry shouted, as a mosquito made a dive at him. The earth was so parched, we couldn't raise a crop of beets and the varmints were getting downright ornery. Then, as I stood there, I felt my shoes getting tighter and tighter.

"Thunderation!" I exclaimed. "Our topsoil's so dry it's gone in reverse. It's *shrinking* things."

Didn't I lay awake most of the night! Our wonderful one-acre farm might shrink to a square foot. And all night long the skeeters rattled the windows and hammered at the door. Big? The *smallest* ones must have weighed three pounds. In the moonlight I saw them chase a yellow-billed cuckoo.

Didn't that make me sit up in a hurry! An idea struck me. Glory be! I'd break that drought.

First thing in the morning I took Will and Chester to town with me and rented three wagons and a birdcage. We drove straight home, and I called everyone together.

"Shovels, my lambs! Heap these wagons full of topsoil!"

But Larry and little Clarinda were still worried about Fourth of July. "We won't be able to grow fireworks, Pa!"

"You have my word," I declared firmly.

Before long, we were on our way. I drove the first wagon, with the young'uns following along behind in the other two. It might be a longish trip, and we had loaded up with picnic hampers of food. We also brought along rolls of chicken wire and our raincoats.

"Where are we going, Pa?" Jill called from the wagon behind.

"Hunting."

"Hunting?" Tom said.

"Exactly, my lambs. We're going to track down a rain cloud and wet down this topsoil."

"But how, Pa?" asked Tim.

I lifted the birdcage from under the wagon seat. "Presto," I said, and whipped off the cover. "Look at that lost-looking, scared-looking, long-tailed creature. Found it hiding from the skeeters under a milk pail this morning. It's a genuine rain crow, my lambs."

"A rain crow?" Mary said. "It doesn't look like a crow at all."

"Correct and exactly," I said, smiling. "It looks like a yellow-billed cuckoo, and that's what it is. But don't folks call 'em rain crows? Why, that bird can smell a downpour coming sixty miles away. Rattles its throat and begins to squawk. All we got to do is follow that squawk."

But you never heard such a quiet bird! We traveled miles and miles across the prairie, this way and the other, and not a rattle out of that rain crow.

The Big Dry had done its mischief everywhere. We didn't see a dog without his tongue dragging, and it took two of them to bark at us once. A farmer told us he hadn't been able to grow anything all year but baked potatoes!

Of course, we slept under chicken wire—covered the horses, too. My, what a racket the gallinippers made!

Day after day we hauled our three loads of topsoil across the prairie, but that rain crow didn't so much as clear its throat.

The young'uns were getting impatient. "Speak up, rain crow," Chester muttered desperately.

"Rattle," Hester pleaded.

"Squawk," said Peter.

"Please," said Mary. "Just a little peep would help."

Not a cloud appeared in the sky. I'll confess I was getting a mite discouraged. And the Fourth of July not another two weeks off!

We curled up under chicken wire that night, as usual, and the big skeeters kept banging into it, so you could hardly sleep. Rattled like a hailstorm. And suddenly, at daybreak, I rose up laughing.

"Hear that?"

The young'uns crowded around the rain crow. We hadn't been able to hear its voice rattle for the mosquitoes. Now it turned in its cage, gazed off to the northwest, opened its yellow beak, and let out a real, ear-busting rain cry.

"K-*kawk*! K-*kawk*! K-*kawk*!"

"Put on your raincoats, my lambs!" I said, and we rushed to the wagons.

"K-*kawk*! K-*kawk*! K-*kawk*!"

Didn't we raise dust! That bird faced northwest like a dog on point. There was a rain cloud out there and before long Jill gave a shout.

"I see it!"

And the others chimed in one after the other. "Me, too!"

"K-*kawk*! K-*kawk*! K-*kawk*!"

We headed directly for that lone cloud, the young'uns yelling, the horses snorting, and the bird squawking.

Glory be! The first raindrops spattered as large as quarters. And my, didn't the young'uns frolic in that cloudburst! They lifted their faces and opened their mouths and drank right out of the sky. They splashed about and felt mud between their toes for the first time in ages. We all forgot to put on our raincoats and got wet as fish.

Our dried-up topsoil soaked up raindrops like a sponge. It was a joy to behold! But if we stayed longer, we'd get stuck in the mud.

"Back in the wagons!" I shouted. "Home, my lambs, and not a moment to lose."

Well, home was right where we left it.

I got a pinch of onion seeds and went from wagon to wagon, sowing a few seeds in each load of moist earth. I didn't want to crowd those onions.

Now, that rich topsoil of ours had been idle a long time——it was rarin' to go. Before I could run back to the house, the greens were up. By the time I could get down my shotgun, the tops had grown four or five feet tall—onions are terrible slow growers. Before I could load my shotgun, the bulbs were finally bursting up through the soil.

We stood at the windows watching. Those onion roots were having a great feast. The wagons heaved and creaked as the onions swelled and lifted themselves——they were already the size of pumpkins. But that wasn't near big enough. Soon they were larger'n washtubs and began to shoulder the smaller ones off the wagons.

Suddenly we heard a distant roaring in the air. Those zing-zanging, hot-tempered, blood-sucking prairie mosquitoes were returning from town with their stingers freshly sharpened. The Big Dry hadn't done their dispositions any good——their tempers were at a boil.

"You going to shoot them down, Pa?" Will asked.

"Too many for that," I answered.

"How big do those onions have to grow?" Chester asked.

"How big are they now?"

"A little smaller'n a cow shed."

"That's big enough," I nodded, lifting the window just enough to poke the shotgun through.

Well, the gallinippers spied the onions——I had planted red onions, you know——and came swarming over our farm. I let go at the bulbs with a double charge of buckshot and slammed the window.

"Handkerchiefs, everyone!" I called out. The odor of fresh-cut onion shot through the air, under the door, and through the cracks. Cry? In no time our handkerchiefs were wet as dishrags.

"Well! You never saw such surprised gallinippers. They zing-zanged every which way, most of them backwards. And weep? Their eyes began to flow like sprinkling cans. Onion tears! The roof began to leak. Mud puddles formed everywhere. Before long, the downpour was equal to any cloudburst I ever saw. Near flooded our farm!

The skeeters kept their distance after that. But they'd been mighty helpful.

With our farm freshly watered we grew tons of great onions——three or four crops a day. Gave them away to farmers all over the country.

The newspaper ran a picture of the whole family——the rain crow, too.

The young'uns had a splendid Fourth of July. Grew all the fireworks they wanted. They'd dash about with bean shooters——shooting radish seeds. You know how fast radishes come up. In our rich topsoil they grew quicker'n the eye. The seeds hardly touched the ground before they took root and swelled up and exploded. They'd go off like strings of firecrackers.

And, mercy, what a racket! Didn't I say I'd rather catch a skunk by the tail than tell a fib? Well, at nightfall a scared cat ran up a tree, and I went up a ladder to get it down. Reached in the branches and caught it by the tail.

I'd be lying if I didn't admit the truth. It was a skunk.

McBroom the Rainmaker

Meet the Author

Sid Fleischman was born on March 1, 1920, in New York, but he grew up in San Diego, California. During his school years, sleight of hand performers fascinated him. After graduating at the age of seventeen, he had a traveling act of his own, performing tricks countrywide. He later went to college, after which he became a reporter and writer for the San Diego paper. He started writing for young readers by making up stories for his own children. He writes at a huge table stacked with story ideas, library books, research, letters, notes, pens, pencils, and a typewriter. His cat, Nora, sits close by to help him when he needs it. One of his most popular book characters is McBroom, who is the star of several tall tales.

Meet the Illustrator

Bill Ogden lives on five acres of land in New Hampshire, with his wife and his son. He is a true nature lover, who shares his land with a wide variety of animals, such as deer, foxes, beavers, coyotes, hawks, mice, ducks, geese, raccoons, otters, owls, giant blue herons, crows, and "extremely large tomato horn worms." When he's not drawing, he says he can be found in the great outdoors, "stalking the wild mushroom, catching the wily bass, and chasing the dreaded, garden-eating woodchuck."

Theme Connections

Think About It

With a small group of classmates, discuss this selection's relationship to the American West.

- What were some of the challenges settlers faced from natural phenomena, such as the "Big Dry"?
- Why did many large families move to the American West?

Check the Concept/Question Board to see if there are any questions there that you can answer now. If the selection or your discussions about the selection have raised any new questions about the American West, put the questions on the Concept/Question Board. Maybe the next selection will help answer the questions.

Record Ideas

Why is the tall tale a common genre for stories about the American West? Use your Writing Journal to record your notes and ideas.

Research Ideas

Explore the geographical features of the American West and the challenges the region's terrain and severe weather posed to the settlers.

The Search

from . . . *And Now Miguel*
by Joseph Krumgold
illustrated by Antonio Castro

Miguel Chavez's great wish is to be allowed to accompany his father, uncles, and older brothers on their annual move to the Sangre de Cristo Mountains with the family's sheep herds. Miguel feels that at twelve he is old enough to spend the summer with the men of the family in the mountains rather than stay at home with his mother and younger brother and sister. When some of the family's sheep are lost as the result of a spring storm, Miguel thinks that his chance has come to prove his worth as a shepherd. He intends to find the sheep. However, fearing that Miguel will only get in the way, his father will not allow him to join the search.

My friend Juby was playing basketball when I came to the yard of the schoolhouse. That is, Juby and some of the others were playing just shooting for baskets, and as soon as he saw me, he waved his hand and quit, and came over.

"How're you doing?" he asked me.

I said, "Pretty good," because what's the use telling everybody your troubles?

"D'you folks lose any sheep?" he asked me.

"What?" I made one grab at his arm and held tight.

"Sheep," he said. "What's the matter?"

"Now look, Juby," I said. "What's the use talking you and me? How do you know we got missing sheep? What about them?"

"I saw them."

"What?"

"At least I think they're yours. From the shape of the numbers they look like yours." We don't put our brand on the sheep until after we shear them. But our numbers had a different shape to them than any of the others in the neighborhood.

"Where?"

"Then you did lose some sheep?"

"Juby!" I was a little excited. "What's the use, Juby? Just to talk? Where did you see them?"

"Well——you know Carlotta?"

"Who?"

"Our milk cow."

"Cows? What about the sheep?"

"I'm telling you. She got loose last night, Carlotta, and when I went to herd her back I saw those sheep."

"Where? Where? Where?"

"What's the matter with you, Mike? Something wrong?"

"Juby," I said. "You and me, you're my oldest friend, aren't you?"

"Sure."

"Then tell me, where are the sheep?"

"Give me a chance. I saw them across the river. Maybe fifteen, ewes and lambs. They looked like they were heading straight for Arroyo Hondo." It was just in the opposite direction from where my older brother Blasito and the sheep wagon was, from where he looked this morning. "Were they yours?"

"You don't know what this could mean, Juby. That is for me."

But just then the bell started to ring, and Mrs. Mertian, who is the teacher of our school over there in Los Cordovas, she came to the door and told everybody to come in.

"Let's go." Juby went with the others into the class.

And that's the way things stood.

On one side, Mrs. Mertian with the bell ringing. And on the other side the big mountains, looking very dark and a little mad, if you can think of mountains like they were mad. But that was the way they looked, and at that moment there came thunder from behind them.

And in the middle, I stood. If it ever happened that I came home with the missing sheep? Could anything ever be better?

Mrs. Mertian said, "Miguel."

From the Sangre de Cristo there came thunder, very low.

I did not stand too long. Because there was no question about it! Nothing, that is to say, nothing at all could ever be better.

I headed straight for the *Boys* on the other side of the yard.

"Miguel!" It was Mrs. Mertian yelling. I didn't even look back. I jumped into this whole bunch of bushes and started down the hill.

Big champion jumps, every one breaking a world's record, that's the way I came down that hill. With each jump, everything went flying. My books banging at the end of the rope in my hand, swinging all around. My arms, like I had a dozen of them, each one going off by itself. My feet, like I was on a bike, working away to keep my balance. But I couldn't balance. Except by jumping. I couldn't stop. Each jump bigger than the last. I cleared a bush, then a big cracked rock. Then, I wasn't going to make it but I did, a high cactus. Each jump I thought was the last. Each jump was going to end with a cracked head, a split rib, or maybe two broken legs. But it didn't. I don't know why. There was nothing I could do. I came down that hill, like a boulder bumping in bigger and bigger bumps, bumping its way down a cliff. Straight for the river. Until I wasn't scared of falling

anymore. I had to fall! Or land in the river. But how? I grabbed a
bush. That didn't stop me. And then my books caught, between
a couple of rocks. I slipped, grabbed at another bush. Slid a
couple of feet, and then took off again. And then I landed. On
my face. I landed in a whole piled up bunch of mesquite. No
one, I'm sure ever since that hill was first there, ever came down
it so fast.

I wasn't hurt. Except for a scratch stinging near my eye, I was
all right. It didn't even bleed. All I needed was to catch my
breath. I lay there in the bushes until I did. Breathing and
listening for Mrs. Mertian, in case she came to the top of the hill
and was yelling down at me. But I didn't hear any yelling. When
I looked she wasn't there. The school bell stopped, too. All there
was to hear was the thunder, now and then, far off, and the wind
blowing quiet.

I got up thinking, I'd done it. After what Juby told me there
was only one thing to do, and now I'd done it. Here I was, just
me, Miguel, getting the sheep that were lost, all alone. And there
would be no one bringing them home but me. All I had to do
was to get up there, on the mesa across the river, round up the
bunch and march them back to where everyone could see. It
would be something worth watching, me herding the ewes and
lambs that were lost back into the corral at home. My father
would tell me how sorry he was about what happened at
breakfast, the way he wouldn't let me go help. And I would tell

my father, it was nothing, he didn't have to feel sorry.

I felt good. Looking at the mountains, and the mountains looking down at me as if to see what I was going to do next.

I hopped across the river. The easy place to cross was downstream a way, where there were more rocks to jump on. I didn't bother to go to the easy place. I could have made it even if the rocks were twice as far from each other, feeling good like I was, and all in practice from the way I'd come jumping down the hill. I only slipped into the water twice, without much water getting into my shoes at all.

To get up the cliff on the other side was not easy. It was steep in this place and wet and slippery with the rain, the stones high and smooth with nothing to grab on to except sometimes a juniper bush. And besides having the books in one hand. It would be better without the books. But I couldn't leave them around or hide them, seeing they might get wet. I made it all right, pulling and crawling my way up. Steep places and books, that wasn't too hard. Not to find a bunch of lost sheep, it wasn't.

When I got up to the top and looked, I didn't see them. I guess I did expect a little bit they'd be up there waiting for me. But they weren't. I didn't mind too much. The kind of thing I was doing had to be hard. Such a big thing couldn't be too easy. It'd be like cheating. I set out, walking to the north.

Up on the mesa, it looked empty. Like one of those pictures that my little brother Pedro draws. One straight line across the middle of the page and big zigzags off to one side which is the mountains. Then dark on top for the clouds, which he makes by smudging up all the pencil lines. And dark on the bottom for the mesa, which he makes with a special black crayon. That's all there is in the picture. And that's why it's a good picture. Because that's all there is. Except for some little bushes, juniper and chaparral and sagebrush. With nothing sticking up, only a high soapweed or a crooked-looking cactus. Nothing else.

Especially, no sheep.

I walked from one rise to the next. Every three or four steps turning all around as I walked. And when I got near to the top of each rise I had to run. Because I thought in the next ten, fifteen steps up top there, sure, I'd see them. The first few times I saw nothing, which I didn't mind too much. And the next few times, I saw nothing, too. Pretty soon I was getting ready to see them, because after an hour or so of walking and turning around and running I figured it was hard enough. Even for something big.

Besides I had a pebble in my left shoe. I felt it down there coming up the cliff. I didn't mind then, because it only made everything even harder. And that was all right with me. But now it was getting to hurt good. And I couldn't sit down and take it out. That would be like giving up.

Besides, I didn't have any time to waste. The mesa spread out, as far as you could see, with many breaks——everywhere little canyons and washes. And it was sure that on top of the next canyon, maybe, I was going to see them, those sheep. If I didn't waste time getting up there. Which I didn't. But all I saw was the same kind of nothing that I saw from the last high place, just this wide straight line stretching right across the middle.

Walking down was harder than walking up. For one thing, walking down on my left heel made the pebble bigger. It was getting to feel like a rock. And for another, walking down, you've already seen what there is to see all around, and there's nothing to look forward to until you start to walk up again. It got so I was running more than I was walking. Running downhill because I wanted to get that part over with, and running up because I couldn't wait to get to the top. And all the time, turning around. I got pretty good at being able to turn around and keep running at the same time.

Except what good was it, getting pretty good at anything? When the only thing that counted was to get one look, one quick look at those sheep.

All the turning around did was to get me so mixed up I didn't know whether I was going north, south, east or west. Not that it made any difference, I guess. The sheep weren't particular which direction you went to find them. They weren't in any direction. There were just no sheep. There was all the dark sky, and all this straight flat plain you'd ever want to see. But, no sheep.

And after a couple of hours of seeing no sheep, I would've been glad to see any sheep, even if they weren't ours. I kept trying to see sheep so hard, it was like my eyes got dry and thirsty just to see sheep. To see nothing for two, three hours, especially sheep, it gets hard on your eyes.

It was getting hard on my left foot, too, with that big rock pressing in.

And it wasn't so easy on my hands, either, on account of the books. The books weren't heavy, but when you keep that rope wrapped around your hand it can pinch. And even if you take it off one hand and put it on the other, it don't take long before it's pinching that hand, too.

Another thing was it got to be hard breathing. Because there was no time to stop and get a good breath. There was always somewhere to go take a look, and you couldn't stop because maybe that very second the sheep were moving away out of sight, and that very second if you were up on a top you'd see them.

After so many hours of it being so hard, I figured it was hard enough by then. It was getting long past the time I ought to find our sheep. Only it didn't make any difference how I figured. They weren't there to be found. Not anywhere.

And after a while, walking, walking, every place started to look like you'd been there before. You'd see a piece of tumble weed. And you were sure it was one you saw an hour before. It didn't help to think that maybe you were just walking up and around the same hill all the time.

Then looking, looking, I thought I heard a bell. I listened hard in the wind. One of the ewes that was lost might have a bell. In the flock there are ten or a dozen sheep with bells. Each one is like the leader of a bunch. I stood still, listening. Then I heard it again, and it was for sure a bell. But it was the school bell, far away, back in Los Cordovas. It must've already become noon, and that was the bell for noontime. Soon the ringing far away stopped. And there was nothing to listen to again, except the quiet wind.

It was never the same, after I heard that bell. It made me feel hungry. Because the bell meant going home to eat. And feeling hungry, I got to feel not so good in the other parts of me. Like lonely. At the beginning being alone was the best part of it, going off by myself to bring home the sheep. But now it was getting to look like I wasn't bringing home any sheep. And that made a lot of difference about being alone, while everybody else was back there going home to eat. The only way I could go home was to find them. It wasn't only so I could bring the sheep back. I had to find them so I could go back, too.

From then on, I got very busy. I didn't stop to walk any more.
I ran. Everywhere I went I kept up running, and I did most of
my breathing going downhill when I didn't have to try so hard
to keep running. There was hardly any breath left over to keep
looking with. And that was the hardest part of all, the looking.
Because there was never anything to see.

And after a long while, I heard the bell again. School was out
for the day.

It was hard to figure out what to do next.

I could leave home. That's about all there was left. I couldn't
go back without the sheep. Not after what my father said at
breakfast, and especially not after the way he looked. And it was
clear enough that in all this whole empty place I was never going
to find them, those sheep. I could just as well stop, that's all. I
could take some time and do a lot of breathing. I could bury my
books under a bush. I could sit down and take off my shoe and
get rid of that rock with all the sharp edges on it. Then I could go
somewhere until I saw a lot of sheep and sit down and look at
them, till I got enough again of looking at sheep. And then I
could decide where I was leaving home to go to.

Maybe even to the Sangre de Cristo Mountains. On my own,
by myself.

But when I looked at the mountains, I knew that was no
good. It was impossible. There was only one way to go up into
the Mountains of the Sangre de Cristo. And that was to make
everyone see you were ready, and then you would go.

Indeed, in order that I should go this way, that's why I was
looking for the sheep right now. And if I gave up looking for the
sheep, then the idea of going up into the Mountains, I had to
give that up, too. I guess if you are going to leave home you just
left home, that's all, everything.

Except, it wasn't up to me anymore. It wasn't a question that
I should give up looking for the sheep.

It was just no use.

I could keep running from the top of one rise up to the next,
looking, looking with my eyes getting drier and drier, without
any breath, and the bones in my hands like they were cracking,

and the heel of my left foot like it was getting torn away, listening to nothing but the wind——I could keep on doing that forever. It wasn't a question of me giving up, it was a question that just everything had given up, me and everything.

So I sat down. I took a deep breath. And I started to untie the laces from my left shoe. And then——what do you think?

I smelled them.

It is not hard to know that what you're smelling is sheep. If only there are some sheep around to smell. They smell a little sweet and a little old, like coffee that's left over in a cup on the table with maybe used-up cigarettes in it. That's sort of what they smell like.

So when there was this smell, I looked around. I found out from which direction was the wind. And in that direction I went to the top of the next rise, a dozen steps. And no farther away than you could throw a rock, there they were coming up the hill toward me, about fifteen ewes and their lambs, ambling along, having a good time eating, just taking a walk like there was no trouble anywhere in all the world.

"Wahoo!" I took off. Around my head in a big circle I swung my books. Like it was a rope, and I was going to throw a loop on all fifteen at once. "Wahoo!" I took off down that hill as if I were a whole tribe of Indians and the sheep was somebody's chuck wagon that was going to get raided. "Wahoo!"

The sheep looked up, a little like they were a bunch of ladies in church and they were interested to see who was coming through the door.

I showed them who was coming through the door. Before they knew what was happening they were moving. *Whoosh*—— I let my books swing out, and I hit one right in the rump. *Whish*——I kicked another one with my foot that had the rock, so that it hurt me more, I think, than the sheep. I picked up a stone and——*wango*——I let a third one have it in the rear. I got them running right in the opposite direction than they were going.

I kept them going at a gallop. Running first to the one side, then to the other, swinging the books around my head all the time. Yelling and hollering so they wouldn't even dare slow down. They looked scared, but I didn't care. I had waited too long for this. And now I wanted them to know that I was here. I ran them down the hill fast enough to be a stampede. And whichever one ran last, he was the unlucky one. There were a lot of rocks around, and I throw rocks good.

At the bottom of the hill I quieted down. Why was I acting like I was so mad? I had no reason to be mad at the sheep. It wasn't as if they started out to get me in trouble. Indeed, because of them, here I was doing a great thing. I was finding them and bringing them home. If they didn't take it into their heads to go out and get lost, I never would have this big chance.

I quieted down. I stopped and I breathed. The air was good. After the rain it was clean and it smelled sweet, like a vanilla soda in Schaeffer's Drugstore in Taos before you start to drink it with the straw. I took in the air with deep breaths. I sat down and took off my shoe. I found the rock down near the heel. But my goodness, it wasn't any kind of rock at all. Just a little bit of a chip off a stone. In my foot it felt like a boulder. But in my hand it didn't look like anything at all.

I was quieted down. We started off. It was going to be a long drive home. I didn't mind. There were so many good things to think about. What my father would say to me and my grandfather.

It is no great trouble to drive a small bunch of sheep. You just walk behind them, and if one begins to separate you start in the same direction that it starts and that makes it turn back and bunch up again. It was very little work. So there was much time to think what my uncles would say, and my big brothers. And how Pedro would watch me.

There was much time to look around. At the mountains, not so dark now and not so mad. There was much to see, walking along thinking, breathing, and looking around. How the clouds now were taking on new shapes, the dark ones separating and new big white ones coming up. And on the mesa everything looked fine. I saw flowers. Before when I was looking there were no flowers. Now, there they were. The little pink ones of the peyote plants. And there were flowers on the hedgehog cactus, too, kind of pinkish purple some, and others a real red.

I remembered my brother Gabriel's song about the little red flower. And walking along, thinking, breathing, looking around, I began to sing the song. Only the first words over and over again because I didn't remember the rest, which made no difference, because who was listening anyway? It was just I wanted something to sing.

The Search

Meet the Author

Joseph Krumgold was born into a family that was very involved with the early motion picture industry. By the time he was twelve, he also had decided on a career in the movies. After college, he went to Hollywood. He became a writer and producer of screenplays for the first "talkies." During World War II, he worked for the Office of War Information, where he became really interested in people and places. This interest led him to begin making documentary films after the war was over. He traveled all over the United States, Europe, and the Middle East making movies about the lives of interesting people and places. One of his films was about the life of sheepherders in the American Southwest. It was adapted into an award-winning children's book. This is how Mr. Krumgold became a children's book author. He continued writing books for children for the rest of his life.

Meet the Illustrator

Antonio Castro has been working as a freelance artist for the last twenty years, during which time he has achieved much recognition for his art. His work has been exhibited at galleries and museums in El Paso, Texas and Juarez, Mexico. He has illustrated dozens of children's books and created designs for magazines and album covers. In addition, Mr. Castro teaches advanced illustration for the University of Texas in El Paso.

Theme Connections

Think About It

With a small group of classmates, discuss what you have learned about the lives and culture of some descendants of Spanish settlers.

- Why was it so important to Miguel that he find the sheep on his own?
- How did the geography of the region affect Miguel's search for the sheep?

Check the Concept/Question Board to see if there are any questions there that you can answer now. If the selection or your discussions about the selection have raised any new questions about the American West, put the questions on the Concept/Question Board.

Record Ideas

How would the lives of the descendants of Spanish settlers in the West be different today if other settlers had not entered the region? Use your Writing Journal to record your notes and ideas.

Research Ideas

Find out more about the historical background of early Spanish settlers and their influence in the American Southwest.

Bibliography

Black Cowboy Wild Horses

by Julius Lester and Jerry Pinkney. Read this true story about Bob Lemmons, a black cowboy in the Wild West.

Boom Town

by Sonia Levitin. What do Peddler Pete, Cowboy Charlie, and Mr. Hooper have in common? Amanda's gooseberry pies!

Call Me Francis Tucket

by Gary Paulsen. Francis Tucket learned how to survive in the Wild West, but acquiring a family of his own offered him a whole new set of challenges.

Dear Levi: Letters from the Overland Trail

by Elvira Woodruff. Join twelve-year-old Austin as he travels the Overland Trail in 1851 and encounters the daily hardships of disease, bad weather, danger and even death.

Indian Chiefs

by Russell Freedman. Photographs and short biographies tell the story of these great Native Americans.

Mr. Mysterious and Company

by Sid Fleischman. If you can imagine having one exciting adventure after another while traveling across the deserts and plains of the West in the 1880s, this is the book for you.

Pioneer Girl: Growing Up on the Prairie

by Andrea Warren. What was it like in the late 1880s growing up on the lonely, windswept prairie of Central Nebraska in a one-room house? Join Grace as she adapts to life on the wide prairie and grows into a spirited and self-reliant pioneer.

Wagon Train: A Family Goes West in 1865

by Courtni C. Wright. Snakebites and broken wagons don't take away from the joy that Ginny and her family feel when they finally reach California. But what a long ride it has been to get there from Virginia.

Some people spend their lives searching for something—freedom, adventure, excitement, and knowledge. Sometimes their search takes them on fantastic journeys and quests. What motivates these searchers? What makes them keep going, always searching?

The Story of Jumping Mouse

Native American legend retold and illustrated by John Steptoe

O nce there was a young mouse who lived in the brush near a great river. During the day he and the other mice hunted for food. At night they gathered to hear the old ones tell stories. The young mouse liked to hear about the desert beyond the river, and he got shivers from the stories about the dangerous shadows that lived in the sky. But his favorite was the tale of the far-off land.

The far-off land sounded so wonderful the young mouse began to dream about it. He knew he would never be content until he had been there. The old ones warned that the journey would be long and perilous, but the young mouse would not be swayed. He set off one morning before the sun had risen.

It was evening before he reached the edge of the brush. Before him was the river; on the other side was the desert. The young mouse peered into the deep water. "How will I ever get across?" he said in dismay.

"Don't you know how to swim?" called a gravelly voice.

The young mouse looked around and saw a small green frog. "Hello," he said. "What is swim?"

"This is swimming," said the frog, and she jumped into the river.

"Oh," said the young mouse, "I don't think I can do that."

"Why do you need to cross the river?" asked the frog, hopping back up the bank.

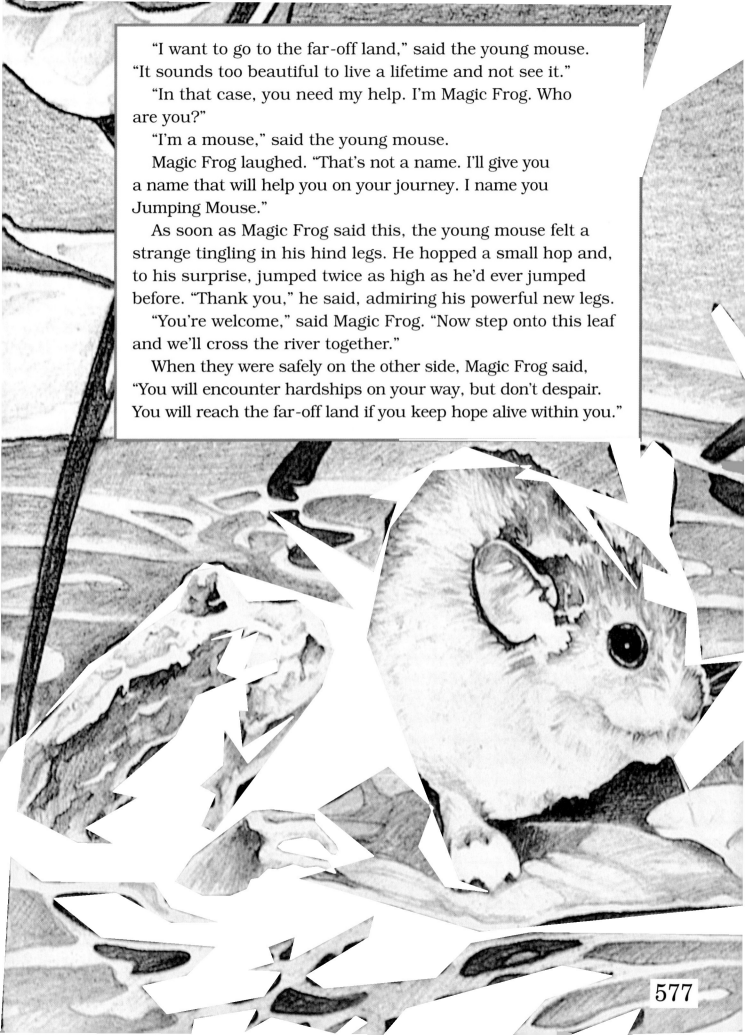

"I want to go to the far-off land," said the young mouse. "It sounds too beautiful to live a lifetime and not see it."

"In that case, you need my help. I'm Magic Frog. Who are you?"

"I'm a mouse," said the young mouse.

Magic Frog laughed. "That's not a name. I'll give you a name that will help you on your journey. I name you Jumping Mouse."

As soon as Magic Frog said this, the young mouse felt a strange tingling in his hind legs. He hopped a small hop and, to his surprise, jumped twice as high as he'd ever jumped before. "Thank you," he said, admiring his powerful new legs.

"You're welcome," said Magic Frog. "Now step onto this leaf and we'll cross the river together."

When they were safely on the other side, Magic Frog said, "You will encounter hardships on your way, but don't despair. You will reach the far-off land if you keep hope alive within you."

Jumping Mouse set off at once, hopping quickly from bush to bush. The shadows circled above, but he avoided being seen. He ate berries when he could find them and slept only when he was exhausted. Days passed. Though he was able to travel quickly, he began to wonder if he'd ever reach the other side of the desert. He then came upon a stream that coursed through the dry land. Under a large berry bush he met a fat old mouse.

"What strange hind legs you have," said the fat mouse.

"They were a gift from Magic Frog when she named me," said Jumping Mouse proudly.

"Humpf," snorted the fat mouse. "What good are they?"

"They've helped me come this far across the desert, and with luck they'll carry me to the far-off land," said Jumping Mouse. "But now I'm very tired. May I rest here a while?"

"Indeed you may," said the fat mouse. "In fact, you can stay forever."

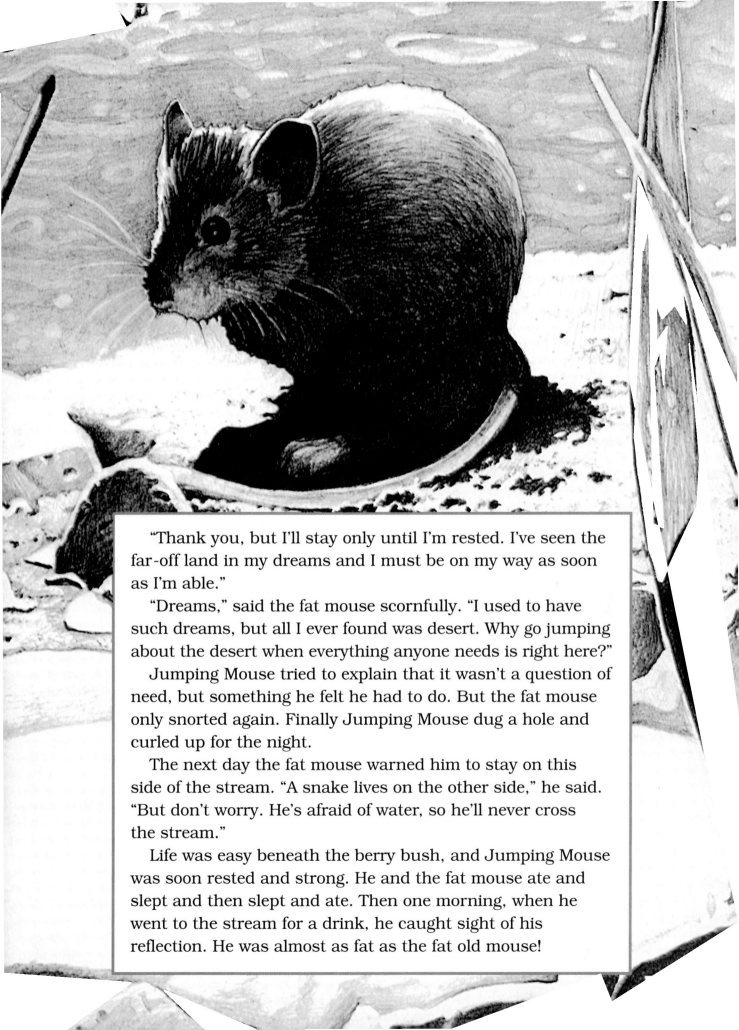

"Thank you, but I'll stay only until I'm rested. I've seen the far-off land in my dreams and I must be on my way as soon as I'm able."

"Dreams," said the fat mouse scornfully. "I used to have such dreams, but all I ever found was desert. Why go jumping about the desert when everything anyone needs is right here?"

Jumping Mouse tried to explain that it wasn't a question of need, but something he felt he had to do. But the fat mouse only snorted again. Finally Jumping Mouse dug a hole and curled up for the night.

The next day the fat mouse warned him to stay on this side of the stream. "A snake lives on the other side," he said. "But don't worry. He's afraid of water, so he'll never cross the stream."

Life was easy beneath the berry bush, and Jumping Mouse was soon rested and strong. He and the fat mouse ate and slept and then slept and ate. Then one morning, when he went to the stream for a drink, he caught sight of his reflection. He was almost as fat as the fat old mouse!

"It's time for me to go on," thought Jumping Mouse. "I didn't come all this way to settle down under a berry bush."

Just then he noticed that a branch had gotten caught in the narrow of the stream. It spanned the water like a bridge——now the snake could cross! Jumping Mouse hurried back to warn the fat mouse. But the mousehole was empty, and there was a strange smell in the air. Snake. Jumping Mouse was too late. "Poor old friend," he thought as he hurried away. "He lost hope of finding his dream and now his life is over."

Jumping Mouse traveled throughout the night, and the next morning he saw that he had reached a grassy plain. Exhausted, he hopped toward a large boulder where he could rest in safety. But as he got closer, he realized the boulder was an enormous, shaggy bison lying in the grass. Every once in a while it groaned.

Jumping Mouse shivered at the terrible sound. "Hello, great one," he said bravely. "I'm Jumping Mouse and I'm traveling to the far-off land. Why do you lie here as if you were dying?"

"Because I *am* dying," said the bison. "I drank from a poisoned stream, and it blinded me. I can't see to find tender grass to eat or sweet water to drink. I'll surely die."

Jumping Mouse was sad to see so wondrous a beast so helpless. "When I began my journey," he said, "Magic Frog gave me a name and strong legs to carry me to the far-off land. My magic is not as powerful as hers, but I'll do what I can to help you. I name you Eyes-of-a-Mouse."

As soon as he had spoken Jumping Mouse heard the bison snort with joy. He heard but he could no longer see, for he had given the bison his own sight.

"Thank you," said Eyes-of-a-Mouse. "You are small, but you have done a great thing. If you will hop along beneath me, the shadows of the sky won't see you, and I will guide you to the mountains."

Jumping Mouse did as he was told. He hopped to the rhythm of the bison's hooves, and in this way he reached the foot of the mountains.

"I am an animal of the plains, so I must stop here," said Eyes-of-a-Mouse. "How will you cross the mountains when you can't see?"

"There will be a way," said Jumping Mouse. "Hope is alive within me." He said good-bye to his friend; then he dug a hole and went to sleep.

The next morning Jumping Mouse woke to cool breezes that blew down from the mountain peaks. Cautiously he set out in the direction of the coolness. He had not gone far when he felt fur beneath his paws. He jumped back in alarm and sniffed the air. Wolf! He froze in terror, but when nothing happened he gathered up his courage and said, "Excuse me. I'm Jumping Mouse, and I'm traveling to the far-off land. Can you tell me the way?"

"I would if I could," said the wolf, "but a wolf finds his way with his nose, and mine will no longer smell for me."

"What happened?" asked Jumping Mouse.

"I was once a proud and lazy creature," replied the wolf. "I misused the gift of smell, and so I lost it. I have learned not to be proud, but without my nose to tell me where I am and where I am going, I cannot survive. I am lying here waiting for the end."

Jumping Mouse was saddened by the wolf's story. He told him about Magic Frog and Eyes-of-a-Mouse. "I have a little magic left," he said. "I'll be happy to help you. I name you Nose-of-a-Mouse."

The wolf howled for joy. Jumping Mouse could hear him sniffing the air, taking in the mountain fragrances. But Jumping Mouse could no longer smell the pine-scented breezes. He no longer had the use of his nose or his eyes. "You are but a small creature," said Nose-of-a-Mouse, "but you have given me a great gift. You must let me thank you. Come, hop along beneath where the shadows of the sky won't see you. I will guide you through the mountains to the far-off land."

So Jumping Mouse hopped to the rhythm of the wolf's padding paws, and in this way he reached the far-off land.

"I am an animal of the mountains, so I must stop here," said Nose-of-a-Mouse. "How will you manage if you can no longer see or smell?"

"There will be a way," said Jumping Mouse. He then said good-bye to his friend and dug a hole and went to sleep.

The next morning Jumping Mouse woke up and crawled from his hole. "I am here," he said. "I feel the earth beneath my paws. I hear the wind rustling leaves on the trees. The sun warms my bones. All is not lost, but I'll never be as I was. How will I ever manage?" Then Jumping Mouse began to cry.

"Jumping Mouse," he heard a gravelly voice say.

"Magic Frog, is that you?" Jumping Mouse asked, swallowing his tears.

"Yes," said Magic Frog. "Don't cry, Jumping Mouse. Your unselfish spirit has brought you great hardship, but it is that same spirit of hope and compassion that has brought you to the far-off land. You have nothing to fear, Jumping Mouse. Jump high, Jumping Mouse," commanded Magic Frog.

Jumping Mouse did as he was told and jumped as high as he could. Then he felt the air lifting him higher still into the sky. He stretched out his paws in the sun and felt strangely powerful. To his joy he began to see the wondrous beauty of the world above and below and to smell the scent of earth and sky and living things.

"Jumping Mouse," he heard Magic Frog call. "I give you a new name. You are now called Eagle, and you will live in the far-off land forever."

The Story of Jumping Mouse

Meet the Author and Illustrator

John Steptoe was born on September 14, 1950. He grew up in the Bedford-Stuyvesant section of Brooklyn, New York. As a teenager, he was sent to a special art school in Manhattan. While still in high school, he took his portfolio of artwork to the editors of *Harper's Magazine*. They suggested he use his artwork for a children's book. *Stevie* became his first children's book and was published by the time he was 19 years old. By the age of 20, the John Steptoe Library in Brooklyn was dedicated to him.

Over the next two decades, Mr. Steptoe illustrated over a dozen books. His first goal was to create books that could be enjoyed especially by African-American children. However, he said later in his career, "I hope I have made a statement that is even greater than my discovery of reasons to be proud of African ancestors. I hope my writing is also a statement of brotherhood in the wide world into which I was born."

Theme Connections

Think About It

With a small group of classmates, discuss how this selection added to your knowledge of journeys and quests. During discussion, address the following questions.

- What did this story teach us about obstacles to our goals?
- How and why did Jumping Mouse choose to share his strengths with all the animals he met?
- What did the Magic Frog mean when he said that Jumping Mouse would reach the far-off land if he kept his hopes alive?

Record Ideas

Record in your Writing Journal any thoughts, ideas, or new questions you may have about the unit theme.

Create a Storyboard

With a small group of classmates, create a storyboard of the main events and characters in "The Story of Jumping Mouse." Make sure that all of the main ideas, goals, and obstacles are depicted in the order in which they occurred in the story. Also, accompany each storyboard frame with dialogue from the selection.

Sacagawea's Journey

from *Sacagawea*
by Betty Westrom Skold
illustrated by Craig Spearing

In 1803, President Thomas Jefferson purchased the Louisiana Territory, an area that extended from the Mississippi River to the Rocky Mountains and that doubled the size of the United States. In 1804, he sent an expedition headed by Meriwether Lewis and William Clark to explore this region and to find a route through it to the Pacific Ocean. About forty-five men set off from St. Louis and traveled up the Missouri River to the territory of the Mandan Indians. There they met a French fur trader, Toussaint Charbonneau, and his wife, Sacagawea. Sacagawea was not a Mandan. She was a Shoshone, a member of a group living in the Rocky Mountains. Sacagawea had been captured as a young girl and brought east. At the time she met Lewis and Clark she was sixteen or seventeen years old and had recently given birth to a son that the men nicknamed Pompy. She and her husband were hired to go with the expedition as interpreters and guides.

Sacagawea stuffed a little more soft, dry grass into Pompy's cradleboard, put the child into it, and tied the rawhide thongs. Her eyes swept the room that had sheltered her through the winter, now stripped of the buffalo robes and the hunting and cooking gear. The last fire was dying on the hearth as she stepped outside.

The ground under her moccasins was spongy and damp from the melting snow. Tender new buds dotted the cottonwoods. For several days Lewis and Clark had seen swans and wild geese flying northeastward in the evening.

The Hidatsas had been leaping across the ice cakes to catch the buffalo floating downstream. Soon the river would be ice-free and ready. The captains had taken charge of the final packing, carefully separating the maps, papers, and wildlife specimens that would be sent back to President Jefferson from the provisions that would go farther up the Missouri with their Corps of Discovery.

Now it was April 7, 1805. Today they would say good-bye to the Mandans and Hidatsas, who watched from the banks of the river. It would also be a day of parting for six American soldiers and two French traders, who would return to St. Louis with the keelboat and two canoes. The main part of the Corps of Discovery——Captains Lewis and Clark, Sacagawea, Pompy, Charbonneau and another interpreter, three sergeants, twenty-three privates, and a black slave named York——would follow the Missouri westward in the two long pirogues and six dugout canoes.

Shadows were lengthening into late afternoon when the big keelboat and two canoes began to move back down the Missouri toward St. Louis. Almost at the same time, the six dugout canoes and two pirogues of the westbound party pushed away from the shoreline and started up the river.

The men were in good spirits——talking, laughing, waving at the Indians along the banks. Sacagawea began the journey

more quietly. No sign of excitement showed on her face, and her voice was calm. Only months later would the others realize the depth of her feeling as she started the journey.

Sacagawea took her turn with the others, sometimes paddling in one of the boats, often walking along the shore. The world of the plains seemed to flow by. Flocks of geese fed in the young grass, while sparrow hawks wheeled across the sky. Patches of juniper spread along the sides of the hills. Maple trees were budding and plum bushes were in bloom, but winter was not quite over. Once in a while snow would sift down briefly on a land that had already felt the touch of spring.

At Fort Mandan Sacagawea had become acquainted with the military life of the Americans. She had grown used to the uniforms, the salutes, the sentinels, the commands, and had learned the names of the thirty men whom her family had joined. As the real work of the expedition began, she came to know each person as an individual. Each one had been chosen for the skills that would help the Corps of Discovery as a whole.

Captain Lewis was a brave and thoughtful leader who enjoyed walking alone out on the prairie, studying the animals or gathering bits of plant life. It was he who learned to chart their route by the stars. Captain Lewis also served as doctor for the expedition, giving out medicines from his small leather bag. Sacagawea learned that Captain Clark's talents as mapmaker and peacemaker were equaled by his leadership skills.

Private Cruzatte, whose violin music had delighted her at Fort Mandan parties, was experienced in river travel. Sergeant Gass was a carpenter, and Private Shields was an expert gunsmith. Drewyer served as an interpreter, but he was also an able hunter. The black man, York, worked as Captain Clark's personal servant, and he provided entertainment for the whole Corps with his story-telling. Sergeant Ordway became a capable commander whenever the captains were not around. John Colter, from the Kentucky woods, had been chosen for hunting skills, and in a single day he bagged an elk, three deer, a wolf, and five turkeys. Charbonneau proved to be a surprisingly good trail cook.

Even Scannon, Captain Clark's big, black, Newfoundland dog, had his chores. An alert watchdog, he frightened away animals who wandered into camp during the night. He also helped with Pompy, lying like a faithful guardian beside the baby's cradleboard.

Sacagawea cheerfully kept pace along the trail, moving with a light, firm step. Food-gathering skills from her Shoshone childhood proved useful again and again. Just two days from Fort Mandan, when they had halted for dinner, she sharpened a digger stick and began to poke around in small piles of driftwood. She uncovered a good supply of wild artichokes, buried there by mice.

Day after day Sacagawea walked along the shore or rode in a canoe with the others, but in a sense she made the journey alone. Not even the child on her shoulders shared her experience. No one else could share her dream of homecoming.

Evenings around the campfire were a pleasant time. After supper the men would often throw quoits, a game in which they tossed rope rings at stakes. Sometimes they danced to the music of violin and mouth harp. The captains and several of the others faithfully wrote down each day's events in their journals by the dim light of the fire. Sacagawea sat cross-legged on the ground, mending buckskins and watching over Pompy.

For several days they passed through prairie country like one large grassy pasture. Gentle herds of buffalo, elk, and antelope gazed at them curiously, sometimes following the men who walked on shore. Deer peered shyly from the brush.

By late April they had reached the woodlands at the mouth of the Yellowstone River. Happy to have arrived at this first important landmark, they celebrated with music, dancing, and a small ration of spirits.

May 14 brought troubles to the expedition. Six of the hunters wounded a brown grizzly. Crazed by pain, the bear charged and chased them along the bank. The men plunged into the river, and others in the party were able to kill the bear with eight shots.

After sunset that evening the white pirogue was almost destroyed. The sail had been raised to take advantage of a brisk wind. Steering was Charbonneau, a timid and clumsy river pilot. A sudden squall struck the boat at an angle, ripping the brace of the sail from the man who held it, and the boat tipped over on its side. Charbonneau had never learned to swim. He cried out to God in terror and dropped the rudder. Cruzatte, in the bow, threatened to shoot him if he did not take hold of the rudder and do his duty. A trembling Charbonneau obeyed.

Meanwhile Sacagawea, balancing the baby on her back, calmly reached far out over the side and grabbed the valuable cargo that had fallen overboard. After the pirogue had been dragged to shore and bailed out with kettles, the

592

rescued articles were spread out on the ground to dry. By her quick thinking Sacagawea had saved many things of value to the expedition. She had rescued instruments for navigation, scientific books needed by the captains for their work, and trading goods needed to make peaceful contact with Indians they would meet along the way.

Almost every day the travelers reached some new tributary of the Missouri. They remembered maps drawn on skins or in the earth by Hidatsa warriors back at Fort Mandan. As each river was identified by its Hidatsa name, they could feel confident that they were on the right track. When they came to a river with water the tan color of milky tea, they named it the Milk River. This was the river known to the Hidatsas as "The River Which Scolds At All Others." Small, unnamed streams were given new names by Lewis and Clark. When a lively, clear-running river was named for Sacagawea, she accepted the honor with shy pleasure. Another stream was called Blowing Fly Creek for the hordes of flies that swarmed over their meat. Judith's River was named for a friend of Captain Clark's from Virginia.

In the high country near the mouth of Judith's River, they found the remains of a large Indian camp that had been deserted a short time before. All over the hills were the scattered ashes of cooking fires where tipis had stood. A child's ball and a moccasin found on the site were brought to Sacagawea. She looked at them carefully, then shook her head. They were not Shoshones.

In early June the party came to a branching of the river that gave them a problem. Which of the branches was the "true Missouri"? Was it the one that seemed to come from the north, or was it the branch that flowed from the southwest? Most of the Corps were sure that the northern branch was the Missouri. It looked like the river they had followed all the way from the Mississippi, broad and thick with mud. The captains, on the other hand, wanted to follow the southern branch, a clear, swift-running stream with a rock and gravel bed. They reasoned that the Missouri had its source in the mountains and that a mountain stream would be swift and clear.

A wrong decision could be a costly mistake. Already they could see snow-topped mountains in the distance. Even if they should find the "Northwest Passage," crossing the mountains in winter would be a risky business. If they should turn up the wrong river, it could waste precious weeks of summer travel time. The captains decided that a camp should be set up for a few days at the fork of the rivers. Small exploring parties would go up each of the branches and decide which fork led to the Great Falls described by the Hidatsas, and from there to Shoshone country.

Clearly it was a good time to pause. Those not in the exploring parties could spend their time dressing skins for clothing. Uniforms had fallen to shreds, and buckskin clothing had to be made to replace them. Moccasins had been so cut by the rocky trails that they had been thrown away, and the men could barely walk on their bruised feet. Many of them were exhausted from towing the boats free from sandbars or sloshing through cold water up to their armpits. Poor diet and muddy water caused diarrhea and nausea, while chilling rains brought raging fever.

Lewis was so sure that the muddy northern branch could not be the Missouri that he named it Maria's River, after his cousin, Maria Wood. Nevertheless, he agreed to take a party up this river while Captain Clark explored the southern branch. The Lewis party found out that the northern branch flowed through a picture book country of beautiful birds, wild roses, and herds of game animals, but both he and Clark were still convinced that the southern branch was the Missouri. To find out for sure, they decided that Lewis would take four men and follow the southern branch on foot in search of the Great Falls.

Lewis and a small land party pushed up into the rolling hills and across a level plain. Suddenly he heard the distant sound of falling water and saw spray rising above the horizon. He followed the sound of roaring water until he stood on a pile of rocks and looked in wonder at the water cascading over huge bluffs, nine hundred feet wide and eighty feet high. In some places the water fell in great sheets, while at other points it was broken by rocks into glittering spray. He had reached the Great Falls of the Missouri River. Back at camp, he reported that there was no way to pass this point by water. They would have to organize a portage around the falls, but they had followed the "true Missouri."

Captain Lewis learned that Sacagawea had become ill during his absence. The young woman who had met all the hardships of the journey now lay sick in the covered part of the white pirogue, shaded from the July heat. She was gripped by many pains, weak, and exhausted. Her pulse was irregular, and her fingers twitched. Captain Clark had tried medicines and had bled her, but she was no better.

The white explorers were worried. They had grown fond of this brave Shoshone woman, and she had been useful to them in finding roots, sewing buckskin, and pointing out the landmarks along the way. Now, just when they needed her most, on the very edge of Shoshone country, she lay close to death.

Finally, in desperation, Captain Lewis had mineral water brought from a nearby sulfur spring and poured it down her throat. Within minutes Sacagawea began to perspire, and her pulse grew stronger. The crisis had passed.

The captains decided that the Maria's River camp would be a good place to leave the large red pirogue and some of

the provisions to lighten the load for the portage around the falls and for travel through the mountains. The men dug deep, bottle-shaped holes called caches in the ground and filled them with salt, tools, powder, and lead. Signs of the digging were removed. They dragged the pirogue up on an island, tied it to trees, and covered it with brush.

To move the six dugouts around the falls, they built makeshift wagons. The mast of the white pirogue was cut up for axles and rounds were sliced from a huge cottonwood tree to form wheels.

The eighteen-mile portage around the Great Falls was an eleven-day struggle. The explorers limped in thin moccasins over needle-sharp ground covered with buffalo tracks and prickly pear cactus, shoving the two heavy, clumsy carts. Axles cracked and wagon tongues broke, so new ones had to be made from willow trees. In a stiff breeze the men hoisted a sail on one of the canoes and the wind helped carry it along on the wagon wheels.

One day a sudden storm pelted the party with huge, bouncing hailstones. Water filled runoff channels, almost sweeping Captain Clark, Sacagawea, and Pompy away in a flash flood. They found shelter under a rock shelf and watched a wall of water moving down the creek. Pushing the mother and baby ahead of him, Captain Clark scrambled up the hill to safety just before they would have been swept away.

After they had completed the exhausting portage, they built two canoes and moved up the river, which was narrow and crowded with islands. At a place where the Missouri loops like a rattlesnake, huge rocks hung out over the banks and pressed the river into a narrow channel. Captain Lewis marveled at the scene and called it the "Gates of the Rocky Mountains."

Time had been lost in the portage, and the explorers were impatient to find the Shoshones. Each day they found new signs that the Shoshones were near, including many small, deserted camps among the hills. Sacagawea pointed out remains of willow shelters and trees that had been stripped of bark, explaining that the Shoshones used the soft underpart of the wood for food. One morning they saw smoke rising in the distance. They guessed that the Shoshones might have seen their party and set the prairie afire to warn other families that Blackfeet or Hidatsa warriors might be near.

In a green valley Sacagawea identified White Earth Creek, where her people used to gather earth for their paint. The Three Forks of the Missouri were near. For Sacagawea and for the Corps of Discovery, it was a time of hope. Soon

they would set foot in the land of her people, the Land of the Shining Mountains.

Every day brought fresh signs that the Shoshones were near, creating new hope that contact could be made. Sacagawea rode in the river party with Lewis, while Captain Clark and a few others moved ahead by land, scouting for signs of the Shoshones. The Rocky Mountains crowded in close to the river like tall, rugged giants, and Captain Lewis was worried. They might be headed toward savage rapids or waterfalls. Could the river possibly run through these mountains without suddenly tossing their canoes into some wild, unexpected danger? Sacagawea assured him that the river would not suddenly change. There would be a strong and rapid flow, but no waterfalls that could wreck the canoes.

Misery followed them up the river. Shoulders ached from poling canoes between rocks. Cactus needles pierced their feet, and barbed seeds poked through their leggings. Each evening Sacagawea huddled close to the fire, protecting

Pompy from the mosquitoes and gnats that swarmed around his head. They slept under mosquito biers, gauzy netting stretched over wooden frames.

On the morning of July 27, the river route opened suddenly on a beautiful stretch of plains and meadows surrounded by distant high mountains. Sacagawea grew silent and her body became tense. Her eyes moved quickly from water to shore, and then off to the forest that covered the mountain slopes. Quietly she identified this as the place of the Hidatsa raid five summers before. She pointed to the rocky shoals in the middle of the river where she had been pulled up on the horse of the Hidatsa warrior. No word from her could possibly explain the mixture of feelings that almost overwhelmed her. No word from these white men could take away the painful memory of violence. No word from them could possibly add to the joy of her return.

Sacagawea's Journey

Meet the Author

Betty Westrom Skold's four-and-a-half year battle with tuberculosis made her childhood dream of becoming a teacher impossible. During her sickness, however, she spent a lot of time reading and writing. So, she became a writer on a small town newspaper instead.

Skold met an educational publisher who asked her to write a children's biography of Sacagawea. It became her first book as a professional writer. Today, Skold writes for a variety of age groups and tries new kinds of writing all the time. She has been a journalist, a poet, an essayist, a biographer, and a fiction writer.

Meet the Illustrator

Craig Spearing has a degree in illustration and printmaking. The first trade book he illustrated was *Prairie Dog Pioneers* by Jo and Josephine Harper. Since, he has created many illustrations for children's educational books and magazines.

His father was a geologist and his mother was a historian. He admires that his father was an eternal "Boy Scout" and his mother always valued careful research. He says that both his parents played an important part in shaping the way he does illustrations.

Theme Connections

Think About It

With a small group of classmates, discuss how Sacagawea's journey and quest was similar to that of Jumping Mouse, and how it was different. Then, address the following questions.

- There was one common journey for the expedition members. What types of individual quests were there?
- How did the group members cooperate to overcome obstacles and challenges on their journey?
- What other challenges might the Lewis and Clark expedition have encountered in the rest of their journey?

Record Ideas

Record in your Writing Journal the ideas you thought and talked about with others. Note how new knowledge of journeys and quests could be added to your unit activity.

Make a Character Web

Create a character web for each person involved in the Lewis and Clark expedition. Each web should include that person's skills, knowledge, and goals. When you have completed your webs, share and compare them to your partner's, examining them for differences and similarities.

Tanya's Reunion

by Valerie Flournoy
illustrated by Jerry Pinkney

It was Saturday. Baking day. One of Grandma's special days. Tanya had just popped the last spoonful of bread pudding made that morning into her mouth when Grandma announced, "Got a card from Aunt Kay and Uncle John today. They've invited me to the farm before all the family arrives for the big reunion. And I've decided to go."

A silence fell across the dinner table. Neither Tanya nor her brothers, Ted and Jim, could remember their grandmother going *anywhere* without the rest of the family.

"Aren't *we* going to the farm and reunion too?" Tanya asked. She had been looking forward to the big family event and her first trip to a farm ever since the announcement had arrived.

602

"Yes, Tanya. We're still going," Papa reassured her.

"We can all go to the farm together *after* the boys' football summer camp is over," Mama suggested, glancing toward Papa.

Grandma sucked her teeth and sighed. "Now, what's all the fuss? My baby sister asked me to come home early. I suspect she needs help working out all the sleeping arrangements and finding just the right spot for all the history people will be bringing with them."

Tanya remembered Mama and Grandma talking about the plan to have as many items that were once part of the homestead . . . the farm . . . returned for the biggest family gathering ever!

"But, Mother," said Mama, "you were sick not too long ago. Do you really think this trip is wise?"

Tanya watched Grandma reach out and touch Mama's hand.

"That was then, honey, and this is now, and I'm just fine. So I'm gonna go while I'm able," the old woman said firmly. "Besides, if you're so worried about me, you can always send Tanya along to see I stay out of trouble."

A trip with Grandma! Just the two of them. Tanya couldn't believe her ears.

"*May* I go with Grandma to the farm?" she pleaded excitedly.

Mama looked from Tanya to Papa to Grandma.

"Ted and Jim *are* going to football camp," Papa gently reminded Mama. "And we *will* be joining them shortly."

Grandma pulled a letter from her apron pocket. "I think Kay mentioned some of *her* grandchildren would be visiting early too. So Tanya will have someone to play with."

Mama looked from Grandma to Papa to Tanya again. "All right," she finally agreed. "You can go."

Tanya couldn't hide the pride she felt when she saw the surprised looks on Ted's and Jim's faces.

"We've had some special days on that old farm," Grandma said with satisfaction. "And so will Tanya. You'll see."

The sun rose slowly in the morning sky as Tanya watched all her familiar places vanish behind her. Past her schoolyard and the park. Past row after row of houses and traffic lights.

And still they traveled on and on. They stopped only to switch from one bus to another. Tanya listened while Grandma spoke about "going home" to the great land of Virginia that "borned four of the first five Presidents of these United States."

And still they traveled on and on. Until the bright sunny sky grew cloudy and gray and the highway turned into never-ending dirt roads that seemed to disappear into the fields and trees, down into the "hollers," the valleys below. Tanya could barely keep her eyes open.

And still they traveled on and on . . . until finally the bus crawled to a stop.

Grandma shook Tanya gently. "We're here, Tanya honey, wake up." Tanya rubbed her eyes awake. "We're home."

Standing on the last step of the bus, Tanya spied a car, trailing clouds of dust, coming toward them. In the distance were a farmhouse and barn.

"I've been sitting for the past eight . . . nine hours," Grandma told Uncle John, who'd come to get them, "so I think I'll just let these old limbs take me the rest of the way."

Tanya watched Grandma walk slowly but steadily up the familiar roadway.

"Memories die hard," Uncle John whispered to Tanya.

Tanya wasn't certain what her great-uncle meant. She only knew that if Grandma was going to walk, she would walk too. And she raced to the old woman's side.

"Take care, honey," Grandma said. "August weather down here's meant to be eased on through, not run through."

Tanya looked up at Grandma as she stared off into the distance, a faraway look in her eyes. What Tanya saw didn't look like the pictures in her schoolbooks or magazines or the pictures in her head.

There wasn't a horse in sight and the farmhouse was just a faded memory of its original color. Tanya noticed clouds of dust floating about her ankles, turning her white socks and sneakers a grayish brown color.

"Just open your heart to it," Grandma said. "Can't you feel the place welcomin' ya?"

Tanya didn't feel anything but hot and tired and disappointed. The farm wasn't what she expected. No, it wasn't what she expected at all.

A dog's bark drew Tanya's gaze back to the farmhouse. Stepping off the porch, a large dog at her side, was Grandma's baby sister, Kay.

"Watchin' you walk up that road, Rose Buchanan," Aunt Kay began, then gave Grandma a hug.

"Yes, on summer days like this it's as if time were standing still just a bit," Grandma finished for her.

Aunt Kay turned to her great-niece, smothering her in a welcoming hug full of warmth and softness that reminded Tanya of Grandma.

A summer breeze suddenly blew across the land, pushing the scattered gray clouds together. Tanya felt raindrops.

"Looks like it's comin' up a cloud," Uncle John said, hurrying the women onto the back porch and into the house. "I think it's *finally* gonna rain!"

Tanya was swept into the house by the laughing, talking grown-ups. Inside the kitchen Tanya met her cousin Celeste and her children, baby Adam and seven-year-old Keisha. The room was filled with wonderful aromas that made Tanya's mouth water—until she noticed the fly strip hanging above the kitchen table.

When Tanya went to bed that night, she was miserable. She barely touched her supper, until Uncle John thought to remove the fly strip dangling overhead. She missed her own room. She missed Mama and Papa, even Ted and Jim. Cousin Keisha and baby Adam were nice. But he was too small to really play with, and Keisha refused to leave her mother's side all night.

Grandma helped Aunt Kay tuck the children in. "What happened to our special days, Grandma?" whispered Tanya.

"Seems to me our first one went just fine," said Grandma. "The land needed the rain and it's finally gettin' it. Makes today kinda special, don't you think?"

Tanya sighed. "I wanna go home," she murmured into her pillow.

Cockle-doodle-do! The rooster's morning wake-up call startled cousin Keisha out of her sound sleep, and she cried until her mother came to take her into her room with the baby.

From the bed by the window, Tanya leaned against the windowsill looking over the empty farmyard. The sky was slate gray, but the air was fresh and clean and a gentle breeze swept through the window. It was also Saturday. Baking day, Tanya remembered before drifting back to sleep.

A single raindrop plopped on Tanya's face . . . then another . . . and another, until she awoke and closed the window. By the time she finished dressing, the rain sounded like a thunderous drumroll along the rooftop.

Hurrying down the staircase, Tanya stopped at the room Aunt Kay had called her sitting parlor. The room she chose to hold the family's memories. Several quilts—including Grandma's—with different colors and designs were draped across the sofa or hanging from the walls. Crocheted tablecloths and napkins, baptismal gowns and baby blankets, and a rocking chair and baby crib were also in place. There were various pots and pans, blacksmithing and gardening tools, candle molds and a few toys. Even a broom that couples jumped over when they married during slavery times. Every item was clearly and neatly labeled by its owner.

"Ahhh! Here's my northern niece. Ready for breakfast?" asked Uncle John.

"Yes! Ready!" Tanya said, turning from the doorway.

It rained through breakfast. It rained through checkers with cousin Celeste and four games of dominoes with Uncle John and Keisha. It rained through Adam's crying and Keisha's temper tantrum when Tanya hid all too well while playing hide-and-seek. It rained all morning long.

"Grandma," Tanya finally called. "Grandma, where are you?"

"In here," Grandma answered.

Tanya found Grandma, Aunt Kay, and cousin Celeste in the kitchen surrounded by boxes and lists about sleeping arrangements and who would cook what for the big reunion.

"Grandma, aren't we gonna bake today?" Tanya asked.

Grandma looked up from her lists. "Oh my," she murmured.

Tanya sighed unhappily and Grandma put her arm around her granddaughter's shoulder, leading her out the back door. The rain fell in a straight, steady stream, like a curtain separating the porch from the barnyard beyond.

Grandma patted the place beside her on the swing and Tanya slid into a familiar spot under her grandmother's arm.

"I'm sorry, Tanya honey. I guess I just plumb forgot what day this was." The old woman sighed, then laughed. "And I guess no number of stories can make you see this place through these old eyes."

"Did you *really* like living on this farm, Grandma?" Tanya asked. "Weren't you *ever* lonely?"

Grandma laughed again. "No, Tanya, I wasn't lonely. Back then, this whole farmyard: the barn, the pasture, fields, and orchard beyond"——she stretched out her arm—— "this place was filled with activity. We had the land and the land had us. We worked over it, tilled and planted it. Then harvested it when it was ready. In turn the land gave us

water, food, clothing, and a roof over our heads."

"If you weren't lonely, Grandma, why did you leave?" Tanya persisted.

Grandma looked out over the land, remembering. "It was after the second World War. My Isaac——your grandpa Franklin——and many other people thought we'd find better opportunities, better jobs closer to the cities up north. And we did. But we still kept the land and paid taxes on it. Sometimes let other people pay to work it, 'til Kay and John came back. But this will always be home."

Tanya and Grandma rocked slowly, silently, looking out across the rain-soaked land.

"Grandma, when you look far away . . . out there . . . what do you see?"

Grandma's eyes glowed. "I see your aunts and uncles and cousins when they lived on the farm. I see *my* father's father and his Indian bride. They built this farm so many, many years ago."

"And do you see Grandpa?" Tanya asked quietly.

"My, yes, Tanya. Your grandpa's always with me. But here on the farm he's 'specially close," the old woman answered.

The steady rain began to taper off. Grandma gave Tanya's shoulder a squeeze. "Now you, and Keisha and Adam, are a part of this farm, child," she said. "Family gatherings of this size can't happen without lists and planning and work. Everybody just pitches in and does the best they can. I know you will too."

When Grandma and Tanya returned to the kitchen, the room was in an uproar. Adam was crying loudly. The phone was ringing and the delivery man was at the door. Aunt Kay was searching for her handbag.

Grandma laughed. "Looks like we're needed."

Cousin Celeste took Adam while Grandma handled the delivery man. Tanya answered the phone and with Keisha's help found the missing box of diapers. All was calm when Aunt Kay returned with her handbag.

"Aunt Kay, may Keisha and I visit Uncle John in the barn?" Tanya asked.

"I'm sure he'll like the company," Aunt Kay said. "Just put on these old boots before you go."

Tanya and Keisha pulled on the boots and off they marched. The girls watched as Uncle John finished milking the cow. Then with his consent, Tanya sprinkled chicken feed on the ground. While the chickens ate, she and Keisha collected their eggs. After that the girls explored the barn, and when they grew tired, they climbed into the hayloft to rest.

The sun shone bright and hot when the threesome left the barn. "Weather can be right funny down here," Uncle John chuckled.

"John!" Grandma called through the screened window. "We could use some apples."

Uncle John handed each girl her own basket before pointing them in the direction of the orchard.

"Race ya!" Keisha squealed, and away she ran.

Keisha reached the orchard first. Tanya wasn't far behind when she saw something lying on the ground. She picked it up, brushed it off, and put it in the bottom of her basket before she began to pick apples.

The day slipped into dusk when the family finally sat down to supper. They had homemade apple pie for dessert——Tanya had shown Keisha how to roll the dough for the crust——topped with homemade ice cream. Only when the last bite of pie was gone did Tanya bring out what she had found that afternoon: a piece of the fence that had once separated the farmyard from the orchard. Carved in the wood were the initials

R.B.

+

I.F.

Rose Buchanan and Isaac Franklin.

"This is *your* history, isn't it, Grandma? Yours and Grandpa's."

"Oh yes, child. A special memory of your grandpa and me," said Grandma, beaming. "We'll put it in the parlor for everyone to share."

That night Uncle John placed sleeping bags on the porch so Tanya and Keisha could pretend they were camping out. Tanya had never seen so many fireflies or heard so many crickets.

"Doesn't the farmyard *ever* get quiet?" Tanya asked Grandma, who was rocking beside her.

"Those are just night sounds, honey," Grandma said, breathing in the hot, humid night air. "Telling us all is well."

And it was.

Tanya's Reunion

Meet the Author

Valerie Flournoy's book, "Tanya's Reunion," is a sequel to her award-winning book, *The Patchwork Quilt.* She wrote both books from experiences she had as a little girl. One of her favorite themes to write about is the importance of discovering one's heritage. In both books, the main character, Tanya, finds new ways to connect with her grandmother. Through these connections, she learns the value of family, memories, and tradition.

Valerie Flournoy was born on April 17, 1952, in Camden, New Jersey. She received a degree in teaching, and went on to work as an editor in book publishing. She now writes books for both young and adult readers, and lives with her twin sister in New Jersey.

Meet the Illustrator

Jerry Pinkney on his career as an artist: "I've loved to draw as long as I can remember, and in elementary school my teachers were very supportive. I often handled different projects through drawing. I was never an adept speller, but when I sat down to draw, if something didn't work out, I made it work. I was assigned many projects that had to do with drawing. This made me feel special. . . . [Today] I work as a free-lance illustrator. . . . I realize that I have something important to contribute, especially in the area of portraying black people. My growing-up experiences, my family, the neighborhood, and the music, have all found their way to my drawing board."

Theme Connections

Think About It

With a small group of classmates, discuss what you learned about journeys and quests from this selection. During discussion, address the following questions.

- Have you ever experienced disappointment or confusion when visiting a place that is important to an adult or family member?
- What advice would you have given Tanya when she wanted to return home?
- What would you label in your home as historical or significant?
- Why did Tanya begin to assist others with the family reunion?
- How did Tanya know that the fence piece would be an important part of her Grandmother's history?

Record Ideas

Record in your Writing Journal any new ideas or questions that came out in discussion.

Create a Chart for Planning a Trip

With a partner, think of a place to which you would like to travel and discuss your reasons for wanting to go there. Then create a chart of things you need to do before going on the trip, items that need to be packed, and activities that can be done while you're on the way to your destination.

Wander-Thirst

by Gerald Gould
illustrated by Jane Kendall

Beyond the East the sunrise, beyond the West the sea,
And East and West the wander-thirst that will not let me be;
It works in me like madness, dear, to bid me say good-by!
For the seas call and the stars call, and oh, the call of the sky!

I know not where the white road runs, nor what the blue hills are,
But man can have the sun for friend, and for his guide a star;
And there's no end to voyaging when once the voice is heard,
For the river calls and the road calls, and oh, the call of a bird!

Yonder the long horizon lies, and there by night and day
The old ships draw to home again, the young ships sail away;
And come I may, but go I must, and if men ask you why,
You may put the blame on the stars and the sun and the white
   road and the sky!

Roads Go Ever Ever On

by J. R. R. Tolkien
illustrated by Jane Kendall

Roads go ever ever on,
Over rock and under tree,
By caves where never sun has shone,
By streams that never find the sea;
Over snow by winter sown,
And through the merry flowers of June,
Over grass and over stone,
And under mountains in the moon.

When Shlemiel Went to Warsaw

from the book by Isaac Bashevis Singer
illustrated by Krystyna Stasiak

Though Shlemiel was a lazybones and a sleepyhead and hated to move, he always daydreamed of taking a trip. He had heard many stories about faraway countries, huge deserts, deep oceans, and high mountains, and often discussed with Mrs. Shlemiel his great wish to go on a long journey. Mrs. Shlemiel would reply: "Long journeys are not for a Shlemiel. You better stay home and mind the children while I go to market to sell my vegetables." Yet Shlemiel could not bring himself to give up his dream of seeing the world and its wonders.

A recent visitor to Chelm had told Shlemiel marvelous things about the city of Warsaw. How beautiful the streets were, how high the buildings and luxurious the stores. Shlemiel decided once and for all that he must see this great city for himself. He knew that one had to prepare for a journey. But what was there for him to take? He had nothing but the old clothes he wore. One morning, after Mrs. Shlemiel left for the market, he told the older boys to stay home from cheder and mind the younger children. Then he took a few slices of bread, an onion, and a clove of garlic, put them in a kerchief, tied it into a bundle, and started for Warsaw on foot.

There was a street in Chelm called Warsaw Street and Shlemiel believed that it led directly to Warsaw.

While still in the village, he was stopped by several neighbors who asked him where he was going. Shlemiel told them that he was on his way to Warsaw.

"What will you do in Warsaw?" they asked him.

Schlemiel replied: "What do I do in Chelm? Nothing."

He soon reached the outskirts of town. He walked slowly because the soles of his boots were worn through. Soon the houses and stores gave way to pastures and fields. He passed a peasant driving an ox-drawn plow. After several hours of walking, Shlemiel grew tired. He was so weary that he wasn't even hungry. He lay down on the grass near the roadside for a nap, but before he fell asleep he thought: "When I wake up, I may not remember which is the way to Warsaw and which leads back to Chelm." After pondering a moment, he removed his boots and set them down beside him with the toes pointing toward Warsaw and the heels toward Chelm. He soon fell asleep and dreamed that he was a baker baking onion rolls with poppy seeds. Customers came to buy them and Shlemiel said: "These onion rolls are not for sale."

"Then why do you bake them?"

"They are for my wife, for my children, and for me."

Later he dreamed that he was the King of Chelm. Once a year, instead of taxes, each citizen brought him a pot of strawberry jam. Shlemiel sat on a golden throne and nearby sat Mrs. Shlemiel, the queen, and his children, the princes and princesses. They were all eating onion rolls and spooning up big portions of strawberry jam. A carriage arrived and took the royal family to Warsaw, America, and to the river Sambation, which spurts out stones the week long and rests on the Sabbath.

Near the road, a short distance from where Shlemiel slept, was a smithy. The blacksmith happened to come out just in time to see Shlemiel carefully placing his boots at his side with the toes facing in the direction of Warsaw. The blacksmith was a prankster and as soon as Shlemiel was sound asleep he tiptoed over and turned the boots around. When Shlemiel awoke, he felt rested but hungry. He got out a slice of bread, rubbed it with garlic, and took a bite of onion. Then he pulled his boots on and continued on his way.

He walked along and everything looked strangely familiar. He recognized houses that he had seen before. It seemed to him that he knew the people he met. Could it be that he had already reached another town,

Shlemiel wondered. And why was it so similar to Chelm? He stopped a passerby and asked the name of the town. "Chelm," the man replied.

Shlemiel was astonished. How was this possible? He had walked away from Chelm. How could he have arrived back there? He began to rub his forehead and soon found the answer to the riddle. There were two Chelms and he had reached the second one.

Still, it seemed very odd that the streets, the houses, the people were so similar to those in the Chelm he had left behind. Shlemiel puzzled over this fact until he suddenly remembered something he had learned in cheder: "The earth is the same everywhere." And so why shouldn't the second Chelm be exactly like the first one? This discovery gave Shlemiel great satisfaction. He wondered if there was a street here like his street and a house on it like the one he lived in. And indeed, he soon arrived at an identical street and house. Evening had fallen. He opened the door and to his amazement saw a second Mrs. Shlemiel with children just like his. Everything was exactly the same as in his own household. Even the cat seemed the same. Mrs. Shlemiel at once began to scold him.

"Shlemiel, where did you go? You left the house alone. And what have you there in that bundle?"

The children all ran to him and cried: "Papa, where have you been?"

Shlemiel paused a moment and then he said: "Mrs. Shlemiel, I'm not your husband. Children, I'm not your papa."

"Have you lost your mind?" Mrs. Shlemiel screamed.

"I am Shlemiel of Chelm One and this is Chelm Two."

Mrs. Shlemiel clapped her hands so hard that the chickens sleeping under the stove awoke in fright and flew out all over the room.

"Children, your father has gone crazy," she wailed. She immediately sent one of the boys for Gimpel the healer. All the neighbors came crowding in. Shlemiel stood in the middle of the room and proclaimed: "It's true, you all look like the people in my town, but you are not the same. I came from Chelm One and you live in Chelm Two."

"Shlemiel, what's the matter with you?" someone cried. "You're in your own house, with your own wife and children, your own neighbors and friends."

"No, you don't understand. I come from Chelm One. I was on my way to Warsaw, and between Chelm One and Warsaw there is a Chelm Two. And that is where I am."

"What are you talking about. We all know you and you know all of us. Don't you recognize your chickens?"

"No, I'm not in my town," Shlemiel insisted. "But," he continued, "Chelm Two does have the same people and the same houses as Chelm One, and that is why you are mistaken. Tomorrow I will continue on to Warsaw."

"In that case, where is my husband?" Mrs. Shlemiel inquired in a rage, and she proceeded to berate Shlemiel with all the curses she could think of.

"How should I know where your husband is?" Shlemiel replied.

Some of the neighbors could not help laughing; others pitied the family. Gimpel the healer announced that he knew of no remedy for such an illness. After some time, everybody went home.

Mrs. Shlemiel had cooked noodles and beans that evening, a dish that Shlemiel liked especially. She said to him: "You may be mad, but even a madman has to eat."

"Why should you feed a stranger?" Shlemiel asked.

"As a matter of fact, an ox like you should eat straw, not noodles and beans. Sit down and be quiet. Maybe some food and rest will bring you back to your senses."

"Mrs. Shlemiel, you're a good woman. My wife wouldn't feed a stranger. It would seem that there is some small difference between the two Chelms."

The noodles and beans smelled so good that Shlemiel needed no further coaxing. He sat down, and as he ate he spoke to the children:

"My dear children, I live in a house that looks exactly like this one. I have a wife and she is as like your mother as two peas are like each other. My children resemble you as drops of water resemble one another."

The younger children laughed; the older ones began to cry. Mrs. Shlemiel said: "As if being a Shlemiel wasn't enough, he had to go crazy in addition. What am I going to do now? I won't be able to leave the children with him when I go to market. Who knows what a madman may do?" She clasped her head in her hands and cried out, "God in heaven, what have I done to deserve this?"

Nevertheless, she made up a fresh bed for Shlemiel; and even though he had napped during the day, near the smithy, the moment his head touched the pillow he fell fast asleep and was soon snoring loudly. He again dreamed that he was the King of Chelm and that his wife, the queen, had fried for him a huge panful of blintzes. Some were filled with cheese, others with blueberries or cherries, and all were sprinkled with sugar and cinnamon and were drowning in sour cream. Shlemiel ate twenty blintzes all at once and hid the remainder in his crown for later.

In the morning, when Shlemiel awoke, the house was filled with townspeople. Mrs. Shlemiel stood in their midst, her eyes red with weeping. Shlemiel was about to scold his wife for letting so many strangers into the house, but then he remembered that he himself was a stranger here. At home he would have gotten up, washed, and dressed. Now in front of all these people he was at a loss as to what to do. As always when he was embarrassed, he began to scratch his head and pull at his beard. Finally, overcoming his bashfulness, he decided to get up. He threw off the covers and put his bare feet on the floor. "Don't let him run away," Mrs. Shlemiel screamed. "He'll disappear and I'll be a deserted wife, without a Shlemiel."

At this point Baruch the baker interrupted. "Let's take him to the Elders. They'll know what to do."

"That's right! Let's take him to the Elders," everybody agreed.

Although Shlemiel insisted that since he lived in Chelm One, the local Elders had no power over him, several of the strong young men helped him into his pants, his boots, his coat and cap and escorted him to the house of Gronam Ox. The Elders, who had already heard of the matter, had gathered early in the morning to consider what was to be done.

As the crowd came in, one of the Elders, Dopey Lekisch, was saying, "Maybe there really are two Chelms."

"If there are two, then why can't there be three, four, or even a hundred Chelms?" Sender Donkey interrupted.

"And even if there are a hundred Chelms, must there be a Shlemiel in each one of them?" argued Shmendrick Numskull.

Gronam Ox, the head Elder, listened to all the arguments but was not yet prepared to express an opinion. However, his wrinkled, bulging forehead indicated that he was deep in thought. It was Gronam Ox who questioned Shlemiel. Shlemiel related everything that had happened to him, and when he finished, Gronam asked, "Do you recognize me?"

"Surely. You are wise Gronam Ox."

"And in your Chelm is there also a Gronam Ox?"

"Yes, there is a Gronam Ox and he looks exactly like you."

"Isn't it possible that you turned around and came back to Chelm?" Gronam inquired.

"Why should I turn around? I'm not a windmill," Shlemiel replied.

"In that case, you are not this Mrs. Shlemiel's husband."

"No, I'm not."

"Then Mrs. Shlemiel's husband, the real Shlemiel, must have left the day you came."

"It would seem so."

"Then he'll probably come back."

"Probably."

"In that case, you must wait until he returns. Then we'll know who is who."

"Dear Elders, my Shlemiel has come back," screamed Mrs. Shlemiel. "I don't need two Shlemiels. One is more than enough."

"Whoever he is, he may not live in your house until everything is made clear," Gronam insisted.

"Where shall I live?" Shlemiel asked.

"In the poorhouse."

"What will I do in the poorhouse?"

"What do you do at home?"

"Good God, who will take care of my children when I go to market?" moaned Mrs. Shlemiel. "Besides, I want a husband. Even a Shlemiel is better than no husband at all."

"Are we to blame that your husband left you and went to Warsaw?" Gronam asked. "Wait until he comes home."

Mrs. Shlemiel wept bitterly and the children cried, too. Shlemiel said: "How strange. My own wife always scolded me. My children talked back to me. And here a strange woman and strange children want me to live with them. It looks to me as if Chelm Two is actually better than Chelm One."

"Just a moment. I think I have an idea," interrupted Gronam.

"What is your idea?" Zeinvel Ninny inquired.

"Since we decided to send Shlemiel to the poorhouse, the town will have to hire someone to take care of Mrs. Shlemiel's children so she can go to market. Why not hire Shlemiel for that? It's true, he is not Mrs. Shlemiel's husband or the children's father. But he is so much like the real Shlemiel that the children will feel at home with him."

"What a wonderful idea!" cried Feyvel Thickwit.

"Only King Solomon could have thought of such a wise solution," agreed Treitel the Fool.

"Such a clever way out of this dilemma could only have been thought of in our Chelm," chimed in Shmendrick Numskull.

"How much do you want to be paid to take care of Mrs. Shlemiel's children?" asked Gronam.

For a moment Shlemiel stood there completely bewildered. Then he said, "Three groschen a day."

"Idiot, moron, donkey!" screamed Mrs. Shlemiel. "What are three groschen nowadays? You shouldn't do it for less than six a day." She ran over to Shlemiel and pinched him on the arm. Shlemiel winced and cried out, "She pinches just like my wife."

The Elders held a consultation among themselves. The town budget was very limited. Finally Gronam announced: "Three groschen may be too little, but six groschen a day is definitely too much, especially for a stranger. We will compromise and pay you five groschen a day. Shlemiel, do you accept?"

"Yes, but how long am I to keep this job?"

"Until the real Shlemiel comes home."

Gronam's decision was soon known throughout Chelm, and the town admired his great wisdom and that of all the Elders of Chelm.

At first, Shlemiel tried to keep the five groschen that the town paid him for himself. "If I'm not your husband, I don't have to support you," he told Mrs. Shlemiel.

"In that case, since I'm not your wife, I don't have to cook for you, darn your socks, or patch your clothes."

And so, of course, Shlemiel turned over his pay to her. It was the first time that Mrs. Shlemiel had ever gotten any money for the household from Shlemiel. Now when she was in a good mood, she would say to him, "What a pity you didn't decide to go to Warsaw ten years ago."

"Don't you ever miss your husband?" Shlemiel would ask.

"And what about you? Don't you miss your wife?" Mrs. Shlemiel would ask. And both would admit that they were quite happy with matters as they stood.

Years passed and no Shlemiel returned to Chelm. The Elders had many explanations for this. Zeinvel Ninny believed that Shlemiel had crossed the black mountains and had been eaten alive by the cannibals who live there. Dopey Lekisch thought that Schlemiel most probably had come to the Castle of Asmodeus, where he had been forced to marry a demon princess. Shmendrick Numskull came to the conclusion that Shlemiel had reached the edge of the world and had fallen off. There were many other theories. For example, that the real Shlemiel had lost his memory and had simply forgotten that he was Shlemiel. Such things do happen.

Gronam did not like to impose his theories on other people; however, he was convinced that Shlemiel had gone to the other Chelm, where he had had exactly the same experience as the Shlemiel in this Chelm. He had been hired by the local community and was taking care of the other Mrs. Shlemiel's children for a wage of five groschen a day.

As for Schlemiel himself, he no longer knew what to think. The children were growing up and soon would be able to take care of themselves. Sometimes Shlemiel would sit and ponder. Where is the other Shlemiel? When will he come home? What is my real wife doing? Is she waiting for me, or has she got herself another Shlemiel? These were questions that he could not answer.

Every now and then Shlemiel would still get the desire to go traveling, but he could not bring himself to start out. What was the point of going on a trip if it led nowhere? Often, as he sat alone puzzling over the strange ways of the world, he would become more and more confused and begin humming to himself:

> *"Those who leave Chelm*
> *End up in Chelm.*
> *Those who remain in Chelm*
> *Are certainly in Chelm.*
> *All roads lead to Chelm.*
> *All the world is one big Chelm."*

When Shlemiel Went to Warsaw

Meet the Author

Isaac Bashevis Singer was born in Poland in 1904 and grew up in Warsaw. He said of his childhood home, "My father was an orthodox rabbi, and our house was a house of holy books and learning. Other children had toys. I played with the books in my father's library.

Singer and his brother came to the United States in 1935. Isaac learned English but wrote all of his books first in Yiddish. He then translated them into his new language. He said of his writing for children, "Children are the best readers of genuine literature. . . . The young reader demands a real story, with a beginning, a middle, and an end, the way stories have been told for thousands of years."

Meet the Illustrator

Krystyna Stasiak was born in Poland, but she became a permanent resident of the United States in 1969. As a child, her parents tried to guide her into the world of music. However, she naturally gravitated toward the world of art. She received her art degree from the Academy of Fine Arts in Warsaw, Poland. Today she is a free-lance artist. She exhibits her art in museums and illustrates books for both children and adults.

She loves animals and believes they have their own distinct personalities. She also loves to travel and has visited Italy, Switzerland, and Austria. Her other hobbies include skiing, tennis, literature, languages, and music.

Theme Connections

Think About It

With a small group of classmates, discuss what you learned about journeys and quests from this selection. During discussion, address the following questions.

- Is it possible to have journeys in one's own mind, rather than physically?
- Shlemiel wanted to travel to a place he had heard was grand. Where do you want to travel, and why do you want to go there?
- What might have happened to Shlemiel if he had continued his journey?
- What does Shlemiel believe he has learned from his journey?

Record Ideas

Record in your Writing Journal what you have learned about using humor in folk tales. Give three examples of humorous situations from this selection and tell why you think they are funny.

Create an Advice Column for Travelers

With a small group of students, brainstorm and write down all the different problems that might occur for travelers. Then brainstorm possible solutions to these problems. Choose two of the problems you brainstormed. Then write your advice column as a group.

FINE Art

May, from Les Tres Riches Heures de Duc de Berry.
1413–1416. **Limbourg Brothers.** Ink, tempera, and gold on
parchment. $8\frac{1}{2} \times 5\frac{1}{2}$ in. Musée Conde, Chantilly, France.
Photo: Giraudon/Art Resource, NY.

Landscape with a Solitary Traveler.
c.1780. **Yosa Buson.** Hanging scroll. Ink
and light colors on silk. 101.5 × 36.4 cm.
Courtesy of the Kimbell Art Museum,
Fort Worth, Texas.

Don Quixote. 1955. **Pablo Picasso.**
Drawing. Musée d'Art et d'Histoire,
St. Denis, France. ©1999 Estate of Pablo
Picasso/Artist Rights Society (ARS), New
York. Photo: SCALA/Art Resource, NY.

The Return of Ulysses.
1976. **Romare Bearden.**
Silkscreen. Gift of
Brandywine Graphic
Workshop, Philadelphia
Museum of Art.
© Romare Bearden
Foundation/ Licensed by
VAGA, New York, NY.

Alberic the Wise

by Norton Juster

illustrated by Leonard Baskin

More than many years ago when fewer things had happened in the world and there was less to know, there lived a young man named Alberic who knew nothing at all. Well, almost nothing, or depending on your generosity of spirit, hardly anything, for he could hitch an ox and plow a furrow straight or thatch a roof or hone his scythe until the edge was bright and sharp or tell by a sniff of the breeze what the day would bring or with a glance when a grape was sweet and ready. But these were only the things he had to know to live or couldn't help knowing by living and are, as you may have discovered, rarely accounted as knowledge.

Of the world and its problems, however, he knew little, and indeed was even less aware of their existence. In all his life he had been nowhere and seen nothing beyond the remote estate on which he lived and to whose lands he and his family had been bound back beyond the edge of memory. He planted and harvested, threshed and winnowed, tended the hives and the pigs, breathed the country air, and stopped now and again to listen to the birds or puzzle at the wind. There were no mysteries, hopes or dreams other than those that could be encompassed by his often aching back or impatient stomach. This was the sum of his existence and with it he was neither happy nor sad. He simply could not conceive of anything else.

Since the days were much alike he measured his life by the more discernible seasons—yet they too slipped easily by, and would have continued to do so, I'm sure, had it not been for the lone traveler who appeared unaccountably one chill morning at the close of winter. Alberic watched him make his weary way along the road until, when they stood no more than a glance apart, he paused to rest before continuing on his journey. A curious old man—his tattered tunic was patched on patches and his worn shoes left hardly a suggestion of leather between himself and the cold ground. He carried a massive bundle on his

back and sighed with the pleasure of letting it slide gently from his shoulder to the ground—then just as gently let himself down upon it. He nodded and smiled, mopped his face carefully with a handkerchief easily as old as himself, then acknowledged Alberic's timid greeting and finally began to speak, and when he did it was of many, many things. Where he had come from and where he was bound, what he had seen and what there was yet to discover—commonwealths, kingdoms, empires, counties and dukedoms— fortresses, bastions and great solitary castles that dug their fingers into the mountain passes and dared the world to pass—royal courts whose monarchs dressed in pheasant skins and silks and rich brocades of purple and lemon and crimson and bice all interlaced with figures of beasts and blossoms and strange geometric devices—and mountains that had no tops and oceans that had no bottoms.

There seemed no end to what he knew or what he cared to speak about, and speak he did, on and on through the day. His voice was soft and easy but his manner such that even his pauses commanded attention. And as he spoke his eyes sparkled and his words were like maps of unknown lands. He told of caravans that made their way across continents and back with perfumes and oils and dark red wines, sandalwood and lynx hides and ermine and carved sycamore chests, with cloves and cinnamon, precious stones and iron pots and ebony and amber and objects of pure tooled gold—of tall cathedral spires and cities full of life and craft and industry—of ships that sailed in every sea, and of art and science and learned speculation hardly even dreamed of by most people—and of armies and battles and magic and much, much more.

Alberic stood entranced, trying desperately to imagine all these wonderful things, but his mind could wander no further than the fields that he could see and the images soon would fade or cloud.

"The world is full of wonders," he sighed forlornly, for he realized that he could not even imagine what a wonder was.

"It is everything I've said and even more," the stranger replied, and since it was by now late afternoon he scrambled to his feet and once more took up his heavy bundle. "And remember," he said with a sweep of his arm, "it is all out there, just waiting." Then down the road and across the stubble fields he went.

For weeks after the old man had gone Alberic brooded, for now he knew that there were things he didn't know, and what

634

magic and exciting things they were! Warm wet breezes had begun to blow across the land and the frozen fields had yielded first to mud and then to early blossoms. But now this quiet hillside was not enough to hold his rushing thoughts. "It is all out there, just waiting," he said to himself again and again, repeating the old man's words. When he had repeated them often enough, they became a decision. He secretly packed his few belongings and in the early morning's mist left his home and started down into the world to seek its wonders and its wisdom.

For two days and nights and half another day again he walked—through lonely forests and down along the rushing mountain streams that seemed to know their destination far better than he knew his. Mile after mile he walked until at last the trees and vines gave way to sweeps of easy meadowland and in the distance, barely visible, the towers of a city reflected back the sun's bright rays. As he approached, the hazy form became a jumble of roofs and chimney pots spread out below, and each step closer embellished them with windows, carved gables, domes and graceful spires. All this in turn was circled by a high wall which seemed to grow higher and wider as he descended towards it until at last it filled his vision and hid all else behind it. The stream which only days before had been so gay and playful now broadened and as if aware of its new importance assumed a slow and dignified pace as it passed through the city. Alberic paused for a moment to catch his breath, then, with a slight shiver of anticipation, passed beneath the cool dark gates and entered the city too.

What a teeming, busy place! Houses and shops, music and movement, all kinds of noises, signs and smells, and more people than he ever knew existed. He wandered along the cobbled streets delighted by each new discovery and noting with care the strange new sights and sounds so unfamiliar to his country senses. He soon learned too that he had come to a city famous above all others for the beautiful stained glass manufactured in its workshops.

"A noble and important profession," he decided soberly, "for surely beauty is the true aim of wisdom!" Without delay he went off to apprentice himself to the greatest of the master glassmakers.

"Well, well," growled the old craftsman after examining Alberic carefully, "so you want to make glass. Very well, we shall see. Your duties will be few and simple. Each morning you'll rise before the birds and with the other apprentices fetch sixty barrows of firewood from the forest. Then in each furnace bank a fire precisely hot enough to melt the lead and fuse the glass, and keep them tended constantly so that none goes out or varies even slightly in its heat. Then, of course, work the bellows, fetch the ingots from the foundry, run errands, assist the journeymen as they need, sharpen and repair all the chisels, files, knives, scrapers, shears, mallets and grozing irons so that each is in perfect order, make deliveries quickly and courteously, grind and mix the pigments, work the forge, sweep out the shop, fetch, carry, stoop, haul and bend, and in your spare time help with the household chores. You can of course eat your fill of the table scraps and sleep on the nice warm floor. Well, don't just stand there, you've only started and you're already hours behind in your work." When he finished he smiled a benevolent smile, for he was known for his generous nature.

Alberic applied himself to his new tasks with diligence, working from early morning until late at night when he would

curl up in one corner of the shop to dream happily of the day's accomplishments and carefully sort and pack into his memory everything he'd learned. For some time he did only the menial jobs, but soon under the watchful eye of the master he began taking part in more important and exacting procedures. He learned to chip and shape the glass into pieces often no larger than the palm of his hand and then apply the colors mixed in gum or oil with a delicate badger brush and fire these to permanence in the glowing kilns. Then from measurements and patterns he learned to set each piece in the grooved strips of lead and solder them carefully at each joint. For almost two years he worked and watched as all these small and painstaking operations took form in great windows and medallions of saintly lives or tales of moral instruction which glowed in deep splendid blues and vivid rubies.

Finally the time came for Alberic to prove his skill and take his place among the glassmakers—to create a work entirely on his own. He was determined that it would be a rare and lovely thing and he set about it with quiet intensity.

"What will it be, Alberic?" they all asked eagerly.

"Beautiful," he replied with never a moment's doubt, and that was all he'd say.

And for weeks he worked secretly in one corner of the shop until the day came when his work was to be judged. Everyone gathered to see it. The master looked long and carefully. He stood back to view it in the light and squinted close at matters of fine detail, and then he rubbed his chin and then he tapped his finger and then he swayed and then he sighed and then he frowned.

"No," he said sadly and slowly, "certainly not. You will never be a glassmaker." And everyone agreed, for despite the best of intentions Alberic's work was poor indeed.

How miserable he was! How thoroughly miserable! Why wasn't it beautiful when he had tried so hard? How could he have learned so much and yet still fail? No one knew the answer. "There is no reason now for me to stay," he said quietly, gathering up his bundle, and without even as much as a last look back he walked out into the lonely countryside. For several days he wandered aimlessly, seeing nothing, heading nowhere, his thoughts turned inward to his unhappy failure. But it was spring and no one who has ever worked the land can long ignore the signs this season brings. Sweet promising smells hung gently in the warm air, and all around the oxlips, daisies and celandine splashed the fields in lively yellow. A graceful bird and then another caught Alberic's eye. The busy buzz and click of small things were reassuring to his ear and even the bullfrogs' heavy thump set his heart beating once again. His spirits and then his hope revived. The world seemed large and inviting once again.

"There are other places and other things to learn," he thought. "Beauty isn't everything. The true measure of wisdom is utility. I'll do something useful." He hurried now and before long came to a city whose stonecutters and masons were renowned throughout the world for the excellence of their work. His thoughts turned to castles and cloisters, massive walls, towering vaults and steeples which only miracles of skill could hold suspended in the air.

"Everything of use and value is made of stone," he concluded and rushed to seek employment with the master stonecutter.

And for two more years he busied himself learning the secrets of this new vocation——selecting and cutting only the finest stone from the quarry——matching, marking and extracting the giant blocks to be moved on heavy wheeled carts to each new building——and then noting carefully how each shaped stone was fitted in its place so that walls and buttresses grew and arches sprang from pier to pier with such precision that no blade however sharp could slip between the joints. Soon he learned to mix and measure mortar and operate the windlasses whose ingenious ropes and pulleys allowed one man to lift for fifty. Then to make his first careful cuts with bolster and chisel and then stop and watch again as surer hands than his cut and shaped the graceful moldings and intricate tracery which brought the stone to life. As he worked he questioned and remembered everything he saw and heard, and as each day passed, his confidence and his knowledge grew and he began to think of his future life as a great and skillful stonecutter.

When the time came for him to prove his skill to the masons and sculptors of the guild, Alberic chose a piece of specially fine, delicately veined marble and set to work. It was to be the finest carving they had ever seen. With great care he studied and restudied the block and planned his form, then cut into the stone in search of it. He worked in a fever of excitement, his sharp chisels biting off the unwanted material in large chips and pieces. But the image he saw so clearly in his mind seemed always to be just out of sight, a little deeper in the stone. The block grew smaller and the mound of dust and chips larger, and still, like a phantom, the form seemed to recede and still he chased it. Soon there was nothing left at all. The great block of stone had disappeared and soon afterwards, the stonecutter too. For again, without a word, Alberic gathered up his belongings and passed through the city gate. He had failed once more.

"Usefulness isn't everything," he decided after roaming about disconsolately for several days. "Innovation is surely a measure of wisdom. I'll do something original."

The opportunity presented itself in the very next town, where the goldsmiths, it was said, produced objects of unsurpassed excellence and fancy. Bowls and magic boxes, mirrors, shields and scepters, crowns, rings, enchanted buckles and clasps, and candlesticks and vases of incredible grace and intricacy spilled from these workshops and found their way to every royal court and market in the land. It was here that Alberic learned to draw and shape the fine gold wire and work the thin sheets of metal into patterns and textures of light and shape and then inlay these with delicate enamels and precious stones. It was here also that he worked and hoped for the next two years of his life and it was here that for the third time he failed and for the third time took his disappointment to the lonely countryside.

And so it went, from town to town, from city to city, each noted for its own particular craft or enterprise. There were potters who turned and shaped their wet clay into graceful bowls and tall jugs fire-glazed with brilliant cobalt, manganese and copper oxides. Leather finishers who transformed smooth soft skins into shoes and boots, gloves, tunics, bombards, bottles and buckets. There were weavers and spinners who worked in wools and silks, carpenters and cabinetmakers, glassblowers, armorers and tinkers. There were scholars who

spent their days searching out the secrets of ancient books, and chemists and physicians, and astronomers determining the precise distances between places that no one had ever seen. And busy ports which offered men the sea and all it touched, and smiths and scribes and makers of fine musical instruments, for anyone with such a bent. Alberic tried them all——and watched and learned and practiced and failed and then moved on again. Yet he kept searching and searching for the one thing that he could do. The secret of the wisdom and skill he so desired.

The years passed and still he traveled on—along the roads and trails and half-forgotten paths—across plains and deserts and forests whose tangled growth held terrors that were sometimes real and sometimes even worse—over hills and cruel high mountain passes and down again perhaps along some unnamed sea—until at last, alone and old and tired, he reached the ramparts of the great capital city.

"I will never find wisdom," he sighed. "I'm a failure at everything."

At the edge of the market square Alberic set his bundle down and searched longingly as all the students, artisans and craftsmen went unconcernedly about their

business. He wiped the dust from his eyes and sat for a moment, thinking of his future and his past. What a strange sight he was! His beard was now quite long and gray and the cloak and hat and shoes bore evidence of some repair from every place he'd been. His great bundle bulged with the debris of a lifetime's memories and disappointments and his face was a sad scramble of much the same. As he rummaged through his thoughts, a group of children, struck by his uncommon look, stopped and gathered close around him.

"Where have you come from?"

"What do you do?"

"Tell us what you've seen," they eagerly asked, and poised to listen or flee as his response required.

Alberic was puzzled. What could he tell them? No one had ever sought his conversation before, or asked his opinion on any question. He scratched his head and rubbed his knees, then slowly and hesitantly began to speak, and suddenly the sum of all those experiences, which lay packed up in his mind as in some disordered cupboard, came back to him. He told them of a place or two he'd been and of some lands they'd never known existed and creatures that all their wildest fancies could not invent, and then a story, a legend and three dark mysterious tales remembered from a thousand years before. As he spoke, the words began to come more easily and the pleasure of them eased away his weariness. Everything he'd ever seen or heard or touched or tried was suddenly fresh and clear in his memory, and when the children finally left for home, their faces glowing with excitement, it was to spread the news of the wonderful old man who knew so much.

Since he had no place else to go, Alberic returned to the square each day, and each day the crowds grew larger and larger around him. At first it was only the children, but soon everyone, regardless of age or size, crowded close to listen— and patiently he tried to tell them all they wished to hear. For many of their questions his own experience provided the answers, and for those he could not directly answer he always had a tale or story whose point or artifice led them to answers of their own. More and more he began to enjoy the days and soon he learned to embellish his tales with skillful detail, to pause at just the right time, to raise his voice to a roar or lower it to a whisper as the telling demanded. And the crowds grew even larger.

Workmen came to listen and stayed to learn the secret ways and methods of their own crafts. Artisans consulted him on questions of taste or skill and when they left they always knew more than when they came. Alberic told them everything he had learned or seen through all his failures and his wanderings, and before very long he became known throughout the realm as Alberic the Wise.

His fame spread so far that one day the King himself and several of his ministers came to the square to see for themselves. Cleverly disguised so as not to alert the old man to his purpose, the King posed several questions concerning matters of state and situations in far-off corners of the kingdom. Everything he asked, Alberic answered in great detail, enlarging each reply with accounts of the lore and customs of each region, condition of the crops and royal castles, local problems and controversies, reports on the annual rainfall and the latest depredations by various discontented barons. And for added measure, two songs and a short play (in which he acted all the parts) which he had learned before being dismissed from a traveling theater company.

"You are the wisest man in my kingdom," the astonished King proclaimed, throwing off his disguise, "and you shall have a palace of your own with servants and riches as befits a man of your accomplishments."

Alberic moved into the new palace at once and was more than content with his new life. He enjoyed the wealth and possessions he had never known before, slept on feather

beds, ate nothing but the most succulent and delicate foods and endlessly put on and took off the many cloaks, robes and caps the King had graciously provided. His beard was trimmed and curled and he spent his time strolling about the gardens and marble halls posing with proper dignity before each mirror and repeating to himself in various tones and accents, "Alberic the Wise, ALBERIC THE WISE, A-L-B-E-R-I-C T-H-E W-I-S-E!" in order to become accustomed to his new title.

After several weeks, however, the novelty began to wear thin, for a sable cloak is just a sable cloak and a *poulet poêla a l'estragon* is really just another roast chicken. Soon doubts began to crowd out pleasures and by degrees he grew first serious, then sober, then somber and then once again thoroughly discouraged.

"How is it possible to be a failure at everything one day and a wise man the next?" he inquired. "Am I not the same person?"

For weeks this question continued to trouble him deeply, and since he could not find a satisfactory answer he returned to the square with his doubts.

"Simply calling someone wise does not make him wise!" he announced to the eager crowd. "So you see, I am not wise." Then, feeling much better, he returned to the palace and began to make ready to leave.

"How modest," the crowd murmured. "The sign of a truly

great man." And a delegation of prominent citizens was sent to prevail on him to stay.

Even after listening to their arguments Alberic continued to be troubled and the very next day he returned to the square again.

"Miscellaneous collections of fact and information are not wisdom," he declared fervently. "Therefore I am not wise!" And he returned and ordered workmen to begin boarding up the palace.

"Only the wisest of men would understand this," the people all agreed and petitions were circulated to prevent his leaving.

For several more days he paced the palace corridors unhappily and then returned for a third time.

"A wise man's words are rarely questioned," he counseled gently. "Therefore you must be very careful whom you call wise."

The crowd was so grateful for his timely warning that they cheered for fully fifteen minutes after he had returned to the palace.

Finally, in desperation, he reappeared that very afternoon and stated simply, "For all the years of my life I have sought

wisdom and to this day I still do not know even the meaning of the word, or where to find it," and thinking that would convince them he ordered a carriage for six o'clock that afternoon.

The crowd gasped. "No one but a man of the most profound wisdom would ever dare to admit such a thing," they all agreed, and an epic poem was commissioned in his honor.

Once again Alberic returned to the palace. The carriage was canceled, the rooms were opened and aired. There was nothing he could say or do to convince them that he wasn't what they all thought him to be. Soon he refused to answer any more questions or, in fact, to speak at all and everyone agreed that because of the troubled times this was certainly the wisest thing to do. Each day he grew more morose and miserable, and though his fame continued to grow and spread he found no more satisfaction in his success than he had in all his failures. He slept little and ate less and his magnificent robes began to hang like shrouds. The bright optimism that had shone in his eyes through all his travels and hardships began to fade and as the months passed he took to spending all his time at the top of the great north tower, staring without any interest at nothing in particular.

"I am no wiser now than I was before," he said one afternoon, thinking back across the years. "For I still don't know what I am or what I'm looking for." But as he sat there remembering and regretting, he sensed in the air the barest suggestion of some subtle yet familiar scent that drifted in on the freshening breeze. What it was he didn't know——perhaps the pungent tangled aroma of some far eastern bazaar or the sharp and honest smell of a once-known workshop, or it might have been simply the sweet clean air of an upland field the memory of which had long been lost in detail yet retained in some more durable way; but whatever it was it grew stronger and stronger stirring something deep within him and taking hold of all his thoughts and feelings. His spirit suddenly quickened in response and each breath now came faster than the one before. And then for just a moment he sat quite still——and then at last he knew.

"I am not a glassmaker nor a stone cutter, nor a goldsmith, potter, weaver, tinker, scribe or chef," he shouted happily and he leaped up and bounded down the steep stone stairs. "Nor a vintner, carpenter, physician, armorer, astronomer, baker or boatman." Down and around he ran as fast as he could go, along the palace corridors until he reached the room in which all his old things had been stored. "Nor a blacksmith, merchant, musician or cabinetmaker," he continued as he put on the ragged cloak and shoes and hat. "Nor a wise man or a fool, success or failure, for no one but myself can tell me what I am or what I'm not." And when he'd finished he looked into the mirror and smiled and wondered why it had taken him so long to discover such a simple thing.

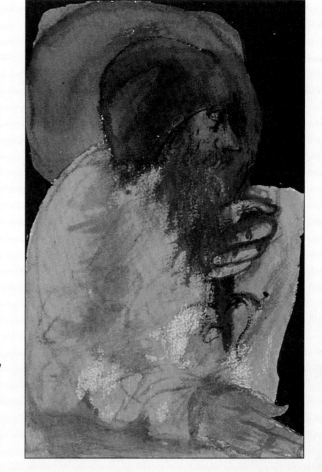

So Alberic picked up his bundle, took one last look through the palace and went down to the square for the last time.

"I have at last discovered one thing," he stated simply. "It is much better to look for what I may never find than to find what I do not really want." And with that he said goodbye and left the city as quietly as he'd come.

The crowd gasped and shook their heads in disbelief.

"He has given up his palace!"

"And his wealth and servants!"

"And the King's favor!"

"And he does not even know where he is going," they buzzed and mumbled. "How foolish, how very foolish! How could we ever have thought him wise?" And they all went home.

But Alberic didn't care at all, for now his thoughts were full of all the things he had yet to see and do and all the times he would stop to tell his stories and then move on again. Soon the walls were far behind and only his footsteps and the night were there to keep him company. Once again he felt the freedom and the joy of not knowing where each new step would take him, and as he walked along his stride was longer and stronger than was right somehow for a man his age.

Alberic the Wise

Meet the Author

Norton Juster, like his father before him, became an architect. However, he also had a love of telling stories that led him to become an author of children's books. One of his favorite things to write about is "the awakening of the lazy mind." His stories are often about people who have become bored by their lives because they are ignorant of all the possibilities that surround them. These characters often do not know how to relieve their boredom until they stumble across someone or something that teaches them how to learn. Once they begin to learn, they find that their lives will never be dull unless they stop pursuing knowledge.

Meet the Illustrator

Leonard Baskin first knew he wanted to be an artist when he was fourteen years old. He decided this after watching an artist, at Macy's department store, sculpt a human head out of clay. He bought five pounds of clay that day.

Baskin practiced sculpting and carving on his own for about a year. He wanted so much to learn more about it, that he "forced" himself on a well-known sculptor and asked for lessons. The sculptor decided to take him under his wing. Baskin studied with this sculptor for three years, and began to receive critical acclaim for his work. He continued his studies in art school and through research. He went on to become a successful painter, draftsman, and printmaker, as well as a sculptor.

Theme Connections

Think About It

With a small group of classmates, discuss what you learned about the reasons for journeys and quests from this selection. During discussion, address the following questions.

- Why would Alberic leave behind everything he knew to venture out into the unknown?
- Did Alberic make his decision wisely?
- Would you have made the same decision to leave home?
- What wisdom could your own journeys through life bring?
- What type of career do you think would bring you happiness, and why?

Record Ideas

Record in your Writing Journal anything new you have learned about journeys and quests. Reread entries written at the beginning of this unit, and make a note of any questions that have been answered.

Create a Word Wheel

Choose three or four descriptive words from this story selection. Draw a small circle within a large circle. Then draw lines, or spokes, to connect the two circles, forming a wheel. Write one of your descriptive words in the center circle. Then on each of the spokes, write a synonym for that word.

Underground to Canada

by Barbara Smucker
illustrated by Ed Tadiello

There was barely time for Julilly and Liza to look about the cabin, when three raps were heard on the door, and the Captain's voice whispered, 'A friend with friends. Open the door, lassies, there's trouble aboard.'

Julilly turned the lock. The Captain's face puffed with anger.

'I've had word there's a slave hunter and sheriff coming aboard, with a warrant to search the schooner before we set sail.' He peered closely at the girls.

'I've a notion that ye're the lassies they're making all the stir about.'

He picked up their bundles and hurried them out of the door. They ran down the narrow corridor and up the winding stairs. It was nearly dark on the open deck. Firefly-looking lanterns bobbed here and there. The wind was full of the smell of fish, and it was cold.

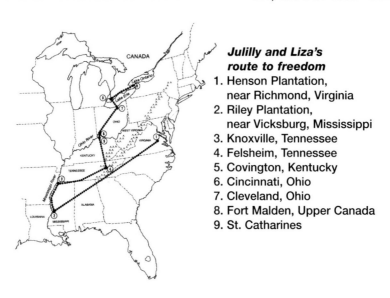

Julilly and Liza's route to freedom
1. Henson Plantation, near Richmond, Virginia
2. Riley Plantation, near Vicksburg, Mississippi
3. Knoxville, Tennessee
4. Felsheim, Tennessee
5. Covington, Kentucky
6. Cincinnati, Ohio
7. Cleveland, Ohio
8. Fort Malden, Upper Canada
9. St. Catharines

The girls ran with the Captain across the deck to the far side of the schooner where the little life-boat, covered with canvas, hung against the side. The Captain pulled back the canvas and helped Julilly and Liza inside.

'Ye'll find blankets, water, and a bite of food in there. Take care and pray that the Good Lord will protect ye.' He pulled down the canvas and left them alone.

The girls shivered. They felt about for the blankets and crawled under them, partly for warmth and partly for protection.

'We're gonna jump into the water,' Julilly said solemnly, 'if that sheriff comes near this little boat and takes the canvas off the top.'

Liza clutched Julilly's shoulder.

'We're never goin' back to bein' slaves again.'

It was a pledge between them. They were near the end of their journey. Massa Ross had said that Canada and freedom were on the other side of Lake Erie. There was no more walking through the woods, or climbing mountains, or hiding in wet swamp water.

'After all our trials, Liza,' Julilly said slowly, 'anythin' is better than goin' back to slavery.'

There was a small opening between the canvas and the top of their little boat, and the girls found that by looking through it they could see onto the deck.

People walked aboard with baskets and bundles in their arms. Sailors pulled at ropes and lifted rolls of heavy white cloth. Near the plank where the people came on board, the Captain stood scowling—his cap still pulled down over one eye and his moustache looking stiff and forbidding.

The girls kept their eyes on him. Two large men shoved their way up the plank and approached him. They could be the sheriff and the slave hunter. Julilly and Liza didn't know. They had never seen them before. The men spoke to the Captain, waving their arms in his face and pacing impatiently up and down beside him. They seemed like horses pawing the ground, wanting some kind of action. But the words they spoke were lost to Liza and Julilly in the wind and the splashing noise of lapping water.

The Captain shook his head. He threw his arms into the air as though in despair. He walked towards the thin stairway. The big men followed.

'They are going to search the cabins, Liza!' Julilly gasped, realizing just how lucky their escape had been. 'We're gonna get to Canada, if we've got to hang onto the bottom of this boat and get pulled across Lake Erie.' Julilly was angry now. What right

had these men to keep chasing them right up to the border, as if they were two runaway dogs? She and Liza were not going to be slaves no more.

It was night now. The grey fringes of daylight had slipped from the sky. Dark clouds foamed and raced above the *Mayflower*. Then they parted and a half-moon dazzled the schooner with yellow light. The North Star shone above with radiant steadiness. A bell clanged and the boat swayed impatiently as though eager to break away from the shore.

The Captain and the two large men popped out of the stairway. They heaved and puffed and ran to the entrance plank. They shook their fists in the Captain's face, but he shoved them onto the plank and waved good-bye.

The *Mayflower* turned. It swung around into the wind. The sails high above began cutting through the water.

'I feel that I'm flyin' through the sky just like those sails.' Liza hugged Julilly as they both pushed a wider opening in the canvas so they could see more of the outside.

The joy that Julilly felt was so intense that there was pain around her heart.

'Liza,' Julilly said finally, 'Mammy Sally is watchin' that same North Star. I've got to keep myself from hopin' too much, but I'm hopin' that it's led her to freedom, too.'

Liza began feeling about for the bundle of food and the flask of water. The girls ate and drank all of it. They drew the blankets close around them and watched the billowing sails catch the rushing wind.

Without wanting to, they slept in the hollow shelter of the small life-boat. When the Captain found them later, peaceful and warm, he left them to rock through the night and be refreshed for the morning.

A crisp, bright morning came quickly with thin, white frost powdering the deck. The air was strong with fresh fish smells. They mixed with the land smells of pine and pungent walnut bark and fertile earth still warm from summer. The waves on Lake Erie lapsed into gentle ripples. Sails were pulled in and the *Mayflower* drifted ashore.

Julilly and Liza woke with the sudden stillness of the schooner's landing. They grasped each other's hand for comfort, at once remembering the *Mayflower*, Lake Erie, and their nearness to Canada.

They pushed up the canvas on their little boat and the bright sun showered over them. The Captain ran towards them shouting with his trilling r's and upturned sentences.

'Ahoy.' He waved for the girls to join him. 'All passengers ashore.'

He grabbed the girls by their arms and ushered them down the plank to the shoreline. He pointed to rows of tall, silent trees and the long, bleak shore.

'See those trees,' he shouted. 'They grow on free soil.'

Julilly and Liza ran down the plank and jumped to the ground.

'Canada?' they cried together.

The Captain nodded.

Liza dropped to her knees. She spread out her arms and kissed the ground. 'Bless the Lord, I'm free!' she cried.

Julilly stood as tall and straight as she could. She pulled the cap from her head and held her head

high. There was no longer any need to hide her black skin. She was Julilly, a free person. She was not a slave.

'Thank you, Lord,' she said aloud. She filled her lungs as full as she could with the air of this new free land. No one else was near them except the Captain, who was wiping tears from his eyes and blowing his nose. But he seemed nervous and jumpy and kept watching each passenger who walked from the schooner.

'Ye are safe now,' he said warmly to the girls, 'and it does me heart good to have brought ye here.' Then he lowered his voice. 'But ye must remember that I must go back to Ohio this very day. I can't be getting myself arrested for helping slaves escape

to freedom, and I can't be revealing that I'm a "conductor" on the Underground Railway, even though my part of the train goes on top of the water.' He laughed suddenly.

Julilly looked at the Captain with new admiration. In her great joy to be standing on the soil of Canada, she had forgotten how this man was risking his job and maybe his life to bring them across Lake Erie on the *Mayflower*.

'Liza and I will never forget how you and all the people of the Underground Railway helped us, Captain,' Julilly said. She wanted to give him something, but her bundle was limp and empty.

Liza seemed not to hear them. She was still kneeling on the ground praying.

'I'm giving ye a little money from Mr Ross,' said the Captain, awkwardly shoving some paper bills into Julilly's hand. 'Far down the shore there is a coloured man with a cart waiting to take ye and your friend to the town of St Catharines. Mr Ross arranged it. Your cousin Lester has a job in that town and he'll take care of ye for a bit.'

Julilly looked quickly down the long stretch of rocks and sand that ran beside the lapping blue water of the great Lake Erie, and, sure enough, there *was* a man with a cart waiting beside one of the roads.

Underground to Canada

Meet the Author

Barbara Smucker first knew she wanted to be a writer when her sixth grade teacher told everyone in class to write an original fairy tale. She continued to love reading and writing as an adult. She used both to become an English teacher, a newspaper reporter, and a children's librarian.

The books she writes are often about imaginary people who live during real points in history. "Underground to Canada" takes place during the Civil War. Smucker believes people can learn from what has happened in the past and use it to make things better in the present and the future.

Meet the Illustrator

Ed Tadiello has completely immersed himself in the study of art. He has been a student at two New York City art schools. He also has held memberships in associations especially for artists and illustrators. The focus of his studies has been the human form. According to Mr. Tadiello, one of the biggest challenges in drawing characters is that they have a "natural quality to them." It is when this "natural quality" is achieved that he feels he has created a work of art, one he hopes "will touch and inspire the viewer."

Theme Connections

Think About It

With a small group of classmates, discuss what you learned about the risks people take when trying to realize their quests. Address the following questions during your discussion.

- Were the girls on a journey, a quest, or both?
- How did the girls know about the secret passage to Canada? Where did they get this information?
- What would have happened to the girls if they were caught by the slave owners?
- Why was the boat captain helping slaves escape?
- Why did the girls fall asleep when their lives were at risk?

Record Ideas

Record in your Writing Journal what you have learned about the unit theme. Write about how your understanding of journeys and quests has changed throughout this unit.

Create a Plot Line

With the help of your teacher, work with the rest of your class to create a plot line of "Underground to Canada." On this plot line, you will need to identify the selection's problem, conflicts, climax, and resolution. After the plot line has been completed, post it on the Concept/Question Board for possible use in your unit activity.

Maps

by Dorothy Brown Thompson

High adventure
And bright dream—
Maps are mightier
Than they seem:

Ships that follow
Leaning stars—
Red and gold of
Strange bazaars—

Ice floes hid
Beyond all knowing—
Planes that ride where
Winds are blowing!

Train maps, maps of
Wind and weather,
Road maps—taken
Altogether

Maps are really
Magic wands
For home-staying
Vagabonds!

Travel

by Edna St. Vincent Millay
illustrated by Doug Knutson

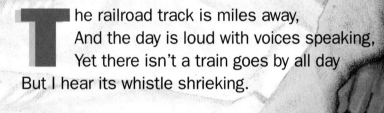

The railroad track is miles away,
And the day is loud with voices speaking,
Yet there isn't a train goes by all day
But I hear its whistle shrieking.

All night there isn't a train goes by,
Though the night is still for sleep and dreaming,
But I see its cinders red on the sky,
And hear its engine steaming.

My heart is warm with the friends I make,
And better friends I'll not be knowing,
Yet there isn't a train I wouldn't take,
No matter where it's going.

Bibliography

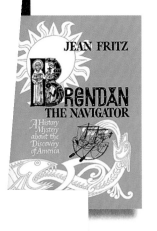

Brendan the Navigator: A History Mystery about the Discovery of America

by Jean Fritz. Saint Brendan was said to have set off from Ireland in a leather boat more than 1,500 years ago and to have found Paradise. Could he have found America?

Cosmic Journeys: A Beginner's Guide to Space and Time Travel

by Sarah Angliss. Black holes, wormholes, time travel. This book has it all. The sky isn't the limit anymore!

El Güero: A True Adventure Story

by Elizabeth Borton de Treviño. What happens when your father is exiled to a new country, one that is unsettled, bandit-infested, and very different from the land you have grown up in?

Grass Sandals: The Travels of Basho

by Dawnine Spivak. Wearing his tree bark hat and his grass raincoat, Basho walked hundreds of miles across his country and wrote a poem everywhere he went.

My Name is York

by Elizabeth Van Steenwyk. Captain Clark's slave, York, has dreams to fulfill as he travels west with Lewis and Clark in the early nineteenth century. Does he achieve them?

Our Journey From Tibet

by Laurie Dolphin. Nine-year-old Sonam makes a dangerous journey over the Himalayas to escape Chinese-occupied Tibet so that she may continue to study her traditional culture.

Paddle-to-the-Sea

by Holling Clancy Holling. Follow this miniature carved canoe and paddler from Canada down the St. Lawrence Seaway to the Atlantic Ocean.

Sacagawea

by Judith St. George. Where would Lewis and Clark have been without their guide? Meet brave, young Sacagawea.

Writer's Handbook

Grammar, Mechanics, and Usage

Table *of* Contents

Grammar, Mechanics, and Usage

Study Skills

Writer's Handbook

Grammar, Mechanics, and Usage

Writing and Technology

Writer's Handbook

Grammar, Mechanics, and Usage

Complete and Incomplete Sentences

Rule: A **sentence** is a group of words that expresses a complete thought.

A sentence must have a subject and a predicate to be complete. The **subject** of a sentence tells *who* or *what*.

Subjects:
The experiment with sand was interesting.
(What? The experiment with sand)

Ted and Janet reported their observations.
(Who? Ted and Janet)

The **predicate** of a sentence tells *what happens* or *happened*.

Predicates:
The sand worked as an insulator.
(What happened? Worked as an insulator.)

The other insulators did not work as well.
(What happened? Did not work as well.)

A sentence is incomplete if it is missing a subject.

Incomplete:
Left the containers in the sun.
(Who left the containers in the sun?)

Checked them every hour.
(Who checked them every hour?)

A sentence is incomplete if it is missing a predicate.

Incomplete:
Each team of students.
(What happened to each team of students?)

Our science teacher, Ms. Kemp.
(What happened to our science teacher, Ms. Kemp?)

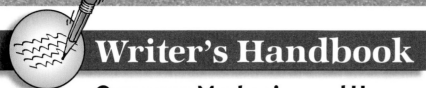

Writer's Handbook

Grammar, Mechanics, and Usage

Compound Subject and Predicate

Rule: A subject of a sentence that has two or more parts is called a **compound subject**. A predicate of a sentence that has two or more parts is called a **compound predicate**. **Conjunctions** are words used to join sentence parts.

A compound subject has two or more parts. The parts are usually connected with the conjunctions *and, but,* or *or.*

> **Subjects with one part:**
> <u>King Midas</u> lived in a fine castle.
> <u>His daughter</u> lived in a fine castle.
>
> **Compound subject:**
> <u>King Midas and his daughter</u> lived in a fine castle.

A compound predicate has two or more parts. The parts are usually connected with the conjunctions *and, but,* or *or.*

> **Predicates with one part:**
> The king <u>counted his money every day.</u>
> The king <u>arranged it in piles every day.</u>
>
> **Compound predicate:**
> The king <u>counted his money and arranged it in piles every day.</u>

If a compound subject or compound predicate has three or more parts, use commas to separate the parts. Put the conjunction just before the last part.

> **Compound subject:** <u>Gold, jewels, and money</u> were the king's most prized possessions.
>
> **Compound predicate:** The King <u>counted, hoarded, and hid his prized possessions.</u>

Grammar, Mechanics, and Usage

Compound Sentences

Rule: You can combine two sentences expressing related ideas. The combined form is called a **compound sentence**.

Follow these rules to form compound sentences:

Use conjunctions such as *and*, *or*, and *but* to combine sentences expressing closely related ideas. Place a comma before the conjunction.

Two sentences:
The library opens at eight o'clock.
It closes at six o'clock.

Compound sentence:
The library opens at eight o'clock, <u>and</u> it closes at six o'clock.

Two sentences:
The books could be due today.
The books could be due next week.

Compound sentence:
The books could be due today, <u>or</u> they could be due next week.

Two sentences:
The books were due today.
I renewed them.

Compound sentence:
The books were due today, <u>but</u> I renewed them.

Grammar, Mechanics, and Usage
Compound Sentences (continued)

Use a semicolon to combine two closely related sentences. The semicolon takes the place of the comma and conjunction.

Two sentences:
The library opens at eight o'clock. It closes at six o'clock.

Compound sentence:
The library opens at eight o'clock; it closes at six o'clock.

If two sentences do not express closely related ideas, keep them separate. For example, do not combine these sentences:

Jim lives near the library.
His favorite books are adventure stories.

Grammar, Mechanics, and Usage

Phrases and Clauses

Rule: A **phrase** is a group of words that does not contain a subject and a predicate. A **clause** is a group of words containing a subject and a predicate.

Use phrases to add precise or interesting details to your writing. One type of phrase is the prepositional phrase. A **preposition** shows how one word is related to another word in the sentence. A **prepositional phrase** always begins with a preposition and is followed by a noun or a pronoun and any of its modifiers.

The prepositional phrases are underlined in the following sentences:

> We stayed at the park and played on the swings.
>
> Up the tree scurried the cat.
>
> Near the ocean you can hear the waves as they crash against the shore.

In your writing, place a phrase as close as possible to the word the phrase modifies. Study these two examples:

> **Misleading:** I saw a little monkey in a magazine photo with a very long tail.
> (What has a very long tail?)
>
> **Clearer:** I saw a little monkey with a very long tail in a magazine photo.

Use different kinds of clauses to show connections between ideas. There are two types of clauses, independent and dependent.

An **independent clause** can stand by itself as a sentence. A **dependent clause** has a subject and a predicate, but it cannot stand by itself because it begins with a connecting word. It depends on the

Grammar, Mechanics, and Usage
Phrases and Clauses (continued)

independent, or main, clause. Often, a dependent clause tells how, when, where, or why the action in the independent, or main, clause takes place.

dependent clause
although I like soccer

independent clause
I am not good at it

independent clause
Jill and I play tennis

dependent clause
after we leave school

Here are some connecting words that are used to introduce a dependent clause:

after	because	since	until	which
although	before	that	when	while
as	if	though	where	who

If a dependent clause is not necessary to the meaning of the sentence, put a comma between the clauses.

Examples:
I like fishing, which is Dad's favorite sport.
I fish with Dad, who likes to go out in a boat.

If a dependent clause is necessary to the meaning of the sentence, do not put a comma between the clauses.

Examples:
Dad knows the man who sold us our boat.
We looked for a boat that we could rent.

Use a comma after a dependent clause that begins a sentence.

Examples:
After we caught our limit, we went home.
Because we like fish, we had some for supper.

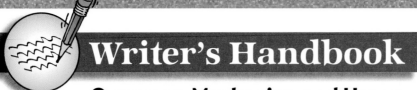

Writer's Handbook

Grammar, Mechanics, and Usage

Using Commas

Rule: Use a **comma** when you write a series of three or more nouns, adjectives, verbs, or phrases. Use a comma when you write dates and addresses, in direct address, and in certain letter parts.

In a **series** of three or more **nouns**, use a comma after each noun that comes before *and* or *or*.

> **Nouns:** Foxes eat <u>lizards</u>, <u>birds</u>, <u>mice</u>, and other small <u>animals</u>.

In a **series** of three or more **adjectives**, use a comma after each adjective that comes before *and* or *or*.

> **Adjectives:** The fur of the Arctic fox is <u>long</u>, <u>white</u>, and <u>silky</u>.

In a **series** of three or more **verbs**, use a comma after each verb that comes before *and* or *or*.

> **Verbs:** Fox cubs <u>wrestle</u>, <u>jump</u>, and <u>play</u> with each other.

In a **series** of three or more **phrases**, use a comma after each phrase that comes before *and* or *or*.

> **Phrases:** Foxes may live <u>among rocks</u>, <u>in underground dens</u>, <u>in caves</u>, or <u>in the hollows of trees</u>.

Follow these guidelines when you use commas in other places:

- In writing **dates**, use a comma to separate the day from the year. When you write a date in a sentence, also place a comma after the year (except at the end of a sentence) to separate it from the rest of the sentence.

Grammar, Mechanics, and Usage
Using Commas (continued)

Date: January 3, 1959, is the date Alaska was admitted to the Union as the forty-ninth state.

- Use a comma to separate the parts of a **place name**. When you write a place name in a sentence, also use a comma after the last word in the place name (except at the end of a sentence) to separate it from the rest of the sentence.

  Place name: Nome, Alaska, is south of the Arctic Circle.

- When you address the person you're speaking to by name, use one or two commas, as necessary, to separate the person's name from the rest of the sentence.

  Address a person:
  Dad, may we visit Aunt Ada next summer?
  Yes, Kayla, we will visit your aunt.

- Use a comma after the greeting and after the closing of a friendly letter.

  Friendly letter: Dear Aunt Ada,
  Love,

- Use a comma after the closing of a business letter. Note that the greeting of a business letter ends with a colon, not a comma. For examples, see page 681, **Using Semicolons and Colons**.

  Business letter: Very truly yours,
  Sincerely,

Writer's Handbook

Grammar, Mechanics, and Usage

Using Parentheses, Dashes, and Ellipses

Rule: Parentheses, dashes, and ellipses are special kinds of punctuation marks. Use **parentheses** to show extra information within a sentence. Use **dashes** to show an interruption. Use **ellipses** to show a pause in speech, an unfinished sentence, or a place where words are left out of a quotation.

Put parentheses around extra information in a sentence. The information may tell what one of the words in the sentence means.

> ***Tyrannosaurus rex*** **was a carnivore (meat eater).**

The words in parentheses may give the reader more information.

> **A** ***Tyrannosaurus rex*** **was about 40 feet (12 meters) in length.**

You may also use dashes to set off a phrase that breaks the even flow of a sentence.

> **The Mesozoic Era—the period when the dinosaurs lived—lasted more than 175 million years.**

In dialogue, you can use a dash to show that a sentence was interrupted before it could be finished.

> **Terry pointed at the dinosaur skeleton and exclaimed, "What an enormous —"**

Grammar, Mechanics, and Usage

Using Parentheses, Dashes, and Ellipses (continued)

Use ellipses to show a pause in speech.

The teacher said, "I think that was the largest of the plant-eating dinosaurs . . . or was there a bigger one?"

Use ellipses to show that a sentence was not finished. A period is placed after the sentence, followed by three dots.

I have read about so many dinosaurs: tyrannosaurs, stegosaurs, brachiosaurs. . . .

Use ellipses to show that one or more words from a quotation have been left out.

She wrote, "Nobody knows . . . why the dinosaurs died out."

Grammar, Mechanics, and Usage

Using Semicolons and Colons

Rule: Semicolons and colons are punctuation marks. A **semicolon** (;) is used to separate two connected and complete thoughts in one sentence. A **colon** (:) shows that something more is to follow.

Colons and semicolons look similar, but serve different purposes.

Follow these rules when you use them:

Use a **semicolon** (;) to separate two connected and complete thoughts in one sentence. You may use a semicolon instead of a comma and a conjunction such as *and, but, or,* or *so.*

> **Sentence using comma and conjunction:**
> The fifth graders voted for dogs as their favorite animals, and cats came in second.

> **Sentence using semicolon:**
> The fifth graders voted for dogs as their favorite animals; cats came in second.

Notice that the semicolon separates a sentence into two parts. Each part is a complete thought with a subject and a predicate.

Use a **colon** (:) in a sentence to show that something is to follow. What follows might be a list of items or names, or it might be a complete thought that explains the first part of a sentence. If what follows is a complete thought, begin the sentence with a capital letter.

Grammar, Mechanics, and Usage

Using Colons and Semicolons (continued)

Colon introduces a list:
These animals also received two or more votes: parakeets, hamsters, and goldfish.

Second part of the sentence explains the first part:
There was only one surprise: Three people voted for snakes!

Use a colon between hours and minutes when you write a time.

Use a colon after the greeting in a business letter.

Examples: 6:45 A.M.   6:50 P.M.

Examples: Dear Mr. Cobra: Dear Ms. Windsor:

Writer's Handbook

Grammar, Mechanics, and Usage

Parts of Speech

Rule: All words can be classified into groups called parts of speech. They include **nouns**, **pronouns**, **verbs**, **adjectives**, **adverbs**, **prepositions**, **conjunctions**, and **interjections**.

A **noun** names a person, place, thing, or idea.

> The football <u>players</u> practice on the <u>field</u>.

A **pronoun** takes the place of a noun.

> The football players practice on the field. <u>They</u> practice for two hours.

A **verb** names an action or tells what someone or something is, was, or will be.

> The players <u>practice</u> hard. They <u>are</u> determined to do well. They <u>will listen</u> to their coach.

An **adjective** describes a noun or a pronoun.

> The <u>football</u> players enjoy playing the game. They are <u>strong</u> athletes.

An **adverb** describes a verb, an adjective, or another adverb. An adverb may answer the questions *How? How often? When?* or *Where?*

> The football team plays <u>skillfully</u>. The players are <u>now</u> the best in the league. The fans cheer <u>frequently</u>. TV camera crews and reporters are <u>everywhere</u>.

Grammar, Mechanics, and Usage
Parts of Speech (continued)

A **preposition** shows the relationship between a noun or pronoun and a verb, an adjective, or another noun in a sentence.

> The bleachers are <u>behind</u> the school.
> Meet me <u>after</u> the game.

A **conjunction** is used to connect words, phrases, or sentences.

> Cal <u>and</u> Jake are the best players.
> They are tired <u>but</u> determined.

An **interjection** is a word or phrase that expresses strong emotion.

> <u>Wow!</u> Jake can really run fast.
> <u>Great!</u> He just made a touchdown.

Writer's Handbook

Grammar, Mechanics, and Usage

Using Possessive Nouns

Rule: A **possessive noun** is used to show ownership. Possessive nouns can be singular or plural.

Follow these rules to form possessive nouns:

A **singular noun** names only one person, place, or thing. Form the possessive of a singular noun by adding an apostrophe and *s* (*'s*).

Singular noun:
Juan had a special party for his birthday.

Possessive noun:
Juan's cousin plays in a rock band.

A **plural noun** names more than one person, place, or thing. Form the possessive of a plural noun that ends in *s* by adding an apostrophe after the *s* (*s'*).

Plural noun ending with *s*:
The band members all owned instruments.

Possessive noun:
The band members' instruments were beautiful.

To form the possessive of a **plural noun** that does not end in *s*, add an apostrophe and *s* (*'s*).

Plural noun not ending with *s*:
All the children clapped and cheered.

Possessive noun:
The children's applause made the band feel happy.

Grammar, Mechanics, and Usage

Using the Right Pronoun for the Right Noun

Rule: **Pronouns** are words that take the place of nouns. Pronouns must agree in number, gender, and person with the nouns that they replace.

Use **singular pronouns** to take the place of singular nouns. Singular pronouns, such as *I, you, he, she,* or *it,* stand for one person or thing.

> **Singular nouns and pronouns:**
> Sonia went to the park. She took out her lunch and ate it happily.

Use **plural pronouns** to take the place of plural nouns. Plural pronouns, such as *we, you,* or *they,* stand for more than one person or thing.

> **Plural nouns and pronouns:**
> Sonia and her classmates went to the museum. They returned at three o'clock.

Use **subject pronouns** to take the place of subject nouns. The subject noun of a sentence tells who or what the sentence is about. Subject pronouns include *I, you, she, he, it, we,* and *they.*

> **Subject pronouns:**
> Sonia went to the park. She sat under a tree.

Grammar, Mechanics, and Usage
Using the Right Pronoun
for the Right Noun (continued)

Use **object pronouns** to take the place of object nouns. The object noun of the sentence follows the verb. Sometimes an object pronoun follows words such as *to, for, with, at,* or *from.* Object pronouns include *me, you, him, her, it, us,* and *them.*

> **Object pronoun:**
> Sonia ate some grapes.
> She ate them in the shade of a maple tree.

Use **possessive pronouns** to take the place of possessive nouns. Possessive pronouns show who owns or has something. Such possessive pronouns as *my, your, his, her, its, our,* or *their* appear before a noun. Other possessive pronouns, including *mine, yours, his, hers, its, ours,* or *theirs,* stand alone.

> **Possessive pronouns:**
> Sonia's father is a dentist. His office is on the fifth floor. The entire floor is his.

Always be sure your readers know exactly to *whom* or *what* each pronoun refers. If it is not clear to which noun your pronoun refers, use the noun again.

> **Not clear:** Alex and Ben went to a café for lunch. He ordered cake.

> **Clear:** Alex and Ben went to a café for lunch. Ben ordered cake.

Writer's Handbook

Grammar, Mechanics, and Usage

Using Present-Tense Verbs

Rule: A **verb tense** is a form of a verb that tells the time an action takes place—in the present, in the past, or in the future. A verb in the **present tense** shows action that happens now or action that happens again and again.

Follow these rules when you use present-tense verbs:

If the subject of a sentence is singular (except for the words *I* or *you*), add *-s* or *-es* to the verb to form the present tense. For most verbs, add *-s* to the end of the verb. With some verbs, you add *-es*. For example, if the verb ends with *-ch*, *-sh*, *-s*, *-ss*, *-x*, or *-z*, add *-es*.

Also, if the verb ends with a consonant followed by *y*, change the *y* to *i* and add *-es*.

Add -s: Margaret <u>sees</u> plays often.

Add -es: She <u>coaches</u> the school drama club.

Change *y* to *i* and add -es:
She <u>tries</u> to remember all of the lines.

If the subject of a sentence is plural, do not add an ending to the verb. Also, do not add an ending to the verb if the subject of the sentence is *I* or *you*.

No ending:
The girls <u>love</u> musicals. They <u>buy</u> recordings of their favorite plays. They <u>listen</u> to the songs over and over again. Sometimes I <u>lend</u> them my CDs.

Grammar, Mechanics, and Usage
Using Present-Tense Verbs (continued)

Irregular verbs have special present-tense forms that you must remember. Here are some examples:

Irregular Verbs	Present-Tense Forms
be	I am. You are. We are. They are. He is. She is. It is.
do	I do. You do. We do. They do. He does. She does. It does.
have	I have. You have. We have. They have. He has. She has. It has.

Writer's Handbook

Grammar, Mechanics, and Usage

Using Past-Tense Verbs

Rule: A **verb tense** is a form of a verb that tells the time an action takes place—in the present, in the past, or in the future. A verb in the **past-tense** form tells about an action that happened in the past.

Follow these rules when you use verbs in the past tense:

- Add -*ed* to form the past tense of most verbs.

  Add -*ed*: Ashley played the drums in a band. She taped her group's performance. Her dad asked her opinion. "It sounded good," she replied. "We really jammed."

For some verbs you need to change the spelling before you add -*ed*.

- If the verb ends with *e*, drop *e* when you add -*ed*.

  Drop *e*: tape   taped

- If the verb ends with a consonant plus *y*, change the *y* to *i* and add -*ed*.

  Change *y* to *i* and add -*ed*: reply   replied

- For most verbs that have one syllable, one short vowel, and one final consonant, double that final consonant before adding -*ed*.

  Double final consonant: jam   jammed

Grammar, Mechanics, and Usage
Using Past-Tense Verbs (continued)

Irregular verbs have special forms in the past tense.
Here are some common examples:

Irregular Verbs	Past-Tense Forms
be	I was. He was. She was. It was. You were. We were. They were.
do	did
have	had
go	went
come	came
say	said
give	gave

Grammar, Mechanics, and Usage

Making Subject and Verb Agree

Rule: In a sentence, the verb must **agree** with the subject. A singular subject takes a singular verb. A plural subject takes a plural verb.

The **subject** of a sentence is the word or words that refer to the person(s) or thing(s) that performs or receives the action of the verb. The **verb** is the word that refers to the action.

Most verbs follow this pattern in the present tense:

Present Tense	
Singular	*Plural*
I work.	We work.
You work.	You work.
He, she, it works.	They work.

If the subject is a singular noun, or *he, she,* or *it,* add *-s* to the verb.

> **Takes *-s* ending:** Juan <u>plays</u> tennis. He <u>plays</u> tennis.

However, verbs that end in *-s, -z, -x, -ss, -ch,* or *-sh* take the ending *-es.* In verbs that end in a consonant plus *y,* the *y* changes to *i* before the *-es* ending.

> **Takes *-es* ending:**
> The player <u>smashes</u> the ball across the net.
>
> **Final *y* changes to *i* before *-es*:**
> The player <u>tries</u> a new grip.

Some common verbs, such as *be* and *have,* are irregular. They have special patterns that you must memorize.

Grammar, Mechanics, and Usage
Making Subject and Verb Agree (continued)

Be: Present Tense	
I am.	We are.
You are.	You are.
He, she, it is.	They are.

Have: Present Tense	
I have.	We have.
You have.	You have.
He, she, it has.	They have.

The words *anyone, everyone, somebody, either*, and *each* are singular and take a singular verb.

Everyone plans to attend the assembly.

A subject consisting of two singular words connected by *and* is usually plural and takes a plural verb.

Maria and Franco play outside.

A subject consisting of two singular words connected by *or* or *nor* takes a singular verb.

Neither Betty nor Tim takes the class.

A subject consisting of a singular word and a plural word connected by *or* or *nor* takes a verb that agrees with the word nearer the verb.

Will the football player or the cheerleaders talk at the assembly?

Sometimes other words come between the subject and the verb. Make sure that the verb agrees with the subject.

One of the English teachers is in charge of the debate.

Writer's Handbook

Grammar, Mechanics, and Usage

Using Adjectives and Adverbs

Rule: An **adjective** describes a noun or a pronoun. An **adverb** describes a verb, an adjective, or another adverb. Adverbs answer the question *Where? When? How much?* or *How often?*

Remember these guidelines when you use adjectives and adverbs:

An **adjective** describes a noun. An adjective can also describe a pronoun such as *he, she, it,* or *they*.

> **Adjectives:** The box had a <u>plastic</u> cover on it. The <u>two</u> boys opened the box. They were <u>curious</u>.

An **adverb** describes a verb, an adjective, or another adverb. Adverbs tell *where, when, how much,* or *how often*.

> **Adverbs:** The boys were <u>slightly</u> nervous. <u>Soon</u> they discovered what was in the box. They closed the box <u>quickly</u>.

You can form many adverbs by adding *-ly* to an adjective. Notice that the spelling of a word may change when *-ly* is added to it.

> **Adverbs:**
> Several snakes lay <u>quietly</u> in the box.   (quiet + -ly)
> The boys put the box down <u>gently</u>.   (gentle + -ly)

Writer's Handbook

Grammar, Mechanics, and Usage

Using and Punctuating Dialogue

Rule: In a story, what characters say to each other is called **dialogue**. A speaker's exact words are called a **quotation**. These words are put inside **quotation marks** (" ").

Place quotation marks (" ") around a speaker's exact words.

> **Quotation marks:** Janell said, "My telescope is assembled."

Begin the first word of a quotation with a capital letter, even if it is not at the beginning of a sentence.

> **Capital letter:** Ben called, "My turn, my turn."

In most cases, use a comma to separate a quotation from the speaker tag.

> **Comma:** "Sure, be my guest," replied Janell.

Put the end punctuation mark for the quotation inside the closing quotation marks.

> **End marks:**
> Ben exclaimed, "The moon looks so close!"
> "Can you see any craters?" asked Sue.

Use two sets of quotation marks when a speaker tag interrupts a quotation. Separate the speaker tag from

Grammar, Mechanics, and Usage
Using and Punctuating Dialogue (continued)

the quotation with commas. Do not capitalize the first word after the speaker tag because it is part of the first sentence of the quotation, not a new sentence. If the interrupted quote contains two complete sentences, use a period and a capital letter.

One sentence:
"Yes," said Ben, "they look huge."

Two sentences:
"They are really big," said Sue. "One crater is about 700 miles across."

Always start a new paragraph when the speaker changes.

Example:
"Sue, did you bring the soccer ball?" Ben asked.
"I put it in the green bag, Ben," replied Sue.

Writer's Handbook

Study Skills

Parts of a Book

A book has other parts besides the main part, the part containing a story or information. All books do not have the same number of parts, but each part is usually found in the same place in every book. Many fiction books have only a **title page** and a **copyright page**, but some will also have a **table of contents** and a **glossary**. Nonfiction books have a title page and a copyright page and often a table of contents, glossary, **bibliography**, and **index**.

When you look for information about a story, question, or problem, you usually use several books. However, you will not have time to read every page of every book. Instead, use the parts of a book to help you find the information you need.

The title page, copyright page, and table of contents are at the front of the book.

- The **title page** gives the title of the book, the name of the author or editor, and the name of the publisher.

- The **copyright page** comes after the title page. It gives the publisher's name and location and the year in which the book was published.

- The **table of contents** is a list, in order of appearance, of the units, chapters, or stories in the book, with the page number on which each item begins.

Study Skills

Parts of a Book (continued)

The glossary, bibliography, and index are at the back of the book. Sometimes a bibliography is found, instead, at the end of each chapter or unit.

- The **glossary** is an alphabetical listing of new or special words that are used in the book along with their definitions.

- The **bibliography** is an alphabetical listing of books in which the author of the book found information about the subject. It may also include other writings that the author thinks would interest the reader.

- The **index** is an alphabetical listing of names, places, and topics covered in the book, with the numbers of the pages on which they are mentioned or discussed.

Study Skills

Using the Card Catalog

Each library has a **card catalog**—a list of all the books in a library. Some libraries list the books on cards found in small cabinet drawers. Other libraries have the card catalog on computers. In both systems, you can find a book listed in three ways: by the author's last name, by the title of the book, or by the subject of the book.

The card catalog is a good place to start your research about a subject. The following information can help you get the most out of it:

- The **author** card lists the author's name at the top of the card. A **title** card lists the book's title at the top. A **subject** card lists the subject of the book at the top. On a computer, you can look up an author's name, a book title, or a subject.

- A book entry may contain a **call number**. On each card, the call number is in the upper left-hand corner. This number matches the numbers and letters on the spine of the book. The call number also matches numbers and letters on the shelf on which you can find the book. An R means that a book is in the reference section. A J or JUV before the number means that the book is in the juvenile section.

- Every card shows the year in which the book was published. Make sure you check the **publication date** if you need to obtain recent information.

- The card lists the **number of pages** in the book. This number can give you some idea of how much information is in a book. It might also suggest whether the book is too hard or too easy.

Study Skills

Using the Card Catalog (continued)

- If the book has **illustrations**, the abbreviation *ill.* is shown. Sometimes the abbreviation *col ill.* is shown to let you know that the illustrations are in color. Depending on your research problem, pictures might help you in your research.

- The entry includes a **summary** of the book. The summary briefly tells what the book is about. It will help you decide whether the book has the information you need.

- If the book includes an **index** or **bibliography**, the card also provides that information. An index will help you locate pages where your subject appears. A bibliography might lead you to other books related to your subject.

- At the bottom of each card is a list of **headings**. This list gives all the headings under which the book is listed in the card catalog. If you look under the other headings in the subjects cards, you may find more books on your research problem.

Study Skills

Using a Dictionary, Glossary, or Thesaurus

A **dictionary** is a book that tells the meanings of most of the words that people use when they speak, read, and write. A **glossary** is the section in the back of a book that gives the meaning of words that appear in that book. A **thesaurus** is a dictionary of synonyms and antonyms. Words in it may be organized in alphabetical order or by subject. In that case, check the index to see how to find a certain word.

- Each word listed in a dictionary, glossary, or thesaurus is called an **entry word**. All entry words are listed in alphabetical order and are printed in dark type.

- At the top of each dictionary, thesaurus, or glossary page are two words called **guide words**. These words are usually printed in dark type. The word on the left is the first entry word listed on the page. The word on the right is the last entry word listed on the page. All other words on the page fall in alphabetical order between the two guide words. (A thesaurus may use guide numbers instead of words.) Guide words can help you find the page on which the word you are looking for is listed.

- A **dictionary** or **glossary entry** gives the word's spelling, pronunciation, part of speech, and meaning or meanings. The part of speech is abbreviated; for example, *n.* stands for *noun*. Entries may also give synonyms for the word, spellings of the word with endings added, and the word's history or etymology.

Study Skills

Using a Dictionary, Glossary, or Thesaurus (continued)

flan·nel (flan´ əl) *n.* A soft, woven material made of wool and/or cotton. [Middle English *flanen*, from Welsh *gwlanen*, "woolen cloth," from *gwlân*, "wool."]

- A **pronunciation key** is found at the beginning of a dictionary or glossary. The key has symbols that stand for vowel and consonant sounds. The symbols are shown with example words. Pronounce these to hear the sounds. Then use the symbols to pronounce unfamiliar words.

- A **thesaurus entry** shows a list of synonyms for that word and perhaps an antonym or two.

  neat *adj.* orderly, organized, tidy, uncluttered, well-organized, trim. Antonym—see MESSY

- Select the word that best conveys your meaning. Remember that synonyms have meanings that are similar but not exactly the same. If you are unsure which word to use in your context, you may wish to check the meanings of the word in a dictionary.

Study Skills

Using an Encyclopedia

Encyclopedias are reference books that contain articles on a wide range of subjects. The articles in encyclopedias usually are arranged in alphabetical order (a few are thematic).

An encyclopedia is a good place to start when you begin doing research. It gives you information about your topic in its articles. It can also lead you to other materials about your topic.

Follow these guidelines when you use an encyclopedia:

- Locate the encyclopedia's index. It is usually at the back of a one-volume encyclopedia or a separate volume of a multivolume set. The index is an alphabetical list of all the articles in the encyclopedia.

- Decide what the key word or words in your research question or problem are. Look up those words in the index of an encyclopedia. For a question about *how the Underground Railroad helped slaves*, you might look in the index under "Underground Railroad." If you need information about a person, look under the person's last name.

  Lincoln, Abraham
  Tubman, Harriet

- In the index of a multivolume encyclopedia, after each main article title, you will see a volume number or letter first, then a page number. Other articles that have additional information might be

Study Skills

Using an Encyclopedia (continued)

listed as well. Make a list of the titles, volume numbers or letters, and page numbers of articles that might have information about your topic.

Underground Railroad 18:329; 2:9
   Brown, John 3:328
   Tubman, Harriet 18:254
   Vermont 19:69

- Look at your list and select the encyclopedia volumes that you think will be most helpful. Turn to the given pages to locate the articles.

- Read any headings or subheadings within each article. Headings tell you what information you will find in the article's sections. They might give you some idea of how to narrow your topic or arrange the information in your own report.

- Throughout the article and at its end, look for suggestions of other places in the encyclopedia where you might find more information about your topic. These suggestions are called cross-references.

(See **Quakers***) See also* **Fugitive Slave Law**.

Also, a list of books with more information about your topic may be given at the end of an article.

Blockson, Charles L. *Underground Railroad*
Brandt, Nat. *The Town That Started the Civil War*

Writer's Handbook

Study Skills

Using Maps

Maps are drawings that show where places are located or where important events happened. Maps are made and used for many purposes. Each kind of map gives different information. For example, **historical maps** show information about the past such as where battles were fought, what trails the pioneers followed, or how land was once divided.

Maps can present a great deal of information more quickly than it can be explained in words. Most maps have these features:

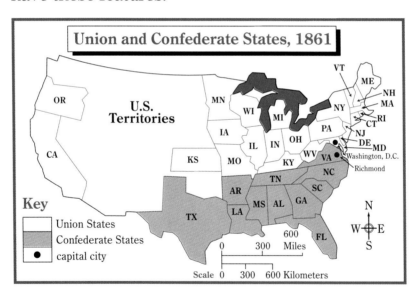

- The **title** tells what information the map shows or what its purpose is. The map shown on this page shows which states remained in the Union during the Civil War and which became Confederate states.

Study Skills
Using Maps (continued)

- The **key** explains what each symbol or color on the map stands for. Notice the key with the map on page 704. It shows that a dot stands for a capital city.

- The **scale** shows how many miles or kilometers are represented by a given measure, usually some fraction of an inch or centimeter, on the map. This map, for instance, shows that one half-inch equals 600 kilometers.

- The **direction arrows** or **compass rose** shows north, south, east, and west on the map.

Use the map features to find more information about states you are researching. For example, this map shows that 34 states were in existence in the year 1861.

Writer's Handbook

Study Skills

Making and Using a Time Line

A **time line** is a graphic device used to show the sequence of important events over a particular period of time and the relative amount of time between them. A time line may cover any chosen length of time, from the lifetime of a person to a historical period of hundreds or thousands of years.

Reading a time line can help you understand and remember the order of important past events. Making a time line can help you present the most important facts gathered in your research.

Here are guidelines for making a time line:

- Decide what you want to show in your time line. Choose a title for it.

  Example: Amelia Earhart

- Make a list of the main events and the time of each one. Use concise, descriptive phrases.

  Examples:

  Born Atchison, Kansas—1897
  First woman to fly across Atlantic as passenger—1928
  Solo flight across Atlantic—1932
  Lost on flight around world—1937

Study Skills

Making and Using a Time Line (continued)

- Draw a line across a sheet of paper. Leave space above and below the line for writing the events and the times—in order, from left to right.

- On the line, make a dot for the time of each event. Vary the space between the dots, according to the length of time between events.

- Below each dot, write a time.

- Above each dot, write an event.

Born Atchison, Kansas	First woman to fly across Atlantic as passenger	Solo flight across Atlantic	Lost on flight around the world
1897	1928	1932	1937

Study Skills

Using Diagrams

A **diagram** is an illustration that shows the parts of an object or shows how something works. Labels on a diagram help explain the parts or steps in the illustration. Diagrams often help readers visualize information that is mechanical or scientific.

Diagrams can show the following kinds of information:

- how something is put together, such as a bicycle
- how something is arranged, such as clothing in a suitcase
- how something works, such as a telescope
- how to make something, such as a quilt
- how two or more things are connected, such as the strings on a violin
- what steps make up a process, such as making lemonade
- what stages make up a cycle, such as the seasons of the year

When you read, diagrams can help you understand technical or scientific material. When you write, you can help your readers understand technical material by using diagrams.

Study Skills
Using Diagrams (continued)

These are the features of a diagram:

Parts of a Telescope

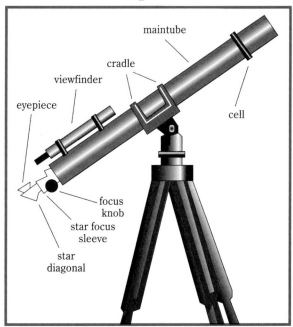

- The **title** of the diagram tells what the diagram is about.

- **Labels** of a diagram tell what each part of an object or step in a process is. On this diagram, for instance, a label tells you that a telescope has both a viewfinder and an eyepiece.

- **Lines** lead from each label to the part or step being identified.

- **Arrows** show in what order the steps of the process or the stages in a cycle take place. Arrows can also show movement or direction. This diagram contains no arrows. However, someone might add an arrow that shows which direction the focus knob turns or what path the light takes.

Writer's Handbook

Study Skills

Organizing Information in a Chart

A **chart** can present much information in a small amount of space. A chart helps organize information so that readers can understand it more easily and quickly.

Sometimes when you are doing research, you might find that you can better understand and compare information if you organize it in a chart. Charts are used for time schedules, work schedules, and other information.

The following guidelines will help you make charts and also understand them:

- Choose information that would be easier and faster to read and understand in a chart. For example, if you want to share information about money from around the world, your chart might include names and symbols for forms of money and different countries.

Money Around the World			
Name	*Symbol*	*Subdivision*	*Country*
Dollar	$	100 cents	United States
Drachma	Dr	100 lepta	Greece
Ruble	R *or* Rub	100 kopeks	Russia

Study Skills

Organizing Information in a Chart (continued)

- Give the chart a **title** that tells what it is about.

- Create **row headings** and write them down the left side of the page. Row headings are the names of the items you will give information about.

- Write short **column headings** across the top of the chart. These headings tell the kinds of information you will give about the items in the row headings.

- To help make the chart easy to read, draw lines between the column headings and between the row headings.

- In the blank spaces, write brief information about the items in the row headings. Complete sentences are not needed.

- To read a chart, find the row or column heading that shows the kind of information you are seeking. Read down or across until you find the information.

Writer's Handbook

Study Skills

Note Taking

Researchers take **notes** to help them remember important information about their research. Notes contain key phrases and short sentences that sum up important facts and ideas.

Follow these guidelines when you take notes:

- Use a different note card for each kind of information that you collect.

- Create a heading for each kind of information. Use the headings to organize your notes.

  <u>Differences Between the North and South</u>
  <u>Before the Civil War</u>
  Different views on states' rights
  South was agricultural; North was industrial.
  South wanted to take slavery to the West.

- Sum up the source's ideas in our own words. Often you need to use only a few meaningful words, phrases, or abbreviations that will remind you of important information.

  Many diffs between N and S eventually led to CW.

- If the author uses especially interesting language to express an idea, you may want to quote her or his words exactly. If so, put quotation marks around the words. Also, record the author's name, the book title (or magazine and article title), and the page number of the quotation.

Study Skills
Note Taking (continued)

"Slowly, darkness lifted and Sumter's shape became more and more distinct. Confederate gunners adjusted the firing angle of their weapons, torches poised near the fuses. At exactly 4:30 a.m., General P. G. T. Beauregard gave the command, and the bombardment—and with it the Civil War—began."

Jim Murphy, "So I Became a Soldier," *The Boys' War: Confederate and Union Soldiers Talk About the Civil War*, page 1.

- Take notes on only the most important information about your research or problem.

- Write neatly and clearly so that you can easily read your notes as you write your report.

Writer's Handbook

Study Skills

Outlining

An **outline** is a written plan that writers use to organize their notes and ideas before they begin to write a first draft. An outline arranges information into main topics and subtopics.

When you are doing research, put your ideas into outline form before you start writing. Then you can be sure that your report or project is organized logically.

Follow these guidelines:

- On a sheet of paper, write the **title** for your outline. This title will be the title of your paper or project.

- Check the **headings** on your note cards. Then separate the cards into piles by their headings. The large, obvious divisions will be **main topics**.

- Next, check your note cards to see how each main topic can be divided. These divisions will be **subtopics** and must relate to the main topic. In the outline here, the two main topics are "Locations of most active volcanoes" and "Famous volcanic eruptions."

- Number each main topic with a Roman numeral (I, II, III, and so on) followed by a period. Your completed outline should include at least two main topics.

- Under each main topic, indent and number each subtopic with a capital letter followed by a period, as shown in the sample outline. Include at least two subtopics under each main topic—or none at all.

Study Skills

Outlining (continued)

- If subtopics need to be divided further, under each subtopic indent again as shown and number each subtopic with an Arabic numeral (1, 2, 3, and so on) followed by a period. If you use **sub-subtopics**, you should have at least two—or none at all.

VOLCANIC ACTIVITY

I. Locations of most active volcanoes

   A. Ring of Fire

      1. Western coast of North and South America

      2. Eastern coast of Asian and Pacific Islands

   B. Mediterranean Sea

II. Famous volcanic eruptions

   A. Mount Mazama

      1. Date

      2. Location

      3. Results

   B. Mount Vesuvius

      1. Date

      2. Location

      3. Results

Study Skills

Making a Bibliography

A **bibliography** is a list of writings about a particular subject. It may include books and other written material, recordings, and photographic collections in which the author found information to use in a book, an article, or a report. A bibliography may also be a list of books in which the reader can find more information about the subject.

A bibliography tells readers where the writer got her or his information. It also tells readers where they can read more about the subject. Provide a bibliography when you write about your research.

Follow these guidelines:

- Make a separate note or card for each book you use in your research. On the card, put the author's full name, with the last name first; the title of the book; the publisher's name; and the date of publication. The publisher's name is found at the bottom of the title page. The date of publication is found on the back of the title page.

When you create your bibliography, put the information in this form:

Meltzer, Milton. Voices from the Civil War: A Documentary History of the Great American Conflict. New York: HarperCollins Children's Books, 1989.

Study Skills
Making a Bibliography (continued)

- Note the form and punctuation: the first and last names are inverted; a comma is placed after the last name and a period after the middle name. The title is underlined or italicized and followed by a period. A colon is placed after the city of the publisher. A comma is placed after the name of the publisher. A period is placed after the date of publication.

- Write the title *Bibliography* in the center of the line at the top of the page. Leave a line space between the title and the first entry. Arrange your entries in alphabetical order by the last name of the author. If a source does not provide an author's name, list the work alphabetically by its title, ignoring the initial word *a, an,* or *the*. Leave a space between entries.

Bibliography

Arnold, Caroline. The Ancient Cliff Dwellers of Mesa Verde. New York: Clarion Books, 1992.

Lauber, Patricia. Painters of the Caves. Washington, D.C.: National Geographic Society, 1998.

Writer's Handbook

Writing and Technology

Doing On-Line Research

On-line research can be interesting, fun, and rewarding. On-line you can find newspaper articles, encyclopedia articles, interviews, dictionaries, and many other kinds of information.

When you do research, you will probably use a **search engine** or a **directory**. A search engine looks for certain keywords. A directory is a list of categories that you can look at and browse through. Many Websites contain both, so they are listed together here. Some of the best-known directories and search engines can be found at the following addresses:

http://www.altavista.digital.com

http://www.hotbot.com

http://www.yahoo.com

These tools will provide you with lists of **URL's** (uniform resource locator), or Internet addresses. To access that site, just click or type the URL. If you type it, be sure you copy every letter, colon, and slash correctly. Type capital letters correctly and include all punctuation except for any at the end. Leave off an end punctuation mark, unless it is a slash (/).

Most sites offer either **search tips** or a **help file**. Read these carefully. They will help you search successfully. For example, at some sites, you can use words such as *AND* to join terms or names. Other sites use symbols or punctuation marks instead. At these sites, you may have to place a name inside quotation marks to search for it.

Writing and Technology
Doing On-Line Research (continued)

When you do research on-line, you should remember and follow a few simple guidelines:

- Use more than one search engine or directory, since each finds Websites in a special way. You may be unsuccessful at one site and successful at another.

- Check the most likely sources first. The Library of Congress or a major university is apt to be a better source of accurate historical information than a personal Website.

- Save information about your sources. If you used an on-line reference book, print out the page that gives its name, publisher, and date. If you used a Website, write down its URL, or Internet address.

Writer's Handbook

Writing and Technology

Comparing Information from Different On-Line Sources

When you select a book or magazine from a library, that document has gone through many people's hands: the writer's, one or more editors', fact checkers', and proofreaders', to name a few. Such material also contains the name of the publisher, whose reputation rests on printing reliable material. Printed material is usually evaluated before it is published.

Web material is different. Material that you find online may be just as reliable as material that you find in print. However, since anyone can publish on the Web, there is a greater chance that material may be inaccurate, wrong, or misleading. Therefore, you must learn to evaluate on-line information carefully.

The following guidelines can help you:

- Look at the person or organization that is sponsoring the site. To do this, look at the home page. Whose name appears on it? Is this a major university or a government organization? Is it a reputable professional person or group? Is it a commercial business, a political organization, or a private person?

- Sometimes the URL address can help you identify the source. Addresses of educational sites end in *edu*; those of government sites end in *gov*; those of businesses end in *com*. However, a personal Web page of a university student might also end in *edu*, so look further.

Writing and Technology

Comparing Information from Different On-Line Sources (continued)

- What is the purpose of the page? Is it designed to inform, persuade, or entertain you? Does it contain advertisements?

- Often, a home page will have a link to more information about the sponsoring organization or person. Click on it to learn more. Is this source likely to be an authority on the subject?

- Where does the information on the site come from? Most reliable sites provide this information somewhere. Sources that are quoted are named.

- Is the information up-to-date? Many pages tell when they were last updated.

- Does it contain links to other valuable sites?

Writing and Technology

On-Line Safety Tips

Computers can connect you to people all over the world. You can look at Websites that were created in another country, and you can post and read messages on bulletin boards that are read throughout the world. You can communicate by e-mail and make new friends all over the world. Computers give you an opportunity to make new friends that you might otherwise never meet.

Meeting people on-line can be fun and exciting. However, you need to follow certain safety rules, just as you do when you meet any stranger.

- Do not believe everything that you read online. Many people make up special online personalities, either for fun or for deception. They may pretend to be older or younger than they really are. They may pretend to have another name or come from a different country.

- Never give out personal information online, unless you are sure that you are dealing with someone that you and your family knows well. Be careful what you post on bulletin boards. Do not give out any of the following information:

   your full name or address
   your school's name or location
   your phone number
   your Social Security number
   your parent's or guardian's name
   where your parent or guardian works

Writing and Technology
On-Line Safety Tips (continued)

- Never reply if someone asks for personal information. If someone writes anything that makes you feel uncomfortable or scared, do not write back. Instead, print out the other person's letter or message and give it to an adult.

- Never send a picture of yourself to someone you don't know. If someone asks for a picture, check with an adult.

- Never give out your password. Do not even tell it to your friends.

- Never agree to meet anyone in person unless you first tell a responsible adult and get that person's permission. Any meetings should be in a public place, not in a car or private home. Do not go alone.

- Never download a file from an unknown source. The file might contain a virus that will harm your computer. It might also contain a program that can damage your computer or gather information about you.

724

Glossary

Pronunciation Key

a as in **at**	**ī** as in **kite**	**o͞o** as in **too**	**ə** as in **about**, **chicken**, **pencil**, **cannon**, **circus**	**sh** as in **shop**
ā as in **late**	**o** as in **ox**	**or** as in **form**		**th** as in **thin**
â as in **care**	**ō** as in **rose**	**ou** as in **out**		**th** as in **there**
ä as in **father**	**ô** as in **bought** and **raw**	**u** as in **up**	**ch** as in **chair**	**zh** as in **treasure**
e as in **set**		**yo͞o** as in **use**	**hw** as in **which**	
ē as in **me**	**oi** as in **coin**	**ûr** as in **turn**, **germ**, **learn**, **firm**, **work**	**ng** as in **ring**	
i as in **it**	**o͝o** as in **book**			

The mark (´) is placed after a syllable with a heavy accent, as in **chicken** (chik´ ən).

The mark (´) after a syllable shows a lighter accent, as in **disappear** (dis´ ə pēr´).

A

abacus (a´ bə kəs) *n.* A tool used to figure math problems by sliding counters.

abolish (ə bol´ ish) *v.* To put an end to.

Word Derivations

Below are some words related to *abolish*.

abolishable	abolishment	abolitionism
abolisher	abolition	abolitionist
abolishes	abolitionary	

abolitionist (ab´ ə lish´ ən ist) *n.* A person who wants to end slavery.

acceleration (ak sel´ ə rā´ shən) *n.* An increase in speed.

accumulation (ə kyo͞o´ myə lā´ shən) *n.* A piled-up mass.

ace (ās) *v.* To easily get all or most answers correct.

adjacent (ə jā´ sənt) *adj.* Next to; touching.

adobe (ə dō´ bē) *n.* Sun-dried brick.

agate (a´ gət) *n.* A striped marble.

agitation (aj´ i tā´ shən) *n.* Disturbance; excitement.

ailment (āl´ mənt) *n.* An illness; a sickness.

alder (ôl´ dər) *n.* A tree in the birch family.

alien (ā´ lē an) *adj.* From another world.

align (ə līn´) *v.* To place in a straight line.

alignment (ə līn´ mənt) *n.* The arrangement of things in a straight line.

allegiance (ə lē′ jəns) n. Loyalty.
amid (ə mid′) adv. In the middle of; among.
amiss (ə mis′) adv. Wrong; not as expected.
ample (am′ pəl) adj. More than enough.
anomaly (ə nom′ ə lē) n. Something that is different from the usual arrangement.
anticipate (an tis′ ə pāt′) v. To know or feel in advance.
anticipation (an tis′ ə pā′ shən) n. The act of expecting; hope.
applicant (ap′ li kənt) n. A person who asks for a position or job.
apprehension (ap′ ri hen′ shən) n. Fear.
apprentice (ə pren′ tis) v. To bind oneself to a craft worker in order to learn a trade.
arc (ärk) v. To move in a curved line. —n. A curve.

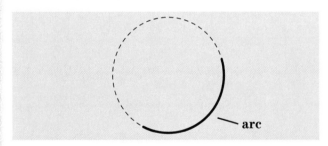

Word Derivations

Below are some words related to arc.

arcade	arcading	arcing
arcaded	arced	arcs

archaeology or **archeology** (är′ kē ol′ ə jē) n. The scientific study of people of the past by digging up things they left behind.

Word History

Archaeology, or archeology, came into English in the year 1837. It is from the Latin word archaeologia, meaning "knowledge gained through the study of ancient objects." This Latin word's origins are with the Greek words archē, meaning "beginning," and logos, meaning "word."

aroma (ə rō′ mə) n. A smell or odor, usually pleasant.
array (ə rā′) n. The order or arrangement of something.
arthritis (är thrī′ tis) n. A disease of inflamed joints, often associated with advanced age.
artifice (är′ tə fis) n. A clever trick in the way a story's plot is constructed.
artillery (är til′ ə rē) n. Mounted guns.
ascend (ə send′) v. To climb up; to rise.
assault (ə sôlt′) n. A sudden attack.
astronomical (as′ trə nom′ i kəl) adj. Having to do with the study of the stars and planets.
astronomy (ə stron′ ə mē) n. The scientific study of stars and planets.
atavistic (at′ ə vis′ tik) adj. Characteristic of people from a much earlier time.
automated (ôt′ ə mā′ təd) adj. Automatic; run by machines.
avert (ə vûrt′) v. To avoid.
avocation (av′ ə kā′ shən) n. Something a person does in addition to or aside from his or her regular job.

B

banish (ban´ish) *v.* To drive away; to force away.

bastion (bas´chən) *n.* A part of a fortified structure that juts out so that defenders can fire at attackers from several angles.

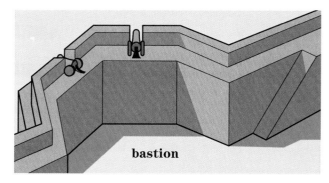
bastion

battery (bat´ə rē) *n.* A group of mounted guns or cannons.

bayonet (bā´ə net) *n.* A swordlike weapon attached to the end of a rifle.

beanie (bē´nē) *n.* A small bill-less cap worn on the crown of the head.

bedclothes (bed´klōz) *n.* Items used to cover a bed, such as sheets, blankets, and quilts.

bedrock (bed´rok) *n.* Solid rock.

benevolent (bə nev´ə lənt) *adj.* Kind; generous.

berate (bi rāt´) *v.* To scold harshly.

bewilderment (bi wil´dər mənt) *n.* Confusion.

bice (bīs) *adj.* Blue or blue-green.

billowing (bi´lō´ing) *adj.* Swelled up by the wind.

blemish (blem´ish) *n.* A stain; a defect.

blintze (blints) *n.* Cheese or fruit wrapped in a thin pancake.

blocade (blo kād´) *v. An old-fashioned spelling of* **blockade.** To cut off an enemy's supplies.

bloody (blu´dē) *adj.* A word used to indicate an extremely negative feeling.

bolt (bōlt) *n.* A roll of material or cloth.

bombard (bom´bärd) *n.* A leather jug or bottle.

bombardment (bom bärd´mənt) *n.* A battering with shots and shells.

boost (boost) *v.* To push up.

bore (bor) *v.* To drill into; to pierce.

bow (bou) *n.* The front part of a ship.

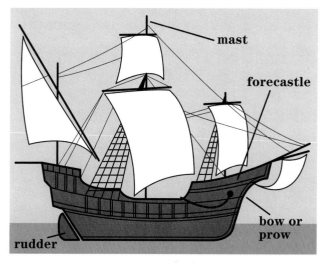
mast

forecastle

bow or prow

rudder

Word History

Bow came into English about 500 years ago. It probably came from the Dutch word *boech*, meaning "bow" or "shoulder." It is also related to *bōg*, a word meaning "bough" (a large tree branch) that dates back more than 800 years.

brazen (brā´zən) *adj.* Bold; cocky.

break (brāk) *v.* To tame a horse.

brocade (brō kād´) *n.* Woven cloth that has a raised pattern.

bronc (bränk) *n.* A wild or poorly broken horse.

brushpopper (brush´po pər) *n.* A person who works in an area covered with low-growing bushes and weeds.

Pronunciation Key: at; l**ā**te; c**â**re; f**ä**ther;
s**e**t; m**ē**; **i**t; k**ī**te; **o**x; r**ō**se; **ô** in b**ou**ght;
c**oi**n; b**oo**k; t**oo**; f**o**rm; **ou**t; **u**p; **ū**se; t**û**rn;
ə sound in **a**bout, chick**e**n, penc**i**l, cann**o**n,
circ**u**s; **ch**air; **hw** in **wh**ich; ri**ng**; **sh**op;
thin; **th**ere; **zh** in trea**s**ure.

bulldog (bool´ dôg´) *v.* To wrestle a
steer, usually by grabbing its horns
and twisting its neck.
buttress (bu´ tris) *n.* A structure built
outside a wall to give the wall support.

C

cairn (kârn) *n.* A pile of stones left as
a landmark or a monument.

cairn

calculation (kal´ kyə lā´ shən) *n.*
1. Counting, computing, or figuring.
2. The result of counting, computing,
or figuring.
calibrate (kal´ ə brāt´) *v.* To measure
by marking off equal amounts.
candor (kan´ dər) *n.* Honesty.
capital (kap´ i tl) *adj.* Excellent.
carcass (kär´ kəs) *n.* The body of a
dead animal.
caribou (kar´ ə boo´) *n.* A reindeer.
catapult (kat´ ə pult´) *v.* To move very
quickly or with great force.
celandine (sel´ ən dīn´) *n.* A plant in

the buttercup family with single
yellow flowers.
ceremonial (ser´ ə mō´ nē əl) *adj.*
Having to do with a formal celebration.
chance (chans) *v.* To take a risk and
try something difficult.
chaparral (shap´ ə ral´) *n.* An area
thick with shrubs and small trees.
cheder (hā´ dər) *n.* Religious school
for teaching Judaism.
chiffon (shi fon´) *n.* A soft, see-through
material made of silk, nylon, or rayon.
cinder (sin´ dər) *n.* Ash or a piece of
partially burnt coal or wood.
circuit (sûr´ kit) *n.* 1. A journey
around an established territory.
2. The path of an electrical current.
short circuit: A condition in which
something gets in the way of the
path of an electrical current and
causes either too much electricity
or not enough.
clamber (klam´ bər) *v.* To climb
with difficulty.
clarify (klâr´ ə fī´) *v.* To make
something clear; to explain.
cloister (kloi´ stər) *n.* A place where
religious people live away from the
world; a convent or a monastery.
cobbler (kob´ lər) *n.* A person who
repairs shoes and boots.
commence (kə mens´) *v.* To begin.

Word History

Commence came into English about 600
years ago. It came from the French word
comencer, and its assumed origin is the
Latin word *cominitiare.* This Latin word is
a derivative of *initiare,* meaning "to initi-
ate." (Also note that the word *commence*
contains the *-ence* suffix, which in this word
means "the action of " or "the process of.")

communal (kə myoon´ l) *adj.* Public; shared by all.

compassion (kəm pash´ ən) *n.* Sympathy; pity.

compel (kəm pel´) *v.* To force.

compensate (kom´ pən sāt´) *v.* To make up for; to offset.

Word Derivations

Below are some words related to *compensate*.

compensated	compensative
compensating	compensator
compensation	compensatory
compensational	

---

compensation (kom´ pən sā´ shən) *n.* Payment.

composition (kom´ pə zish´ ən) *n.* What something is made of.

compromise (kom´ prə mīz´) *n.* A settlement made by both sides each giving up a little.

concave (kon kāv´) *adj.* Curved inward; hollow; like the inner curve of a contact lens.

conceive (kən sēv´) *v.* 1. To start something with a certain point of view. 2. To understand.

conciliatory (kən sil´ ē ə tor´ ē) *adj.* Causing peace to be made.

concrete (kon´ krēt) *adj.* Real.

confine (kən fīn´) *v.* 1. To limit. 2. To keep in a place.

confounded (kon foun´ did) *adj.* Darned.

confront (kən frunt´) *v.* To face.

confrontation (kon´ frən tā´ shən) *n.* A face-to-face meeting.

consecrate (kon´ si krāt´) *v.* To make sacred.

consent (kən sent´) *n.* Permission.

consume (kən soom´) *v.* To destroy.

Word Derivations

Below are some words related to *consume*.

consumed	consumerism	consuming
consumer	consumes	consumption

---

convex (kon veks´) *adj.* Curved outward; like the outer curve of a contact lens.

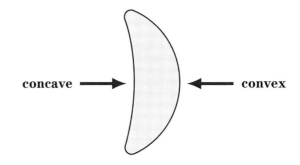

corn pone (korn´ pōn´) *n.* Baked or fried corn bread.

cotangent (kō tan´ jənt) *n.* A term used in trigonometry.

course (kors) *v.* To flow.

cradleboard (krād´ l bord´) *n.* A wooden frame that Native American women wore on their backs to carry their babies.

cringe (krinj) *v.* To back away from something unpleasant; to physically shrink because of fear or excessive humility.

croaker-sack (krō´ kər sak) *n.* A sack usually made of burlap.

crocheted (krō´ shād) *adj.* Made by looping one piece of yarn or thread through itself in an intricate pattern using a hooked needle.

crucial (kroo´ shəl) *adj.* Very important.

crusader (kroo sād´ ər) *n.* A person who fights for a cause.

cultivate (kul´ tə vāt´) v. To till the ground; to grow crops.

curvilinear (kur´ və li´ nē ər) adj. Having rounded or curving lines.

D

decipher (dē sī´ fər) v. To read or translate something written in code; decode.

deduction (di duk´ shən) n. A fact or conclusion figured out by reasoning.

defeatist (di fē´ təst) adj. Expecting and accepting that one will lose or be defeated.

defect (dē´ fekt) n. A fault; a flaw.

defect (di fekt´) v. To leave one's home country for another.

defiant (di fī´ ənt) adj. Openly disobedient; challenging.

Word History

Deliberately came into English about 500 years ago. It is the adverb form of the word *deliberate*, which came from the Latin word *deliberare*, meaning "to consider carefully." It is assumed that the Latin word *libra*, meaning "pound" or "scale," is also in its word history. This brings to mind the modern figure of speech "to weigh one's options." (Also note that *deliberately* contains the *-ly* suffix, which in this word means "in the manner of being.")

degradation (deg´ ri dā´ shən) n. Disgrace; shame.

deign (dān) v. To lower oneself; to stoop to do something that is beneath one.

deliberately (di li´ bə rət lē) adv. On purpose; meaning to.

delicatessen (del´ i kə tes´ ən) n. A shop selling prepared foods such as cooked meats and salads.

democracy (di mok´ rə sē) n. A government run by the people who live under it.

demolish (di mol´ ish) v. To do away with.

depredation (dep´ ri dā´ shən) n. The act of attacking and robbing.

desist (di sist´) v. To stop.

devise (di vīz´) v. To plan; to invent.

diffusion (di fyōō´ zhən) n. A spreading out or scattering.

dike (dīk) n. A bank or wall of earth built to hold back the water of a river or the sea.

diligence (dil´ i jens) n. Steady effort put forth to accomplish a task.

Word History

Diligence came into English about 600 years ago. It is a derivative of the word *diligent*, which has origins in the French word *diligere*, meaning "to love" or "to esteem." *Diligere* can also be divided into the word parts *di-*, meaning "apart," and *legere*, meaning "to select." (Also note that *diligence* contains the *-ence* suffix, which in this word means "the quality of" or "the state of.")

diminish (di min´ ish) v. To decrease; to lessen; to get smaller.

din (din) n. Clamor; uproar; racket.

discernible (di sûrn′ ə bəl) *adj.* Easy to recognize as different.

disconsolately (dis kon′ sə lit lē) *adv.* In a very unhappy way; hopelessly.

disembodied (dis′ em bod′ ēd) *adj.* Without a body.

disown (di′ sōn) *v.* To deny a connection to; to refuse to admit a relationship to.

dissipate (dis′ ə pāt′) *v.* To scatter.

Word Derivations

Below are some words related to *dissipate*.

dissipated	dissipates	dissipation
dissipater	dissipating	dissipative

---

distinct (di stingkt′) *adj.* 1. Clear; plain. 2. Separate.

distort (di stort′) *v.* To change the meaning of something; to misrepresent.

doctrine (dok′ trin) *n.* A principle or position that one believes in.

dogie (dō′ gē) *n.* A calf with no mother.

domesticated (də mes′ ti kāt′ əd) *adj.* Able to exist closely with humans.

domino (do′ mə nō′) *n.* A flat, rectangular game piece made of wood or plastic and divided into two equal parts with a varying number of dots on each part.

downpour (doun′ por′) *n.* A heavy rain.

dramatization (dram′ ə tə zā′ shən) *n.* An acting out of a story.

draught (draft) *n. chiefly British.* A liquid that is drunk; a dose.

dribble (dri′ bəl) *v.* In soccer, to move a ball down the field with a series of short, controlled kicks.

drought (drout) *n.* Dry weather that lasts a very long time.

dubiously (doo′ bē əs lē) *adv.* In a doubtful way.

dwindle (dwin′ dl) *v.* To get smaller gradually.

E

eclipse (i klips′) *v.* To darken; to cover over.

ecstatically (ek stat′ ik lē) *adv.* With great joy.

eddy (ed′ ē) *v.* To whirl into circle shapes.

edible (ed′ ə bəl) *adj.* Eatable.

emancipation (i man′ sə pā′ shən) *n.* The act of setting free.

embattled (em bat′ ld) *adj.* Struggling.

embellish (em bel′ ish) *v.* To make something better or more beautiful by adding to it.

encampment (en kamp′ mənt) *n.* A camp; a temporary stopping place.

encompass (en kum′ pəs) *v.* To include.

encounter (en koun′ tər) *v.* To meet by chance.

emphatically (em fat′ ik lē) *adv.* With spoken firmness or force.

engage (en gāj′) *v.* To take part; to be involved.

enumerate (i noo′ mə rāt′) *v.* To list; to count.

equinox (ē′ kwə noks′) *n.* The two times of the year when day and night are equal in length.

ermine (ûr′ min) *n.* A valuable white fur; the winter white fur coat of some weasels.

erroneous (ə rō′ nē əs) *adj.* Wrong; mistaken.

escort (e skort´) *v.* To go with and help or protect.

establish (i stab´ lish) *v.* To settle in a place.

Word Derivations

Below are some words related to *establish*.

establishable   establisher   establishment
established   establishes

estate (i stāt´) *n.* A large piece of land owned by one individual or family.

eternal (i tûr´ nl) *adj.* Everlasting; always; endless.

ewe (yōō) *n.* A female sheep.

excursion (ik skûr´ zhən) *n.* A pleasure trip; an outing.

exhilarated (ig zil´ ə rāt´ əd) *adj.* Excited.

F

faction (fak´ shən) *n.* A group of people within a larger group or party.

fanatic (fə nat´ ik) *n.* A person whose devotion to a cause goes beyond reason; a person with extreme devotion.

feisty (fī´ stē) *adj.* Having a lively and aggressive personality.

fervently (fûr´ vənt lē) *adv.* With great feeling; with emotion.

festive (fes´ tiv) *adj.* Merry.

festoon (fe stōōn´) *v.* To hang ribbons or banners in curved shapes.

floe (flō) *n.* A large sheet of floating ice.

flounder (floun´ dər) *v.* To struggle.

forage cap (for´ ij kap´) *n.* A small, low military cap.

forlornly (for lorn´ lē) *adv.* Sadly; hopelessly.

Word History

Forlornly is the adverb form of the word *forlorn*, which came into English more than 800 years ago. It is a derivative of the word *forlēosan*, which means "to lose." (Also note that *forlornly* contains the *-ly* suffix, which in this word means "in the manner of being.")

fortify (for´ tə fī´) *v.* To make stronger; to build a stronghold.

foundry (foun´ drē) *n.* A place where metal is melted and formed.

frantically (fran´ ti klē) *adv.* Quickly in a worried way.

frigid (fri´ jəd) *adj.* Very cold.

fume (fyōōm) *v.* To mumble something in an angry or irritated way.

furrow (fûr´ ō) *n.* A trench cut by a plow.

fuse (fyōōz) *v.* To join together by melting.

G

gable (gā´ bəl) *n.* A part of a wall that is enclosed by sloping sides of a roof, making a triangle-shaped section on a building.

gallinipper (gal´ ə nip´ ər) *n. informal.* Any of several insects that sting or bite.

gangly (gang´ glē) *adj.* Gangling; loose and awkward.

gaunt (gônt) *adj.* Very thin; bony.

geyser (gī´ zər) *n.* A hot-water fountain; a jet of hot water that shoots from the ground.

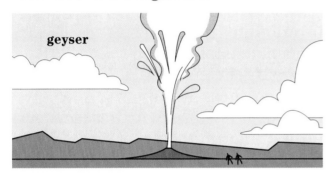

gingerly (jin´ jər lē) *adv.* Cautiously; warily.

gizzard (gi´ zərd) *n.* Intestine.

gore (gor) *v.* To pierce with an animal's horn or tusk.

gourd (gord) *n.* A melon-shaped fruit that can be dried and used as a bowl.

groschen (grō´ shən) *n.* A form of money worth ¹⁄₁₀₀ of a schilling. (A schilling is worth about 7¹⁄₂ ¢.)

grozing iron (grō´ zing ī´ ərn) *n.* A steel tool for cutting glass.

H

haberdasher (ha´ bər da´ shər) *n. chiefly British.* One who sells men's clothing.

haggard (hag´ ərd) *adj.* Exhausted looking; gaunt.

hallow (hal´ ō) *v.* To make holy.

hamlet (ham´ lit) *n.* A small village.

haughtily (hô´ təl ē) *adv.* In an overly proud way.

heirloom (âr´ lōōm´) *n.* An object handed down in a family.

high-falutin' (hī´ fə lōō´ tn) *adj.* Appealing to a higher class of people; fancy; showy.

hogan (hō´ gôn) *n.* A Navaho dwelling.

homespun (hōm´ spən) *adj.* Made at home.

homestead (hōm´ sted) *n.* A home and land surrounding it that belonged to one's family or ancestors.

hone (hōn) *v.* To sharpen.

honeycomb (hun´ ē kōm´) *v.* To make full of holes like a bee's honeycomb.

hover (huv´ ər) *v.* To hang in the air.

Word History

Hover came from an older English word, *hoven*, which may have come into use as many as 800 years ago. Since the earliest records of this word, it has always had the same meaning.

hue (hyōō) *n.* A tint; a shade of color.

humiliate (hyōō mil´ ē āt´) *v.* To shame.

Word Derivations

Below are some words related to *humiliate*.

humiliated	humiliating	humility
humiliates	humiliation	

hypnotic (hip not´ ik) *adj.* Causing sleep.

hypotenuse (hī pä´ tə nōōs´) *n.* In a right triangle, the side opposite the right angle.

I

illuminate (i lōō´ mə nāt´) *v.* 1. To throw light upon; to shine upon. 2. To make understandable; to clarify.

immortality (im´ or tal´ i tē) *n.* The state of living forever; enduring fame.

impassable (im pas′ ə bəl) *adj.* Blocked.

impassioned (im pash′ ənd) *adj.* With great feeling.

impenetrable (im pen′ i trə bəl) *adj.* Impossible to get through.

inalienable (in āl′ yə nə bəl) *adj.* Not able to be sold or given away.

inauguration (in ô′ gyə rā′ shən) *n.* The ceremony in which a president takes office.

indenture (in den′ chər) *n.* A person bound by a contract to work for someone else.

indescribable (in′ di skrī′ bə bəl) *adj.* So extraordinary that it cannot be described.

indifferent (in dif′ ər ənt) *adj.* Not interested; not concerned.

inevitable (in ev′ i tə bəl) *adj.* Certain; sure.

inexorable (in ek′ sər ə bəl) *adj.* Absolute; unyielding.

inferno (in fûr′ nō) *n.* A place of extreme, almost unbearable, heat.

infrared (in′ frə red′) *adj.* Having to do with the invisible rays that are closest to the red end of the visible light spectrum. See illustration of **ultraviolet.**

ingenious (in jēn′ yəs) *adj.* Clever; skillful.

ingot (ing′ gət) *n.* A piece of metal in the shape of a bar or a block.

ingratiate (in grā′ shē āt′) *v.* To put oneself in the good graces of others.

innovation (in′ ə vā′ shən) *n.* The act of creating something new or original.

inquisitive (in kwiz′ i tiv) *adj.* Curious.

insurrection (in′ sə rek′ shən) *n.* A revolt; a rebellion.

intelligible (in tel′ i jə bəl) *adj.* Clear; understandable.

intensify (in ten′ sə fī′) *v.* To increase; to strengthen.

intensity (in ten′ si tē) *n.* Great strength.

interstellar (in′ tər stel′ ər) *adj.* Between the stars. **interstellar space:** the part of outer space that is beyond our solar system.

interval (in′ tər vəl) *n.* A time when action stops for a while; a pause.

intimacy (in′ tə mə sē) *n.* A closeness.

intricate (in′ tri kit) *adj.* Tangled; complicated.

Word History

Ingenious came into English about 500 years ago. It comes from the Latin word *ingenium*, which means "natural capacity." Some meanings of the word *capacity* are "the amount that can be held in a space" and "ability or power." (Also note that *ingenious* contains the *in-* prefix, which in this word means "within," and the *-ous* suffix, which in this word means "having" or "possessing.")

J

journeyman (jûr′ nē mən) *n.* A person who has completed an apprenticeship and can now work in a trade under another person.

juniper (joō′ nə pər) *n.* An evergreen shrub with purple berries.

K

kaleidoscope (kə lī′ də skōp′) *n.* A constantly changing pattern.

kasha (kä′ shə) *n.* A soft food made from a grain, usually buckwheat.

kayak (kī′ ak) *n.* A light Eskimo canoe having a wooden or bone framework and covered with skins.

kayak

keelboat (kēl′ bōt) *n.* A shallow boat built with a keel, or long beam, on the bottom.

kiln (kil) *n.* An oven for firing glass, or heating it at very high temperatures, in order to make the color permanent.

knoll (nōl) *n.* A low, rounded hill; a mound.

L

lambent (lam′ bənt) *adj.* Glowing softly.

lance (lans) *n.* A long-shafted spear.

lariat (lâr′ ē ət) *n.* A rope tied with a movable loop at one end, used to catch cows and horses; a lasso.

learned (lûrnd) *v.* Past tense of **learn**: To gain new knowledge or skill. —*adj.* (lûr′ nid) Educated.

legendary (lej′ ən der′ ē) *adj.* From a story that has been passed down from a people's earlier times.

leisurely (lē′ zhər lē) *adv.* In a deliberate way; without hurry.

levity (le′ və tē) *n.* A lighthearted attitude.

limb (lim) *n.* an arm or leg.

lubricant (loo′ bri kənt) *n.* A substance such as oil or grease that makes machine parts slippery, thus making the parts move easily.

lull (lul) *n.* A period of reduced noise or violence.

luxurious (lug zhoor′ ē əs) *adj.* Grand; rich; elegant.

lynx (lingks) *n.* A wildcat; a bobcat.

M

magnification (mag′ nə fi kā′ shən) *n.* The amount of enlargement possible; the amount something is enlarged.

manacled (man′ ə kəld) *adj.* Handcuffed.

Word History

Manacled (which is a *manacle* with the inflectional *-ed* ending) came into English about 600 years ago. It came from the French word *manicle*, which came from a derivation of the Latin word *manus*, meaning "hand."

maneuver (mə noo′ vər) *n.* A movement that calls for planning and skill.

Word Derivations

Below are some words related to *maneuver*.

maneuverable	maneuverer
maneuverability	maneuvering
maneuvered	maneuvers

maneuvering (mə nōō´ vər ing) *n.*
Planning and then acting according
to plans.

manic (man´ ik) *adj.* Overly excited.

marrow (mar´ ō) *n.* 1. The soft
substance in the hollow parts of
bones. 2. The center; the core.

masculine (mas´ kyə lin) *adj.* Male;
having to do with men.

Mass (mas) *n.* The chief service of the
Roman Catholic Church.

mast (mast) *n.* A pole that supports
the sails of a ship or boat. See
illustration of **bow.**

Maya or **Mayan** (mä´ yə) or (mä´ yən)
n. A member of a people who built an
ancient civilization in Mexico and
Central America. **Mayan** *adj.* Having to
do with the civilization of the Mayas.

meditate (med´ i tāt´) *v.* To think
deeply; to contemplate.

Word History

Meditate came into English in the year
1560. It was derived from *meditari*, a verb
form of the Latin word *medēri*, which
means "to remedy." (Also note that the
word *meditate* contains the *-ate* suffix,
which in this word means "to cause to be
affected by.")

medley (med´ lē) *n.* A mixture;
a jumble.

melodrama (mel´ ə drä´ mə) *n.* A
play that exaggerates emotions
and encourages the audience to
be sympathetic.

menial (mē´ nē əl) *adj.* Humble; lowly;
boring; tedious.

merciful (mûr´ si fəl) *adj.* Forgiving.

mesa (mā´ sə) *n.* A small, high plateau
that stands alone, like a mountain
with a flat top.

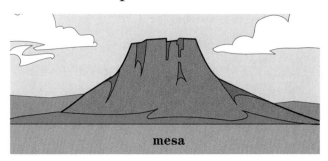

mesa

mesquite (me skēt´) *n.* A spiny shrub
or tree in the legume, or pea and
bean, family.

miaow (mē ou´) *n.* Meow; the sound a
cat makes. —*v.* To meow; to make
the sound a cat makes.

mill (mil) *n.* A factory.

miniature (min´ ē ə chər) *adj.* A small-
sized model of something.

minute (mī nōōt´) *adj.* Detailed;
careful.

mischievous (mis´ chə vəs) *adj.*
Causing trouble in a playful way.

mobilize (mō´ bə līz´) *v.* To put
into action.

monarch (mon´ ərk) *n.* A ruler; a king
or a queen.

morale (mə ral´) *n.* The level of one's
confidence.

morose (mə rōs´) *adj.* Sullen; gloomy.

mossback (môs´ bak) *n.* A wild bull
or cow.

mother-of-pearl (muth´ ər uv pûrl´)
n. A hard, shiny, multicolored
substance found inside some
mollusk shells.

move (mo͞ov) *v.* To make a motion or a suggestion to act on something in a meeting.

muck (muk) *v.* To clean out.

muff (muf) *v.* To do an action poorly; to miss; to mess up.

muster (mus´ tər) *v.* To work up; to gather.

mutilated (myo͞ot´ l āt´ əd) *adj.* Cut up; slashed.

myriad (mir´ ē əd) *n.* An immense number; many.

mystified (mis´ tə fīd´) *adj.* Bewildered; baffled; puzzled.

mythology (mi thol´ ə jē) *n.* A collection of legends or fables.

N

netherworld (neth´ ər wûrld´) *n.* The region below the ground; hell.

nimbly (nim´ blē) *adv.* With quick, light movements.

nobly (nō´ blē) *adv.* In an honorable way.

nomination (no´ mə nā´ shən) *n.* A proposal that someone could hold a government position or office.

Word History

Nomination is a derivative of the word *nominate*, which came into English about 500 years ago. It came from a derivation of the Latin word *nomen*, which means "name." (Also note that the word *nomination* contains the *-ation* suffix, which means "connected to the process of.")

noncombatant (non´ kəm bat´ nt) *n.* A person who is not a part of the fighting during wartime.

novelty (no´ vəl tē) *n.* Something new or different.

nuclear reaction (no͞o´ klē ər rē ak´ shən) *n.* A process in which the centers or cores of atoms are changed.

O

obliterate (ə blit´ ə rāt´) *v.* To destroy completely; to rub out; to erase.

Word Derivations

Below are some words related to *obliterate*.

obliterated	obliterating	obliterative
obliterates	obliteration	obliterator

oblong (ob´ lông) *adj.* Being longer than it is wide.

obscure (əb skyo͞or´) *adj.* Not well known. —*v.* To hide; to cover up.

observatory (əb zûr´ və tor´ē) *n.* A place that is designed for astronomers to study the stars.

observatory

optical (op´ ti kəl) *adj.* Having to do with sight.

optimism (op´ tə miz´ əm) *n.* The belief that everything will happen for the best.

organic (or gan´ ik) *adj.* Produced by living things; was once alive.

orientation (or´ ē ən tā´ shən) n. A person's or object's position in relation to something else.

ornery (or´ nə rē) adj. Mean; grouchy; irritable.

oval (ō´ vəl) adj. Egg-shaped.

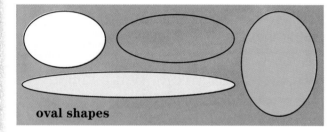

oval shapes

overseer (ō´ vər sē´ ər) n. A supervisor; a manager.

oxlip (oks´ lip) n. A flowering herb with pale-colored flowers.

P

pantaloons (pan´ tl ōōnz´) n. Trousers.

parch (pärch) v. To become very dry.

parliamentary procedure (pär´ lə men´ trē prə sē´ jər) n. A formal way to hold or conduct a meeting, following certain rules.

passion (pash´ ən) n. A strong liking or enthusiasm for something.

peculiarity (pi kyōō´ lē ar´ i tē) n. A strange or unusual feature.

peevishly (pē´ vish lē) adv. With irritation or lack of patience.

perimeter (pə rim´ i tər) n. The distance around the boundary of something.

persecute (pûr´ si kyōōt´) v. To torment; to oppress; to treat badly.

persist (pər sist´) v. To continue trying something; to refuse to give up or quit.

perspective (pər spek´ tiv) n. A way of looking at things in relation to each other.

Word History

Perspective came into English about 600 years ago. It came from the Latin word *perspectivus,* meaning "of sight" or "optical." This Latin word came from a derivation of *perspicere,* which can be broken into the word parts *per-,* meaning "through," and *specere,* meaning "to look." (Also note that the word *perspective* contains the *-ive* suffix, which means "performs the action of.")

persuade (pər swād´) v. To get others to think as you do about a subject or topic.

Word Derivations

Below are some words related to *persuade.*

persuaded	persuading	persuasively
persuader	persuasion	persuasiveness
persuades	persuasive	

pester (pes´ tər) v. To bother; to annoy.

peyote (pā ō´ tē) n. A cactus plant.

phenomenal (fi nom´ ə nl) adj. Remarkable.

pickerel (pik´ ər əl) n. A freshwater fish that is in the pike family.

piñon (pin´ yən) n. A kind of pine tree with edible seeds.

plateau (pla tō´) *n.* A tract of high, flat land; a tableland.

plead (plēd) *v.* To beg.

plumb (plum) *adv.* Completely.

pogrom (pə grum´) *n.* An organized attack on Jews in Russia in the late 1800s. Pogroms were encouraged by the Russian government at that time.

ponder (pon´ dər) *v.* To think about.

popular sovereignty (pop´ yə lər sov´ rin tē) *n.* A policy that said each state could decide whether to have slavery within its borders.

portage (pôr täzh´) *n.* The act of carrying boats and supplies from one waterway to another.

portage

portal (por´ tl) *n.* An entryway.

poultice (pōl´ tis) *n.* A wad of something soft and moist that is placed over a wound to heal it.

prankster (prangk´ stər) *n.* A person who plays tricks on people for fun.

precarious (pri kâr´ ē əs) *adj.* Uncertain; doubtful.

precaution (pri kô´ shən) *n.* Care taken beforehand.

pressure (pre´ shər) *v.* To force.

prevail (pri vāl´) *v.* To persuade.

primary (prī´ mer ē) *adj.* Main.

prime (prīm) *n.* The most successful or important period of time.

procedure (prə sē´ jər) *n.* The steps to follow in carrying out a routine or method.

proclaim (prō klām´) *v.* To announce publicly.

profound (prə found´) *adj.* Deep.

prominence (prom´ ə nəns) *n.* Fame; importance.

prominent (prom´ ə nənt) *adj.* Famous; well-known.

prophet (prof´ it) *n.* A person who tells events before they happen.

proposition (prop´ ə zish´ ən) *n.* An idea that is presented; a principle.

prosper (pros´ pər) *v.* To succeed; to thrive.

Word History

Prosper came into English about 600 years ago. It came from the French word *prosperer*, the origins of which are in the Latin words *prosperare*, meaning "to cause to succeed," and *prosperus*, meaning "favorable."

provisions (prə vizh´ ənz) *n. pl.* Supplies, especially food or tools.

ptarmigan (tär´ mi gən) *n.* A bird also known as a grouse.

pun (pun) *n.* A joke made by using words that sound almost the same but have different meanings.

pungent (pun´ jənt) *adj.* Sharp or strong smelling or tasting.

Q

quail (kwāl) *v.* To shrink back in fear.

quiver (kwi´ vər) *v.* To shake slightly.

quota (kwō´ tə) *n.* The amount one expects to receive.

R

racquetball (ra´ kət bôl´) *n.* A sport played with a racket and small rubber ball in an enclosed room.

rampart (ram´ pärt) *n.* A wall used as a defense for a city.

ramshackle (ram´ shak´ əl) *adj.* Tumbledown; shaky.

rancid (ran´ sid) *adj.* Stale; unpleasant.

rapscallion (rap skal´ yən) *n.* A rascal; a scamp.

ration (rash´ ən) *n.* A limited share of food.

ravage (ra´ vij) *v.* To damage heavily.

ravine (rə vēn´) *n.* A narrow, steep-sided valley worn into the earth by running water.

ravishing (rav´ i shing) *adj.* Very beautiful.

recede (ri sēd´) *v.* To go backward; to back away.

Word Derivations

Below are some words related to *recede*.

receded	recession	recessionary
receding	recessional	recessive
recess		

recoil (ri koil´) *v.* To spring back from.

recrimination (ri krim´ ə nā´ shən) *n.* An accusation made in return for another accusation; blame given in return.

recruit (ri kroot´) *v.* To get new members.

recruitment (ri kroot´ mənt) *n.* Signing up new soldiers.

refracting (ri frak´ ting) *adj.* Passing through an object and changing direction, as a light ray passing into a lens at one angle and coming out at a different angle.

refuge (ref´ yooj) *n.* A place of safety.

regiment (rej´ ə mənt) *n.* A large body of soldiers.

remote (ri mōt´) *adj.* Far away and separate from others.

render (ren´ dər) *v.* To make.

renounce (ri nouns´) *v.* To give up; to reject.

repetitive (ri pet´ i tiv) *adj.* Repeated.

repulse (ri puls´) *v.* To push back.

resonance (rez´ ə nəns) *n.* Richness of sound; echoing.

reveille (rev´ ə lē) *n.* The playing of a bugle to awaken soldiers.

Word History

Reveille came into English in the year 1644. It comes from a derivation of the French word *eveillar*, meaning "to awaken," which is assumed to be derived from the Latin word *exvigilare*, meaning "to keep watch" or "to stay awake."

reverie (rev´ ə rē) *n.* A daydream.

rigid (rij´ id) *adj.* Stiff; unbending.

ritual (rich´ oo əl) *n.* A ceremony of worship; an act always performed on certain occasions.

rivulet (riv´ yə let) *n.* A small stream of water.

rotate (rō´ tāt) *v.* To revolve; to turn around; to spin.

Word Derivations

Below are some words related to *rotate*.

rotated   rotation   rotatory
rotating   rotator

---

roust (roust) *v.* To decisively defeat and chase someone out of a place; to rout.

rowdy (rou´ dē) *adj.* Rough; disorderly.

rudder (rud´ ər) *n.* A broad, flat blade at the rear of a ship used to steer. See illustration of **bow.**

rutting (rut´ ing) *n.* Mating.

S

saber (sā´ bər) *n.* A heavy sword with a curved blade.

sabotage (sab´ ə täzh´) *v.* To damage purposely.

salutation (sal´ yə tā´ shən) *n.* Greeting.

samovar (sam´ ə vär´) *n.* A decorative metal container with a spigot, or faucet, often used in Russia to heat water for tea.

Word History

Samovar came into English in the year 1830. It is a Russian word formed by joining the word parts *samo-*, meaning "self," and *varit'*, which means "to boil."

---

schooner (skōō´ nər) *n.* A large sailing vessel.

scythe (sīth) *n.* A tool with a long, curved blade for cutting grass or grain by hand.

scythe

sear (sēr) *v.* To roast; to burn.

seclude (si klōōd´) *v.* To keep away from others.

second (se´ kənd) *v.* To verbally agree with a motion or suggestion to do something in a meeting.

sensor (sen´ sor) *n.* A device that can identify such things as light, sound, or temperature and send a signal telling what has been identified.

sentinel (sen´ tn l) *n.* A person who stands watch; a guard.

shamefaced (shām´ fāst) *adj.* Embarrassed.

sharecropper (shâr´ krop´ ər) *n.* A farmer who gives part of his or her crop as rent to the owner of the land.

shlemiel (shlə mēl´) *n. slang.* A fool who is both awkward and unlucky.

shmendrick (shmen´ drik) *n. slang.* A nincompoop; a nobody.

shrill (shril) *adj.* High-pitched; piercing.

shroud (shroud) *n.* A covering for a dead body.

siege (sēj) *n.* An army's attempt to force surrender by surrounding the enemy's position, keeping out food and supplies.

Pronunciation Key: at; lāte; câre; fäther; set; mē; it; kīte; ox; rōse; ô in bought; coin; book; too; form; out; up; ūse; tûrn; ə sound in about, chicken, pencil, cannon, circus; chair; hw in which; ring; shop; thin; there; zh in treasure.

simultaneously (sī′ məl tā′ nē əs lē) *adv.* At exactly the same time.

singe (sinj) *v.* To burn the surface of something.

sinister (sin′ ə stər) *adj.* Harmful; threatening.

skedaddle (ski dad′ l) *v. informal.* To run quickly away.

skeeter (skē′ tər) *n. informal.* A mosquito.

skeletal (skel′ i tl) *adj.* Like a skeleton; so thin that the shapes of bones show.

skirmish (skûr′ mish) *n.* A fight between small forces.

skulk (skulk) *v.* To sneak.

slew (sloo) *n.* Many.

slump (slump) *v.* To sit with drooping shoulders.

Word History

Slump came into English in the year 1887. Its origins are probably in the Scandinavian languages. It is related to the Norwegian word *slumpa*, which means "to fall."

smithy (smith′ ē) *n.* A blacksmith's shop; a place where horseshoes are made.

solace (sol′ is) *n.* Comfort.

solar system (sō′ lər sis′ təm) *n.* The sun and all the planets and other bodies that revolve around it.

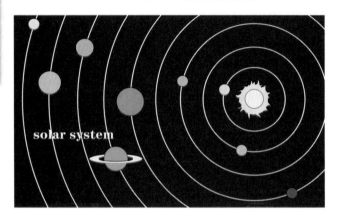

solar system

solder (sod′ ər) *v.* To join metal pieces together by using a highly heated liquid metal at a joint without heating the pieces themselves.

solemnly (so′ ləm lē) *adv.* In a very serious manner.

solitary (sol′ i ter′ ē) *adj.* Alone; single.

solstice (sol′ stis) *n.* The day of the year when the sun appears the farthest north and the day when it appears the farthest south in the sky.

soul-harrowing (sōl′ har′ ō ing) *adj.* Causing suffering to a person's innermost self.

span (span) *v.* To stretch across.

spasm (spaz′ əm) *n.* A seizure; a fit.

spawn (spôn) *v.* To lay eggs and deposit them in water.

speculation (spek′ yə lā′ shən) *n.* Thinking about a subject; pondering.

spew (spyoo) *v.* To pour out; to squirt out.

sphere (sfēr) *n.* A ball; a globe.

sphere

Word Derivations
Below are some words related to *sphere*.

sphered	sphering	spherule
spheric	spheroid	sphery
spherical	spherometer	

spike (spīk) *v.* To forcefully hit a volleyball down the other side of the net.

spire (spīr) *n.* A tall, pointed cone built on top of a tower; a steeple.

spirits (spir´ its) *n.* A liquid containing alcohol.

stabilization (stā´ bə lə zā´ shən) *n.* The act of making something hold steady.

stance (stans) *n.* A person's mental position on a subject.

staple (stā´ pəl) *n.* A basic, or necessary, food.

stockyard (stok´ yärd´) *n.* A place where livestock such as cattle, sheep, horses, and pigs that are to be bought or sold, slaughtered, or shipped are held.

Stonehenge

Stonehenge (stōn´ henj) *n.* A group of large stones in England placed in circular formations around 3,500 years ago, possibly as an astronomical calendar.

straddle (stra´ dəl) *v.* To sit with one's legs on each side of an object.

stroke (strōk) *n.* A sudden attack of illness caused by a blocked or broken blood vessel in or leading to the brain.

stygian (stij´ ē ən) *adj.* Dark; gloomy.

succession (sək sesh´ ən) *n.* One thing happening right after another.

succulent (suk´ yə lənt) *adj.* Juicy; tasty.

sufficient (sə fish´ ənt) *adj.* Enough.

suffocate (suf´ ə kāt´) *v.* To smother; to choke.

sull (sul) *v.* To balk; to stop suddenly and refuse to move.

supple (sup´ əl) *adj.* Easily bent; not stiff.

suppress (sə pres´) *v.* To stop; to put down.

supremacy (sə prem´ ə sē) *n.* A position of the highest power.

surpass (sər pas´) *v.* To go beyond.

sway (swā) *v.* To influence.

swivet (swiv´ it) *n.* A state of worry or fear.

synchronize (sing´ krə nīz´) *v.* To move together at the same rate.

Pronunciation Key: at; lāte; câre; fäther; set; mē; it; kīte; ox; rōse; ô in bought; coin; bŏŏk; tōō; form; out; up; ūse; tûrn; ə sound in about, chicken, pencil, cannon, circus; chair; hw in which; ring; shop; thin; thͯere; zh in treasure.

T

tan (tan) *v.* To turn animal hides into leather.

Word History

Tan came into English about 600 years ago, from the French word *tanner*, a derivation of the Latin word *tanum* or *tannum*. The Latin word means "tanbark," a type of bark that contains an astringent, or drying, substance used in the making of leather.

tangible (tan′ jə bəl) *adj.* Real; actual.

taper (tā′ pər) *v.* To stop slowly; to wind down.

teeming (tē′ ming) *adj.* Overflowing; swarming.

terminal (tûr′ mə nəl) *adj.* Eventually ending in death.

tethered (teth′ ərd) *adj.* Tied by rope to a fixed object.

thresh (thresh) *v.* To separate grain from the stalk by beating it.

tidal flat (tī′ dəl flat) *n.* A flat area of land that is sometimes covered by tidal waters.

till (til) *v.* To turn over soil; to plow.

timpani (tim′ pə nē) *n.* A type of drum.

tipi (tē′ pē) *n.* A tent of the Native Americans of the Plains; a tepee.

Word History

Tipi, or **tepee,** came into English in the year 1743. It is a Native American word, meaning "to dwell," that originated with the Dakota tribe.

toboggan (tə bog′ ən) *n.* A long, narrow sled.

tome (tōm) *n.* One volume of a set of books.

tract (trakt) *n.* A large area of land.

transcribe (trans skrīb′) *v.* To change from one recorded form to another; to translate.

translucent (trans lōō′ sənt) *adj.* Hard to see through. Light is visible, but objects cannot be seen clearly.

transmit (trans mit′) *v.* To send; to communicate; to pass something.

Word Derivations

Below are some words related to *transmit*.
transmittable   transmittance   transmitter
transmittal   transmitted   transmitting

transmitter (trans mit′ ər) *n.* A device that sends out television or radio signals.

treason (trē′ zən) *n.* The act of betraying someone's trust.

trench (trench) *n.* A ditch; a long, narrow channel cut in the earth.

tributary (trib′ yə ter′ ē) *n.* A stream or river that flows into a larger one.

tribute (trib′ yōōt) *n.* Praise, honor, or gifts given to show respect or to show thanks.

trifling (trī′ fling) *adj.* Small and unimportant.

trilling *r*'s (tril′ ing ärz) *n.* *R*'s that are pronounced by rolling the tongue against the roof of the mouth.

trinket (tring′ kit) *n.* A small or cheap piece of jewelry.

tripod (trī′ pod) *n.* A three-legged table or stand.

tripod

tsar (zär) *n.* An emperor of Russia before 1918.

tsarina (zä rē′ nə) *n.* An empress of Russia before 1918.

tumult (tōō′ mult) *n.* A great disorder; an uproar.

tundra (tun′ drə) *n.* A large, treeless plain in the arctic regions.

tunic (tōō′ nik) *n.* A short coat.

turbulent (tûr′ byə lənt) *adj.* Fierce; violent; wild.

Word History

Turbulent came into English in the year 1538. It came from a derivative of the Latin word *turba*, which means "confusion" or "crowd." (Also note that the word *turbulent* contains the *-ent* suffix, which means "the state of" or "the quality of.")

U

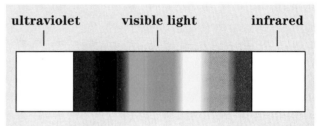

ultraviolet (ul′ trə vī′ ə lit) *adj.* Having to do with an invisible form of light. Ultraviolet rays are found just beyond the violet end of the visible light spectrum.

| ultraviolet | visible light | infrared |

unaccountably (un′ ə koun′ tə blē) *adv.* In a way that cannot be explained.

unanimously (yōō nan′ ə məs lē) *adv.* With the agreement of everyone.

undermine (un′ dər mīn′) *v.* To weaken.

unfurl (un fûrl′) *v.* To open out; to unroll.

unison (yōō′ nə sən) *n.* Behaving the same way at the same time. **in unison** *idiom.* Two or more people saying or doing the same thing at the same time.

unquenchably (un kwench′ ə blē) *adv.* Endlessly; in a persistent way.

upturned sentence (up′ tərnd sen′ təns) *n.* Higher inflection used at the end of a sentence, such as is used for a question.

V

vacuum (vak′ yōōm) *n.* A space with no air. A perfect vacuum is not possible; even in outer space there are some atoms and molecules of gas and radiation, although they are thinly scattered.

vagabond (va´ gə bond´) *n.* One who wanders from place to place.

valiant (val´ yənt) *adj.* Brave; fearless.

velocity (və los´ i tē) *n.* Speed.

Word History

Velocity came into English around the year 1550. It came from the Latin word *velocitas*, a derivative of the word *velox*, meaning "quick." It may also be related to the Latin word *vegēre*, which means "to enliven." (Also note that the word *velocity* contains the *-ity* suffix, which can mean "quality," "state," or "degree.")

verify (ver´ ə fī´) *v.* To prove the truth.

Word Derivations

Below are some words related to *verify*.

verifiability   verification   verifier
verifiable   verified   verifying
verifiableness

vermilion (vər mil´ yən) *adj.* Bright red.

vindicate (vin´ di kāt´) *v.* To prove innocent.

vintage (vin´ tij) *n.* The grapes or wine produced in a vineyard in one year.

vintner (vint´ nər) *n.* A person who makes wine for a living.

vital (vīt´ l) *adj.* Very important; necessary.

vocation (vō kā´ shən) *n.* An occupation; a profession.

W

water buffalo (wô´ tər buf´ ə lō´) *n.* A kind of oxen with large curved horns and a bluish-black hide. Water buffaloes are trained to work in rice fields in Asia.

water buffalo

whopper (hwop´ ər) *n. informal.* A big lie.

wince (wins) *v.* To flinch; to start back from.

windlass (wind´ ləs) *n.* A roller turned with a handle used for lifting heavy weights.

windlass

winnow (win´ ō) *v.* To remove the chaff, or husks, from grain.

wrath (rath) *n.* Anger; rage.

Y

yield (yēld) *v.* To give in; to stop arguing.

YWCA Young Women's Christian Association.

Z

Zulu (zōō´ lōō) *n.* A person from KwaZulu Natal in South Africa.

HarperCollins Publishers Ltd.: "Roads Go Ever Ever On" from THE HOBBIT by J.R.R. Tolkien. Copyright © 1966 by J.R.R. Tolkien. Reprinted with permission of HarperCollins Publishers Ltd.

John Hawkins & Associates, Inc.: **"Good Sportsmanship"** from **NIGHT WITH ARMOUR** by **Richard Armour.** Copyright © **1958** by **Richard Armour.** Reprinted by permission of John Hawkins & Associates, Inc.

Holiday House, Inc.: Excerpts from BUFFALO HUNT by Russell Freedman. Copyright © 1988 by Russell Freedman. All rights reserved. Reprinted from BUFFALO HUNT by permission of Holiday House, Inc. "Sun" and "Secrets" by Myra Cohn Livingston, illustrations by Leonard Everett Fisher. Illustrations copyright © 1988 by Leonard Everett Fisher. All rights reserved. Reprinted from SPACE SONGS by permission of Holiday House, Inc.

Houghton Mifflin Company: "The Coming of Long Knives," an excerpt from SING DOWN THE MOON. Copyright © 1970 by Scott O'Dell. Reprinted by permission of Houghton Mifflin Company. All rights reserved. Illustrations from THE GETTYSBURG ADDRESS. Illustrations and Afterward copyright © 1995 by Michael McCurdy. Reprinted by permission of Houghton Mifflin Company. All rights reserved. Abridged from IN TWO WORLDS: A Yup'ik Eskimo Family, by Aylette Jenness and Alice Rivers. Text copyright © 1989 by Aylette Jenness and Alice Rivers. Photographs copyright © 1989 by Aylette Jenness. Reprinted by permission of Houghton Mifflin Company. All rights reserved. "Roads Go Ever Ever On," from THE HOBBIT. Copyright © 1966 by J.R.R. Tolkien. Reprinted by permission of Houghton Mifflin Company. All rights reserved. "Telescopes," from THE WAY THINGS WORK by David Macaulay. Compilation copyright © 1988 by Dorling Kindersley, Ltd. Text copyright © 1988 by David Macaulay and Neil Ardley. Illustrations copyright © 1988 by David Macaulay. Reprinted by permission of Houghton Mifflin Company. All rights reserved.

James Houston: "The Whole World is Coming" from SONGS OF THE DREAM PEOPLE: Chants and Images from the Indians and Eskimos of North America. Edited and illustrated by James Houston. Atheneum, New York, copyright © 1972 by James Houston.

Alfred A. Knopf, Inc.: "Carrying the Running-Aways" from THE PEOPLE COULD FLY by Virginia Hamilton, illustrated by Leo and Diane Dillon. Text copyright © 1985 by Virginia Hamilton. Illustrations copyright © 1985 by Leo and Diane Dillon. Reprinted by permission of Alfred A. Knopf, Inc.

Ellen Levine Literary Agency, Inc.: "The Night We Started Dancing" from FREE TO BE A FAMILY by Ann Cameron. **Reprinted by permission of Ellen Levine Literary Agency, Inc. Copyright © 1987 by Ann Cameron.**

Wendy Lipkind Agency: "Alberic the Wise" from ALBERIC THE WISE AND OTHER JOURNEYS by Norton Juster. Copyright © 1965 by Norton Juster. Reprinted with permission of Wendy Lipkind Agency.

Lothrop, Lee & Shepard Books, a division of William Morrow & Company, Inc.: "The Siege of Vicksburg" from THE TAMARACK TREE by Patricia Clapp. Text copyright © 1986 by Patricia Clapp. By permission of Lothrop, Lee & Shepard Books, a division of William Morrow & Company, Inc.. THE STORY OF JUMPING MOUSE. A Native American legend retold and Illustrated by John Steptoe. From SEVEN ARROWS copyright © 1972 by Hymeyohsts Storm. Retold and illustrated for children copyright © 1984 by John Steptoe. By permission of Lothrop, Lee & Shepard Books, a division of William Morrow & Company, Inc., with the approval of the John Steptoe Literary Trust.

Macmillan Library Reference USA, a Simon & Schuster Macmillan Company: "Sacagawea's Journey" by Betty Westrom Skold. Reprinted with permission of Macmillan Library Reference USA, a Simon & Schuster Macmillan Company, from SACAGAWEA by Betty Westrom Skold. Copyright © 1977 by Dillon Press.

Mike Makley: "The New Kid" by Mike Makley, from Cricket, The Magazine for Children, Vol. 2, No. 8. Copyright © 1975 by Mike Makley. Reprinted with permission of Mike Makley.

Elsa Marston: "Circles, Squares, and Daggers: How Native Americans Watched the Skies" by Elsa Marston, from the September 1990 issue of Odyssey magazine. Copyright © 1990 by Elsa Marston. Reprinted with permission of Elsa Marston.

Morrow Junior Books, a division of William Morrow & Company, Inc.: An excerpt from CHARLEY SKEDADDLE by Patricia Beatty. Text copyright © 1987 by Patricia Beatty. By permission of Morrow Junior Books, a division of William Morrow & Company, Inc.. An excerpt from CLASS PRESIDENT by Johanna Hurwitz. Text copyright © 1990 by Johanna Hurwitz. By permission of Morrow Junior Books, a division of William Morrow & Company, Inc.. STARS by Seymour Simon. Text copyright © 1986 by Seymour Simon. By permission of Morrow Junior Books, a division of William Morrow & Company, Inc..

Penguin Books Canada Limited: From *Underground to Canada* by Barbara Smucker. Copyright © 1977 by Clarke, Irwin and Company Limited. Illustration by Imre Hofbauer. Copyright © 1978 by Imre Hofbauer. Reprinted by permission of Penguin Books Canada Limited.

Plays, Inc.: "The Book That Saved the Earth" from SPACE AND SCIENCE FICTION PLAYS FOR YOUNG PEOPLE by Claire Boiko. Reprinted with permission of Plays, Inc.

Marian Reiner: "Sun" and "Secrets" from SPACE SONGS by Myra Cohn Livingston. Copyright © 1988 Myra Cohn Livingston. Published by Holiday House. Reprinted by permission of Marian Reiner.

Sand & Sorensen Law Firm: "History of the Tunrit" from SONGS AND STORIES OF THE NETSILIK ESKIMOS, translated by Edward Field from text collected by Knud Rasmussen, illustrated by Pudlo. Reprinted with permission of Sand & Sorensen Law Firm.

Simon & Schuster Books for Young Readers, an imprint of Simon & Schuster Children's Publishing Division: **DEATH OF THE IRON HORSE by Paul Goble.** *Copyright © 1987, by Paul Goble.* Reprinted with permission of Simon & Schuster Books for Young Readers, an imprint of Simon & Schuster Children's Publishing Division. All rights reserved. **S.O.R. LOSERS by Avi.** *Copyright © 1984 by Avi Wortis.* Reprinted with the permission of Simon & Schuster Books for Young Readers, an imprint of Simon & Schuster Children's Publishing Division

Steepletop: "Travel" by Edna St. Vincent Millay. From COLLECTED POEMS, HarperCollins. Copyright © 1921, 1948 by Edna St. Vincent Millay. All rights reserved. Reprinted by permission of Elizabeth Barnett, literary executor.

Navin Sullivan: "Galileo" from PIONEER ASTRONOMERS by Navin Sullivan. Copyright © 1964 by Navin Sullivan. Reprinted with permission of Navin Sullivan.

University of Missouri-Kansas City, University Libraries: "Maps" by Dorothy Brown Thompson. Reprinted with permission of University of Missouri-Kansas City, University Libraries.

Laurence S. Untermeyer: "Wander-Thirst" by Gerald Gould from STARS TO STEER by Louis Untermeyer. Copyright © 1941 by Harcourt Brace and Company. Reprinted with permission of Laurence S. Untermeyer.

Viking Children's Books, a division of Penguin Putnam Inc.: From THE NIGHT JOURNEY by Kathryn Lasky, illustrations by Trina Schart Hyman. Copyright © 1981 by Kathryn Lasky, text. Copyright © 1981 by Trina Schart Hyman, illustrations. Used by permission of Viking Children's Books, a division of Penguin Putnam Inc.